KT-196-912

THE NEW NATURALIST

A SURVEY OF BRITISH NATURAL HISTORY

WOODLAND BIRDS

EDITORS:

Margaret Davies D.Sc.
Sir Julian Huxley M.A. D.Sc. F.R.S.
John Gilmour M.A. V.M.H.
Kenneth Mellanby C.B.E. Sc.D.

PHOTOGRAPHIC EDITOR:

Eric Hosking F.R.P.S.

The aim of this series is to interest the general reader in the wild life of Britain by recapturing the inquiring spirit of the old naturalists. The Editors believe that the natural pride of the British public in the native fauna and flora, to which must be added concern for their conservation, is best fostered by maintaining a high standard of accuracy combined with clarity of exposition in presenting the results of modern scientific research.

The text and line illustrations are here reproduced unaltered, but the process of manufacture used to achieve an economic price does not, unfortunately, do full justice to all the photographs; and those originally in colour appear in black and white.

THE NEW NATURALIST

WOODLAND BIRDS

ERIC SIMMS, D.F.C., M.A.

Bloomsbury Books
London

TO
DAVID AND AMANDA

This edition published 1990 by
Bloomsbury Books an imprint of
Godfrey Cave Associates Limited
42 Bloomsbury Street, London WC1B 3QJ
under license from William Collins Son's & Co. Ltd.

ISBN 1 870630 19 X

©William Collins Son's & Co. Ltd.

CONTENTS

LIST OF TEXT FIGURES

LIST OF TABLES

* As explained on the second page, these plates are here reproduced in black and white.

ILLUSTRATIONS *

EDITOR'S PREFACE

Eric Simms has had a career, of which natural history has been a facet, which has proved him as practical as he is polymathic. During his long service with the British Broadcasting Corporation he became a master of natural sound recordings and thence a strong member of the staff of the BBC's Education Department who excelled as producer and writer as well as broadcaster. Now working as a freelance he can devote all his time and energies to those pursuits and activities closest to his heart.

We are very happy that the *New Naturalist* can publish his synthesis of a lifetime's labour of love on the British-Irish woodland avifauna. He has studied it with scholarly zest and professional understanding and has embellished it from first hand experience with valuable comparisons from Europe and other continents.

Mr Simms's grasp of the ecological mysteries of our woodland bird life is such that he carries the reader with him into the very heart of the woods, or the parkland and suburban and subrural gardenland that is ecologically derived primarily from woodland. His power of re-creating the woodland habitats of England, Wales, Scotland and Ireland is great because he brings to his analysis a proper study of geology, soil, botany, entomology and mankind as the agent of rural change (and pollution) since late glacial times; and a proper study of animal populations and their history which manages to distil the essentials for us without blinding our eyes with figures. He uses tables and lists with care and integrates his own extensive researches with those of other masters with modesty and skill.

Our British and Irish woodland and its avifauna is at what could properly be described as a climax of five thousand years of modification by the hand of man since Neolithic times. Birds, as Mr Simms offers them, are important litmus papers of the ecological changes in our forests, woods, spinneys, parks and gardens. His synthesis offers us a deep analysis of the birds of tree and scrub which will be of abiding interest and value to foresters, farmers and conservationists, and of profound help to those who have to plan our country's rural future.

The Editors

FOREWORD

To have attempted the writing of this book twenty years ago would have been an impossible task, since it is only during the last two or three decades that there have been any lengthy population studies of woodland birds. When I was asked by the Editors of the *New Naturalist* series to undertake the writing of a book about the forest birds of the British Isles, I accepted with excitement and trepidation. However, an author stands squarely on the shoulders of those who have preceded him and my resolve was strengthened by the intensive long-term studies of the birds of Bagley and Wytham Woods by the Oxford research scientists, of Bookham Common by members of the London Natural History Society and of the woods of northern England by Dr Brunsdon Yapp whose *Birds and Woods* was the first book to be wholly devoted to Britain's woodland bird communities. The ecology of our various kinds of woodland is now being studied more intensively than ever before and the reader will become aware of some of the unanswered problems as he reads on. This is perhaps a further justification for undertaking the book since we depend on the continuation of present research as well as the initiation of new projects. For some of the background material I have relied on three general works, all classics in their field – Sir Arthur Tansley's *The British Isles and their Vegetation*, *The Flora of the British Isles* by A. R. Clapham, T. G. Tutin and E. F. Warburg and *The Handbook of British Birds* by H. F. Witherby, F. C. R. Jourdain, N. F. Ticehurst and B. W. Tucker.

I am deeply conscious of my debt to many individuals and organisations who have generously given me advice, granted me countless facilities including access to woods and forests, or allowed me to reproduce published material. I am especially indebted to the Forestry Commission, whose Deputy Surveyors, Information, Wild Life and District Officers and many foresters have all patiently answered and courteously met my many requests for advice, information and access to forests. The Commission has very kindly prepared for this volume the maps reproduced as Figures 9–12 showing the distribution of woodlands and two tree species in Britain. The data for the individual counties are based on the results of a sample census in the case of privately owned woodlands and on existing records for Forestry Commission woodlands, with a base date in both cases of 30th September, 1965. In private woodlands the survey was largely confined to the mainland of Great Britain and the sample was approximately one acre of woodland in every seven with the results collected and calculated on a county basis. The information for the Forestry Commission is based on individual forests and where these overlap county boundaries the areas have been allocated to the county in which they predominantly lie. For this reason, and also because of differences in maximum size of wood and in woodland classification, the data are not strictly comparable with those collected in the 1947 *Census of Woodlands* from which I have also been allowed to quote. The circles on the map in Figure 9 are plotted true to scale; on the other special maps the scale is arbitrary. Table 8, which shows the areas of woodland over 5 acres in Great Britain under the major species of tree, has been specially drawn up as well, and I am very grateful to the Forestry Commission, with whom I have had for many years the most close and valuable professional relations. The Nature Conservancy, too, has always been most sympathetic to my many requests for help.

Much of the research that I have been able to carry out in the Republic of Ireland would not have been possible without the good offices of His Excellency the Irish Ambassador in London, of the Third Secretary at the Embassy, of Dr Fergus O'Gorman of the Game and Wild Life Branch of Roinn Tailte and of many delightfully helpful private landowners. In Northern Ireland I was greatly encouraged by the interest of the Forestry Division of the Ministry of Agriculture which generously gave me much invaluable advice and practical assistance.

In a volume of this kind comparative material is of vital importance, and I wish particularly to thank Dr Yapp and the Oxford University Press for allowing me to quote from the figures of relative abundance in woodland birds given in *Birds and Woods*. I have a special acknowledgment to make to Dr. Charles Elton and Messrs. Methuen for permission to reproduce two quotations from *The Pattern of Animal Communities*, and to Dr David Lack and the Clarendon Press for one figure and two tables from *Population Studies of Birds*. I would also like to record my appreciation to the Editors of *British Birds*, *Bird Study*, the *Journal of Animal Ecology* and the *Quarterly Journal of Forestry* for permitting me to use maps, figures and tables from papers they have published in their journals.

Dr Norman Moore, Mr M. Philips Price, Dr David Lack, Mr P. Hope Jones, Dr Bruce Campbell, Dr Geoffrey Beven, Dr John Stafford, Dr H. N. Southern, Dr D. B. Peakall, Mr A. W. Simpson and the Reverend Peter Hartley have all kindly agreed to my use of material from papers that they have written and I am grateful to them.

I must also mention the contribution of the British Broadcasting Corporation which, by granting me a long period of special leave in 1967, enabled me to see a number of British and Irish woods that I had not been able to visit previously.

I must also pay a sincere tribute to my wife, who has protected me throughout the writing of the book from undue disturbance, and to my children who so understandingly have allowed themselves to be deprived for so long of a father's company.

I have also been greatly sustained by the sympathetic interest both of my old friend James Fisher and of Michael Walter, who has so courteously and attentively kept a watching brief on behalf of the Publishers. I am deeply indebted to both of them.

INTRODUCTION

THE time is five past twelve. It is a still, cool May night and the streets of West London are lying deserted and slightly damp – moonlit pools under the lamp-posts. A thirteen year old boy, haversack over one shoulder, is busily pedalling his way south. His objective is a small wood in Surrey where in about two and a half hours' time the first robin will break into its plaintive, early morning song. So in 1935 I set out to reach Littleheath Woods near Selsdon in order to observe and time my first full dawn chorus in woodland. Since that time I have experienced many dawn choruses and visited many hundreds of woods in Canada, the United States, Africa and many parts of Europe but I still look back with pleasure on my early visits to these woods of southern England. Here I began to come to grips with the warblers, the tits, the woodpeckers, to separate blackcap from garden warbler and marsh tit from willow tit. It was in these woods that I slowly began to master the techniques of my bird-watching – keeping notes, making phonetic renderings of songs, observing behaviour, sketching and locating nests. I learned to appreciate solitude and to allow my mind, in the words of Richard Jefferies, to yield itself "to the green earth, the wind among the trees, the song of birds." Soon I discovered that it was necessary to learn about the trees and the flowers, the rainfall and the soil. I owe a great debt to two men – my father and George Harwood, an artist at Ditchling in Sussex – who both taught me to be just as accurate with my identification of the flora as of the fauna. Butterflies, moths and other insects, reptiles and amphibians began to reveal themselves as intrinsic parts of the overall pattern.

From the southern woods I began to turn my attention to the pine and oakwoods of more remote Britain, comparing them and contrasting them as my experience grew. My quest took me farther and farther afield to the conifers of Canton Vaud, the Coto Donaña and New England, to the cypress swamps of Florida, to the broad-leaved forests of the Smokies and the Rhone and to the riverine jungles of East Africa.

Each woodland is a world in miniature with its own community and system of plant, bird, mammal, insect and invertebrate life keyed to the continuously, although often slowly, changing state of the trees. Forest represents a complex natural community as well as the highest diversity of habitat; it has been called Nature's supreme development. It is difficult to determine each habitat factor in so complex an environment, since it does not work on a plant or animal in isolation but combines with other factors to form a system to which the organisms are adapted. This is why population studies of a single species may be difficult to carry out where a species does not live and move in a closed system. How to separate the factor from the complex whole is one of the chief problems facing ecologists, who have to beware of attributing an adaptation to the factor when the whole deserves the credit. Charles Elton in *The Pattern of Animal Communities* wrote: "Yet any advance on a huge front like that of community ecology clearly needs both strategy and tactics, a context as well as a scatter of only slightly related sentences or paragraphs. I do not believe that the continued stockpiling of innumerable smaller facts and conclusions about life-histories, distribution, populations, habits, interrelations, habitats, productivity, energy flow and the rest, will automatically build up a balanced picture of nature as a piece of inorganic and organic machinery; any more than the piling up of stones taken out of a large quarry will by itself result in the planning and building of a city. But equally, it would be quite pointless to attempt an ecological survey without having a pretty good selection of information on all such topics to work with."

Two thousand years ago forest covered some 60% of Britain and reached high up the mountain slopes to 2,000 ft. or more. Today 80% is agricultural land with an eighteenth-century landscape. Exotic, quick-growing conifers have come to replace the lost hardwoods; in the early days these were planted in serried and unimaginative ranks. This was the Forestry Commission's way of starting to fulfil its original brief of afforesting a million acres of land. Now the Commission has time to stand back and consider the merits of its past labours and to look forward to meeting the demands of conservation, amenity and public access. Farmland today represents a valuable habitat, for many woodland birds have adapted themselves to life among the fields and hedgerows and the biomass there is equal to that of many woods. This is due to the presence of hedges which are similar in character to the ecologically rich edges of woodland. Of the common birds of farmland only a bare half-dozen are not woodland species and the importance of hedgerows to wild life cannot be stressed too strongly. Now hedges are being destroyed and the use of toxic chemicals may damage habitats by indirectly killing the invertebrate life. There are distinct signs that the bird population of farmland may be on the decline.

However, many of the woodland bird species have discovered even more favourable niches for themselves in the suburbs of towns; here they may live at density levels far in excess of those in woods or on farmland. Some adaptable species can live in close proximity to man but others cannot manage this. Man in the twentieth century has a tendency to make organisations, farms, new woodlands, city streets and housing all uniform. When this technique is applied to animal and plant communities it may contain the seeds of its own destruction since a simple community is more open to invasion by unfamiliar organisms from outside. Thus it is essential to preserve the greatest variety of natural and semi-natural habitats and their inhabitants, to maintain as Elton went on to say, "in as rich a form as possible all the communities that may be interspersed among croplands, especially woods, scrub, roadside and field hedgerows and meadows." Many of our woodland species have moved into these habitats as the woods were felled.

The study of woodland ecology is in its very early stages and we cannot as yet readily answer such questions as "Why is this bird absent from that wood? How is this species adapted to all the complex factors in its environment? What would be the effect if this species disappeared?" The gaps in our knowledge are still very large and if this book helps to point them out it will have served part of its purpose.

Before it is possible to make statements about woodland bird communities one must first investigate numbers and proportions. I have visited several hundred British and Irish woods during my life but in order to obtain figures which I could use and compare I had to make a series of counts. These I carried out in nearly three hundred different woodlands in the British Isles and the figures will be discussed under each woodland grouping according to the species of tree. It is interesting to record that, as one would expect, I had more contacts with chaffinches than any other species; in fact, there were almost twice as many as the next most frequent bird – the wren. Then followed the robin and blackbird while the wood pigeon was fifth and the willow warbler sixth.

There are three main factors which decide the kinds of plant and animal that will occur in a region. These are the climate, the soil which results from the erosion of the rocks beneath and the activities of man. Throughout this book we shall be returning to these three themes. We shall see how wind, temperature, rainfall, sunshine and humidity together with the soil influence the species and character of the trees that grow in different areas and how these, in turn, affect the species of bird and other animals that appear. And what about man? Nearly all our woodlands have been interfered with by man and they cannot now be described as natural. The chief division of our woods is into broad-leaved and coniferous woods, of which most of the latter have been planted. Most temperate trees and shrubs lose their leaves in autumn – a defence against physiological drought in the cold of winter – but some like holly and most conifers are evergreen with leaves which have a thickened epidermis enabling them to withstand drought.

The plan of the book is a fairly simple one. It opens with three chapters designed to give the reader some understanding of the ecological factors which can influence tree growth, and to provide an account of the origins and history of the British and Irish woodlands and their birds from Pliocene times to the present day. Chapter 1 is an attempt to provide a simple background to the general environment of trees and thus a framework to any study of woodland birds. Chapter 4 poses the question "What is a woodland bird?" and takes a look at the different types of woodland and the ways in which censuses and sample counts can be carried out within them. The next four chapters are devoted to the bird-life of woodland of the more important tree species – both broad-leaved and coniferous. In Chapter 9 we take a look at woodland bird-songs. The following five chapters are concerned with scrub and developing woodland, including plantations, with small woods, forest edge, farmland and marginal habitats, with the adaptation of certain woodland species to life in towns, with some of the problems of woodland bird populations and the influences at work on them and with the place of birds in the practice of forestry. Finally, there is a systematic list giving the distribution and any changes in status of our woodland birds in Britain and Ireland.

Any work about woodland birds wanders into many other fields. Fortunately most of these have already been well described in companion volumes in the *New Naturalist* series. This book could not hope to be a comprehensive survey of all the aspects of woodland bird communities but it has been a great personal pleasure to write since in the putting of pen to paper I have not only been able to relive many delightful experiences in beautiful surroundings, but I have become increasingly conscious of those unanswered questions, some of which will draw me back to the woods. It is my hope that the book may encourage others to take up some of the difficult and unresolved problems but I cannot think of a more attractive or stimulating laboratory in which to undertake research.

CHAPTER I

THE TREE'S ENVIRONMENT

To find the birds of the British woodlands I have had to visit many different parts and to see many kinds of countryside. Perhaps nowhere else in Europe can one travel so short a distance and find so many contrasts. My search has taken me from the dusty heaths of Breckland with their conifers and crossbills to the Sitka spruce plantations of Glen Urquhart and the whispered stutters of countless goldcrests. I have visited, too, the slippery slopes of chalk beech-hangers, the old pine forests of Caledon, where Vaccinium crackles underfoot, the dank, primeval alder-carrs of East Anglia and the ash trees rooted in the clefts of the Yorkshire limestone pavements. On many occasions I have clambered over the partly buried, bryophyte-covered boulders of the Killarney oak-woods and here, as clearly as anywhere, I have had brought home to me the nature of the physical environment in which trees grow. This environment embraces not only the geology of the region and the soils in which the trees flourish but also the climate, the remainder of the flora and those biotic factors which can affect the natural history of an area. It is here that ecology tries, as I have mentioned earlier, to separate some of the factors from the complex whole and to look more closely at both the organisms and the inorganic parts of their environment which may influence their structure and development. "The ultimate goal of an ecological survey should be to discover and measure the main dynamic relations between all populations of organisms living on an area over some period of time" (Elton 1966). We have to consider the whole ecosystem including not only the fauna and flora but all the inorganic factors as well. In this field our knowledge is still very limited. My intention in this chapter, however, is to bring together some of the more important information, relevant to any study of woodland birds, which is so often scattered through many works of reference on geology, soils, climate, the development of plant communities and so on.

There is already in the *New Naturalist* series a book, *Britain's Structure and Scenery*, which traces very clearly the geological evolution of the British Isles. I shall therefore provide only a simple background of fact against which the story of our woodlands can be set.

Before we can look at the distribution of the various kinds of rock in the

British Isles we must remember that there are three fundamentally different types. First of all, there are the *igneous* rocks which after being deposited in a more or less molten state then cooled and solidified. These may have been erupted from the surface of the land as ash or lava from volcanoes or they may have solidified beneath the surface. Then there are the *sedimentary* rocks which formed layer upon layer on the sea-bed through the deposition of fine materials brought down by rivers and glaciers or as the result of erosion as well as the remains of countless marine animals. Rocks of this type could also form in lakes, river plains or even in deserts. Sometimes igneous rocks pushed their way upwards through the sedimentary layers above them and cooled in their new position. The third group of rocks is known as *metamorphic* and these, originally of the first or second group, may have been the result of great heat and pressure probably when they were far below the earth's surface; it is only through great earth movements and later erosion that they have been revealed to us. The metamorphic rocks are thus often difficult to distinguish from igneous and it has been suggested that volcanic, neptunic (sedimentary) and plutonic (granitic and metamorphic rocks formed underground at great depth) would be more logical terms.

If you draw a line with a ruler across a map of the British Isles from the mouth of the River Tees in Yorkshire down to the mouth of the River Exe in Devon, you will find that north and west of this line lies the region of mountain masses and older rocks. To the south and east of the line are the more recent rocks and the fertile plains of the lowlands. Nearly all the land above 800 ft. and, with the exception of the Cleveland Hills, all that above 1,200 ft. is to be found north and west of the "Highland line". In Ireland the higher ground lies like the rim of a saucer round the coastal edge of a large central plain.

Figure 1 shows the land in the British Isles above 800 ft. The division into two zones corresponds also with differences of structure, topography, and climate and therefore has had a profound effect on their subsequent history and that of the vegetation. The older rocks are chiefly made up of hard slates, grits, crystalline limestones, igneous granites and metamorphic gneisses resulting in shallow soils with forest on only the lower slopes of the hills, with moorland higher up and bogs, especially on the western coasts of Scotland and Ireland. The newer rocks are primarily sedimentary – soft sand and limestones, gravels, clays and marls which form deeper soils on the plains or low hills; these once carried almost continuous forest with swamp and fen forming in the lower, water-logged basins. Today the country of the older rocks with its heavy rains, warm south-westerly winds and cool summers has been largely stripped of its

FIG. I. Land over 800 feet in the British Isles.

natural forests and being unsuitable for arable farming has been turned over either to sheep grazing or to planting with alien conifers. The lowland zone with its deep soils has been largely deforested and turned over to cultivation.

It has already been shown in another volume in this series that the very real difference between the tree cover of the two zones may be partly concealed by the presence of a few species of tree to be found in both areas, as well as by man's erratic planting activities over the whole country.

However, woodlands in the north are found largely along the slopes of valleys or on their floors whereas in the south the trees can flourish on the highest hills. The Highland zone favours the growth of coniferous trees while the south-east is essentially the zone of broad-leaved. Certain trees like the hornbeam, wild service, white beam and field maple are restricted to the south-east and, although the beech has been extensively planted in the north, it, too, is probably native only in the south-east. Typical northern trees include the Scots pine, rowan, wych elm and sessile oak, while the pedunculate oak is largely associated with the lowland area. Of the common trees alder, birch and ash seem to grow equally well in suitable localities in both zones.

Climate plays an important part in the tree's environment and can have a profound effect on the flora of a region. One has only to contrast the tundra of the Arctic with the rain forest of the tropics to appreciate that, whatever the soils, climate is an important ecological factor. Such extremes do not exist in Britain and the differences in climate in the various regions are very much less. Western Europe with its often rainy, warm summers and cooler winters is particularly favourable to the growth of deciduous forest in which the trees, by shedding their leaves in the autumn, do not suffer loss of water at a time when very little water could be drawn up by their roots from a frozen soil.

The British Isles lie in the North Temperate Zone. There is a drop in summer temperatures as one travels north and a rise in winter temperatures as one goes west. Southern Ireland and the south-west of England and Wales lie in the northern part of the 50° F. – 60° F. annual isotherm belt while the remainder is to be found inside the 40° F. – 50° F. belt. The finest development of deciduous summer forest occurs in the Midland Plain and in the south-east of England which on average are drier and warmer in summer than the rest of Britain. In western Ireland and Scotland the mild winters and cool summers with high air humidity have resulted in a climate which varies hardly at all through 10 degrees of latitude; here the natural vegetation is blanket bog in which the stable features of the land are covered by peat, and it is only on the better drained ground that trees can exist. In the north there is a lower range of temperatures at all times of year; here the vegetation is largely limited to that of the northern coniferous forest but oak can exist in sheltered valleys lying south of the 58th Parallel with pine and birch on the hill-slopes above. The 54° F. July isotherm cuts off the north-east corner of Caithness: in northern Europe the July isotherm of 50° F. appears to coincide with the limit of tree growth – this is also the southern limit of the Arctic region. Native Scots pine survives up to an altitude of 2,000 ft. and I have seen trees even above this height on the sharp slope of Craig Fhiaclach in the Cairngorm Mountains. On the whole the high sparse native woods are dominated by birch. There is a decrease in temperature with increasing altitude with a lapse rate of 1° F. for every 300 feet. It may well be that the low summer temperatures on British mountains – the mean July temperature on Ben Nevis is 41.1° F. – are an obstacle to plant growth, and it is this which distinguishes them from their counterparts in Europe and North America. This could be the reason for the much higher tree line in the Swiss Alps. Another factor that can influence temperature is the distance from the sea, for higher temperatures are reached on the coast. The zonation of animals and plants on mountain slopes seems to be directly linked with temperature.

Changes in temperature can also affect the rate of biological processes and if one organism is dependent upon another, e.g. titmice on moth larvae, an alteration in the temperature can desynchronise the two life cycles to the disadvantage of the predator. Temperature, as we shall see later, may also be a factor in the limited distribution of such species as the cirl bunting. It has been suggested that the nightingale may also be affected in the same way.

Rainfall in the British Isles is greatest to the west and north and lowest in the south and east (Fig. 2). Broadly, most of Highland Britain receives more than 30 in. of rain each year while Lowland Britain gets less. However, the belt of high rainfall in the Highlands does not stretch evenly from north to south and it lies, not on the coast, but several miles inland from the sea. The annual rainfall can vary from about 24 in. in London to 77 at Fort William and 150 at 3,000 ft. in parts of western Scotland, yet the Outer Hebrides have to endure only from 40 to 60 in. The high ground intercepts the rain-clouds which tend to come chiefly from the west. The moist heavy air from the Atlantic rises over the mountains and the subsequent cooling causes the moisture to be given out as rain. There is a sharp decline in the amount of rain on the eastern slopes and some parts of the eastern Highlands receive less than 40 in.

It is sometimes more important to know the seasonal distribution of the rainfall. Generally trees grow faster the higher the rainfall but the actual amount varies between species. There is a strong association between high rainfall and high altitude, as the annual figures show, and the western uplands over 500 ft. lie very largely above the rainfall limits of a bog-forming climate. As Pearsall has shown, the average annual rainfall is not necessarily a true guide to the distribution of this type of climate for the absence of soil-drying in summer depends on the evaporation rate as well as other factors such as the presence of cloud, air humidity, mean

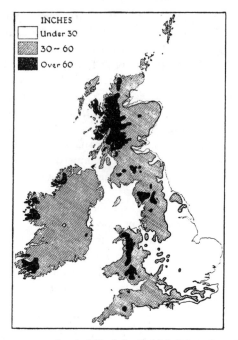

FIG. 2. The mean annual rainfall of the British Isles, showing the contrast between the wetter west and the drier east. From *Britain's Structure and Scenery*, by L. Dudley Stamp, 1946.

temperatures and local topographical features. For those of us who go hill-walking the position of clouds can be a very useful pointer to local differences in rainfall. These two factors of temperature and rainfall are very important in evolving the vegetation of a region. Relative humidity – the amount of moisture in the air expressed as a percentage of the amount the air could hold if it were saturated – may vary, and where rainfall exceeds the potential evaporation the ground can become water-logged. Humidity also has an important effect on the animals that live in the leaf litter that collects below trees. Finally, rainfall can influence the nature of soil by dissolving out the mineral salts, and this factor we shall return to later in the chapter.

In areas of high wind the growth of trees can be held back or even stopped by wind which has a stunting effect by blowing over the leaves, increasing the transpiration rate and drying out the shoots. Many trees growing near the coast or in very open, exposed situations develop asymmetrically through the destruction of leaves and shoots on the windward side. I have seen many small hawthorns on Romney Marsh, oak trees on Lakeland fellsides and sycamores in Shetland with their crowns streaming away from the prevailing wind. In Ireland persistent winds from the Atlantic make tree growth difficult or impossible so that the largest woodlands are found in sheltered valleys or on the eastern slopes of the hills. Near the coast airborne salt may also have a "blasting" effect, and after some south coast gales I have seen trees more than three miles inland with their southern halves turned brown by the salt. At high altitude cold winds can also limit the growth of trees. On the summit of Ben Nevis an average of 261 gales a year over 50 miles per hour have been recorded; this figure is more than six times the average for the nearby and exposed west coast of Scotland. Wind may not only keep down temperature on British hills but it can also operate through the humidity factor by drying out the soil which, in turn, means a loss of water for the plants.

All these climatic factors can work closely together and it may be rather difficult to unravel them. Trees with quite long life spans are also affected by many years of changing weather so that during their lives they may have undergone a whole range of different conditions – severe frost, sun and drought, a rise in rainfall. For the reader who seeks a fuller account of Britain's weather there is another volume in this series by Manley (1952) called *Climate and the British Scene*.

The individual tree and the established wood may also create their own micro-climates. Subtle differences may exist between two sides of an individual tree and conditions in the middle of a wood may be very different from those on the edge. Thus forests can modify the effects of extreme temperatures, rainfall, sunshine and humidity although the differences are not easy to plot. Trees and shrub layers can clearly interrupt the sun's rays and the temperature inside a wood may be considerably less than that on the outside. A wood offers shelter from the wind and can retain its temperature at night. Inside, quite large amounts of water vapour can be evaporated and the relative humidity need not remain constant. When humidity is at a high level the water loss from the surface of the ground is reduced. So forest can provide a shelter in which trees can grow and the success of this environment is clear when one compares the development of a tree inside the wood with that of an isolated member of the same species in an exposed situation where it must struggle against extremes of wind and temperature.

Inside a wood one of the most important of the habitat factors is light. Experiments carried out with an Avo light meter on days with a uniform blue sky gave a reading of 240 foot candles under the fully developed tree crown, of 20, 27 and 48 respectively under the shrubs while the grading in the open away from the wood was 3,600 foot candles. The dominant tree in a wood largely controls the amount and duration of the shade and thus, in turn, the other plants and indirectly the fauna. Oaks cast a heavy shade for more than six months of the year but if the tops of the trees are not too close together quite a bit of light can come through and allow the ground flora to be both rich and varied. There is also appreciable shade in a beechwood under which evergreen hollies and yews may grow, but only where there are gaps in the canopy can other shrubs develop. In many beechwoods the flora at ground level is completely missing and there is nothing but a carpet of dead leaves. Ash, with its many compound, feathery leaves, is responsible for much less shade. Pines and other evergreen conifers cast a continuous shade throughout the year, and in cases where the trees grow close together, as in artificial plantations, no shrubs or other plants can grow beneath them. Plants require starch and this is formed with the aid of chlorophyll from water and carbon dioxide through the use of sunlight – the process of synthesis. This is the first stage in the nutrition of a plant and is followed by the formation of more complex substances. Although light is necessary for photosynthesis the nourishment of the plant is obtained from two sources – the air and the soil.

Soil is the skin on the surface of the earth as well as the material in which trees and other plants grow. The dominance of certain trees depends on several factors of which the nature of the soil can be the most important. In the first place the soil is determined by a parent rock material. It may lie on an unstable surface such as a rocky hillside where under the influence of the weather the fragments of rock are broken down into smaller and smaller particles until they form the basic material of most soils. In the Lowland zone soil may form on more stable surfaces where active erosion is much less. Soil is produced in the first place by chemical changes brought to the rather sterile rock fragments by water often rich in carbon dioxide and secondly by the slow accumulation of organic material such as plant remains, dead roots, rhizomes and leaves. In the British Isles rainfall tends to exceed evaporation and as water moves downwards from the surface any dissolved salts and acid-neutralising bases such as lime and plant foods are also washed downwards – a process known as *leaching*. Local features such as the amount of slope on a hillside may affect the speed of leaching and so a time-factor may be involved in the making of soil-types. Where leaching has taken place the water charged with lime or other bases must appear somewhere else, and where it does it gives rise to enriched or *flushed* soils. Generally speaking leaching takes place typically in upland areas while flushed soils are more characteristic of lowland; both have a profound influence on the vegetation. The mineral requirements of different groups of plants vary and trace elements play an important, sometimes a vital, part in their chemistry. Ground-feeding birds may take in some soil with their food and so absorb them. Further, plants in a state of chemical disbalance may attract pests and, in turn, the predators that feed upon them. Certainly, chemical differences in plants can result in limiting the herbivorous creatures that feed upon them so that they vary, say, from oak to beech, but bird predators need not be limited to one species of tree.

The weathering of the parent rock material forms the subsoil, which is a mass of particles of uneven shape and size threaded by numerous channels and spaces filled with air and water. Many different organisms live in vertical zones in this habitat. Above lies the topsoil – the *humus* – derived from organic plant remains and altered by many physical, chemical and biological processes under differing climatic influences. The layer of humus with its fats, carbohydrates and proteins is full of micro-organisms whose density can vary from one to ten thousand million per gramme of soil. There are three main groups of soil animals – the micro-fauna (protozoa, rotifers, nematodes), the meso-fauna (mites, ants, springtails), and the macro-fauna (millipedes, centipedes, woodlice, earthworms). These animals are often very abundant, and counts made in a square metre suggest than an acre of beechwood might contain 40 million mites and 28 million springtails! The soil animals help by their processes of maceration and excretion to break down the soil so that the humus becomes a pulpy colloid overlying the subsoil, rich in plant food and rarely waterlogged. Much of the micro-fauna seems capable of recognising changes in humidity so that more species and greater numbers of animals appear where the air is permanently saturated.

In the temperate region woodland surface soils are usually divided into two kinds. In a deciduous wood the floor has at the surface a layer of comparatively fresh fallen leaves. Below is a stratum of partly decomposed plant remains and lower still a humus completely integrated with the soil. This type of soil is called *mull*; it is usually less acid and rather richer in calcium than most other soils. Its production depends on moderate or reasonably high temperatures, adequate moisture and good aeration. In coniferous woodlands, however, the surface layer decays fairly slowly and lies as a matted mass of material separate from the mineral soil underneath; this soil is called *mor* and is generally sandy and markedly acid. Soil animals in coniferous woodland may be quite common but earthworms are rare or absent altogether. The total weight of animals in coniferous woodland soils is about half that in deciduous woodland.

Madge has shown that the average leaf fall in temperate woods varies from 1,000 to 3,000 pounds per acre per year. Earthworms are the most important animals in breaking up and removing the leaf litter but springtails and certain fly larvae make a significant contribution. It seems likely that in mixed deciduous English woods some five tons or so of soil per acre are brought up to the surface by earthworms each year. Strong links exist between the members of some woodland bird communities and the fauna of the soil, but on the whole this field has not yet been very widely explored.

It is clearly climate rather than the parent rock which determines the chief characteristics of soils. Water and heat are both important agents in the processes which make soil.

Table 1 shows the most typical of the British soils, but it is not easy to find sections or profiles that have not been disturbed by man.

TABLE 1. *British Soil Types*

	Climatic Soils
BROWN EARTH or Brown Forest Soil	Characteristic soil of lowland Britain, and eastern Ireland. Mull rich and varied. Climax vegetation – deciduous summer forest – oak, beech.
PODSOL	Characteristic of cooler, wetter north and west of Britain. Highly acid humus (mor). Heather-moor, pine forest and birch. On sandy rock can occur in Brown Earth region.
BLANKET BOG	Where surface remains water-logged in podsol climatic region, peat develops. Occurs where rainfall high and exceeds evaporation. Especially in west Scotland, west Ireland and plateaux of 2,000 ft. on Pennines, Dartmoor and Wicklow Mountains.
	Soils Dependent on Special Water or Parent Rock Conditions
MEADOW SOIL	On flat ground with high water-table. Typically developed in river valleys to become pasture and hay, or silage meadows.
FEN PEAT	Constantly water-logged. Humus accumulates but kept alkaline through in-draining of base-rich water. When drained excellent arable land – Broads, Fens, Lough Neagh.
RAISED BOG	In less wet climate, acid peat accumulates in local basins. Ireland, Scotland.
RENDZINA	Derived from parent limestones. Shallow soils on fairly steep slopes. Alkaline in reaction. Leaching slight. Beechwood in south: ashwood in north and west.

The three main climatic soil types are the Brown Earths (or Brown Forest Soils), Podsols and Blanket Bog. The lower column in Table 1 covers most

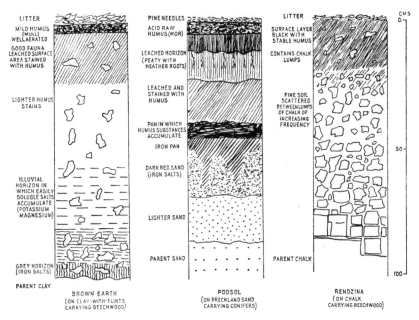

FIG. 3. Three soil profiles.

of the soils regulated by special local water conditions or the nature of the parent rock material such as limestone. The Brown Earths are the truly characteristic soils of the climatic region in which the final vegetation is deciduous summer forest – southern Britain, the Midlands and eastern Ireland. Conditions are comparatively dry and there is only a narrow margin between rainfall and evaporation. Leaching is not severe and there is a good supply of humus. This is the soil that forms the countryside of the broad-leaved forests, but in England most of it is now fine agricultural land. The section, or profile, shows a brown surface layer of excellent humus; it is partially leached in the upper layers which tend to be more acid than the lower ones. Water moves up and down within the profile from the parent rock below; this maintains stability and prevents the soil changing to a podsol where the water moved down (Fig. 3).

The podsol is characteristic of the north and west of the British Isles. Below the highly acid, raw, peaty humus and the humus-stained soil is a greyish layer which has been so heavily leached that the available bases, especially iron and lime, have been washed downwards. Fine particles and some of the humus are taken down as well and these gather at a depth of two or three feet in a brown cemented layer of "humus pan". Farther below is a red-brown or orange "iron pan" full of iron compounds. These pans are often a barrier to drainage. At the bottom is the parent rock material. The podsols generally correspond with the Northern Coniferous Region where pine, birch and *Calluna* heath can flourish and, if the soil is not too shallow, spruce as well. On a podsolic heath *Calluna* will compete very heavily against young trees. Podsols may also form on coarse sandy rock in the south where water can penetrate easily so this soil type is not restricted to its regional climate if conditions are favourable elsewhere and the climate is not too different. Soil conditions within a region can alter the vegetation type "and approximate it to one which is characteristic of an adjoining climatic type" (Tansley 1949), and indeed some of the most highly developed podsols occur on the Tertiary and Post-Tertiary deposits in the south and in Breckland. A profile of a typical Breckland podsol is shown in Fig. 3. Deep ploughing with open ridges and furrows can often be used to break up the whole structure of podsols. When this is done the heather is inhibited by the depth of soil, the drainage is improved and young trees can develop without competition. The Forestry Commission have planted spruce and pine in many parts of Scotland using this method.

In the podsol climatic region heavy rainfall can make the ground water-logged and encourage the growth of deep peat deposits. Peat is a kind of humus formed from plants in wet conditions and with little oxygen for anything growing in it. Gradually the dead plants accumulate in layers and so an organic soil is produced. When the peat spreads over comparatively flat or slightly sloping ground in regions where rainfall is heavy and the air so moist that the amount of rain is in excess of evaporation, this climatic soil type is called blanket bog. Where rainfall is less, raised bog peat which is very acid can accumulate in local basins. If there is regular drainage taking place through the rock layers under the peat, then an extreme form of podsol may eventually appear.

Of the other soils, which are produced not so much by climatic conditions as by the nature of the rock underneath, one of the most important is the rendzina – a soil formed from limestone (see Fig. 3). It is often greyish, or darker, rarely more than a foot thick and appears often on quite steep slopes. The parent rock is often chalk or fairly pure and relatively soft limestones. The rendzina profile is rich in calcium carbonate, alkaline in reaction and with comparatively little leaching. The calcium carbonate is brought upwards through rapid evaporation and the profile is prevented from becoming acid. Young soils derived from the chalk are often shallow and greyish-white in colour in contrast to the deeper, blackish soils, rich in humus, which are typical of the wetter, steeper chalk slopes. On more gentle slopes ferric salts may make the soil red-brown and some leaching may cause an acid reaction. These shallow calcareous soils carry a distinctive vegetation. In the south they may be clothed with beechwoods while ashwoods are characteristic of the north and west. Many of them are largely grassland and can form valuable green pastures.

It might seem from what I have said so far that fully developed, stylised soil profiles are common enough to find. This is not so and, while many profiles have been partially eroded, many have not yet had time to form or have remained permanently immature and undeveloped. Ploughing, as we have seen, can have an effect by altering the upper part of a profile. Manuring can also improve the base quality so that a podsol can be changed into a type more like that of a brown earth. If cultivation were to end there would always be a tendency for the climatic soil type to be re-established.

Soils can be classified according to what Tansley called their "texture". The parent materials are chemically made up in different ways and the resulting soils, evolved by weathering, contain particles of a size which is determined by the quality and composition of the original rock. These particles may be distinguished by their size and grouped as stones (or gravel), coarse sand, fine sand, silt and clay.

The diameter of the particles when greater than 2 mm = stones (or gravel)

from 0.2 to 2 mm = coarse sand

from 0.02 to 0.2 mm = fine sand

from 0.002 to 0.02 mm = silt

under 0.002 mm = clay

Soil texture is of vital importance to plants since it controls the movement of water and the presence of air, both of which, in turn, affect the chemical processes that occur in the soil. Gravel tends to be dry because of easy aeration and water percolation and is not very favourable to plant growth. More than half of the sandy soils are made up of coarse and fine sand with less than one tenth of clay. The particles are big enough to permit free passage of air and water so that thorough leaching takes place and the nutrients are washed away. A "hungry" soil like this needs constant manuring if it is turned over to cultivation. In oceanic and sub-oceanic zones these soils often bear heathy woods of pine and birch. Sandstones with plenty of finer particles can develop into brown earths with broad-leaved forest although the bigger sand grains can affect the other vegetation. If trees are cut down on this kind of soil the profile can turn into a podsol and then heath begins to form.

Silt, which is intermediate between the sands and clay, has the ability to hold its water content and to allow the fairly free circulation of air and water. It is a valuable growing soil and the original alluvial silts which bore alder and oakwood have been turned over mainly into meadowlands for pasture.

Clayey soils and clays contain a good proportion of small particles; they are heavy and plastic, drying from sticky pudding-like masses into solid hard clods. Anyone who gardens on this type of soil knows its characteristics only too well. It holds water which can only move slowly through it and the aeration is poor. It is not a favourable soil for plants but it can be improved by the addition of a mild humus. The typical tree cover is one of damp oakwood but much of this land is now pasture.

Loams are soils which have a smaller proportion of sand and a larger one of silt and clay, but their constitution ranges from "clay loams" through "medium loams" to "sandy loams". The clays and humus give a uniformity to the soil, help in the retention of water and provide various plant nutrients. Amply supplied with bases and good drainage these are ideal soils; they once carried oak and occasionally beech but many are now being cultivated.

Besides texture, soils can also be grouped according to their chemical composition and of these the most important is the calcareous soil – one heavily charged with calcium carbonate. The character of chalk and limestone rendzinas is largely determined by the presence of this mineral. The soil is alkaline and has a characteristic flora of "Calcicoles"; it may be shunned by certain plants usually known as "Calcifuges". In the south and south-east beechwood is typical of calcareous soils, and in the north and east ashwood. Some plants like the military orchid, the chalk milkwort and the horseshoe vetch are confined to chalk and limestone. The foxglove and the broom are calcifuges and excellent guides to the absence of calcareous soils.

The texture of the soils can be directly related to the nature of the original rocks – to their lithology, in fact – and to the local conditions of their formation. If you travel across the British Isles you can see many changes in the soils and this may be attributed to the enormous range of geological strata near the surface. Some knowledge of their appearance and distribution helps to give a more complete background to the environment in which trees grow. The most important of the geological formations can be seen in Fig. 4, but it must be remembered that deposits of recent river alluvium, peat and the debris left by the Ice Ages, although considerably eroded, may still overlie some of the older rock formations in an irregular manner. Some of the glacial drift is of quite fine texture and, where it contains rocks carried by the ice from a distance, it is often called "boulder clay". There are many places in western Scotland and the Outer Hebrides where the ancient Lewisian gneiss is overlaid by boulder clay which, in turn, is capped with a thick layer of peat containing the remains of a once extensive forest. In some places the ice sheets swept the ground clear leaving the pre-Cambrian rocks bare and smooth.

Table 2 shows the Stratigraphical Column whereby the history of the earth can be divided into eras and periods. The major geological divisions are brought together into four Eras – the Primary (or Palaeozoic) of long duration, the Secondary (or Mesozoic), the Tertiary and the Quaternary. The last two are sometimes grouped together as the Caenozoic Era. All the rocks that were formed before life appeared on the earth are usually called Pre-Cambrian or Archaean: the subdivisions of this very early period are rather conjectural since they do not contain fossil remains that can be used to judge their age. The dates shown in the column are subject to amendment as new techniques and discoveries are made but they provide a working basis for the evolution of the world's flora and fauna. They have been arrived at by a combination of methods involving radioactive disintegration and the transformation of uranium and thorium into lead and helium, of potassium into argon and of rubidium into strontium as well as by standard methods of geological investigation.

Table 3, shown deliberately opposite Table 2, is intended to be a guide to the distribution of the more important rocks of the British Isles since they are so closely associated with different types of vegetation.

The earliest rocks of the pre-Cambrian occupy a great part of the Scottish Highlands. The soils from these hard and ancient rocks are often poor and shallow a.id are associated with moorland, heaths, sheep-grazings, deer-forest and, if the rainfall is high, blanket bog. These rocks are much scarcer in England and Wales but drier conditions of climate promote the growth of heathy grassland and occasional dry oakwood. The earlier layers of the Primary Era – the Cambrian, Ordovician and Silurian – can be considered together since they produce, in the cool, wet conditions where they so often occur, very similar soils. The Cambrian rocks are to be found in parts of the English Midlands, in the Southern Uplands and North-West Highlands of Scotland, in North Wales and in south-east Ireland. The largely metamorphic Ordovician and Silurian rocks have a wide distribution in the British Isles. The foothills of these rocks often wear down to make good arable soils but the higher outcrops, in Leinster for example, tend to carry blanket bog while in Wales they support thousands of acres of sheep-grazing. The Old Red Sandstone deposits of the Devonian Period bear heath and moors on the higher land with sessile oakwoods in the valleys. In the wetter, milder district of

TABLE 2. *The Stratigraphical Column*

Era	Period	Approximate Age in Years	Botanical and other Features
	HISTORIC		Present flora within historic times.
QUATERNARY	PRE-HISTORIC		Peat deposits. First effects of Man, especially on woodland.
	PLEISTOCENE	1,000,000	Glacial and inter-glacial deposits.
	PLIOCENE		Temperate flora. Many species still found in British Islands. Structure of Britain now virtually complete.
TERTIARY	MIOCENE	25,000,000	
	OLIGOCENE		
	EOCENE	70,000,000	Tropical swamp-forests: many fossil plants.
SECONDARY or MESOZOIC	CRETACEOUS	135,000,000	Angiosperms (Flowering plants) dominant; flora tropical. Early mammals. Dinosaurs.
	JURASSIC	180,000,000	Era of Gymnosperms (Conifers, cycads, ginkgos, monkey-puzzles). Rocks highly fossiliferous. Dinosaurs.
	TRIASSIC	225,000,000	Reptiles, Brachiopods.
	PERMIAN	270,000,000	Amphibians dominant.
	CARBONIFEROUS	350,000,000	Lycopods, Ferns and Horse-tail-like plants.
PRIMARY or PALAEOZOIC	DEVONIAN	400,000,000	Fossil fish. Earliest known land plants.
	SILURIAN	440,000,000	Fish, Crinoids, Corals and Lamellibranchs.
	ORDOVICIAN	500,000,000	Graptolites.
	CAMBRIAN	600,000,000	Trilobites, Brachiopods, Molluscs.
PRE-CAMBRIAN or ARCHAEAN		4,500,000,000 ?	Pre-fossils.

TABLE 3. *The Geography of the Rocks*

Period	Distribution of the Rocks in the British Isles
HISTORIC	Formation of shingle beaches, estuarine mud.
PRE-HISTORIC	Alluvium of fenland. Peat formation.
PLEISTOCENE	Glaciation: erosion, drift and boulder clay over much of country. Red Crag of East Suffolk and East Norfolk; Weybourne Crag and Cromer Forest Bed. Chalky boulder clay.
PLIOCENE	Shelly sands or "crag" in East Anglia and Kent.
MIOCENE	Little represented in Britain.
OLIGOCENE	Limestone and clays of the Hampshire Basin.
EOCENE	Sands and clays. The London Clay and other sediments of London Basin. Bagshot Sands. Hampshire Basin and northern Isle of Wight. Volcanic rocks and basalt of Skye, Mull and north-east Antrim.
CRETACEOUS	CHALK: broad belt parallel to that of Jurassic from Dorset to Norfolk, North and South Downs, Wolds of North Lincolnshire and South-East Yorkshire. GAULT and GREENSAND: encircling the Weald, in Isle of Wight and along northern fringe of Dorset-Norfolk belt of Chalk. WEALDEN: sands and clay of Kent and Sussex.
JURASSIC	Clays, shales, limestones and ironstones. Belt running NE from Lyme Regis through Dorset, Somerset, Cotswolds, Oxfordshire, Lincolnshire/Northamptonshire Basin to North Yorkshire.
TRIASSIC	New Red Sandstone, pebble-beds and Keuper Marl. Small deposits near Elgin in Scotland and in NE Ireland. In England from Lower Severn valley through centre of England NW to plains of East Cheshire and Lancashire. Also Solway Firth, Yorkshire, Durham, East Devon, Notts.
PERMIAN	Breccias, conglomerates and red sandstones of Eden Valley and East Devon. Magnesian Limestone from Sunderland to Nottingham.
CARBONIFEROUS	THE COAL MEASURES MILLSTONE GRIT: part of West Riding, Peak and mid-Devon. MOUNTAIN LIMESTONE: of Lothians and Fife, the central Irish Plain, the Pennines, Peak and Mendips and parts of North-East and South Wales.
DEVONIAN	OLD RED SANDSTONE of Orkney, Caithness, Moray Firth, Southern Angus and Perth, Berwickshire. Mountains of Kerry, Cork, Tipperary and Tyrone. Parts of Southern Pembroke, Brecon and Monmouth. In England Hereford, Shropshire, North and South Devon, Cornwall.
SILURIAN	Southern part of Southern Uplands of Scotland. Considerable area of North-East Ireland (esp. Down, Armagh, Monaghan). Southern Lake District, in Shropshire and near Birmingham. Large part of North and Central Wales.
ORDOVICIAN	Volcanic and sedimentary. Northern part of Southern Uplands of Scotland. Parts of Wicklow, Carlow, Kilkenny, Monaghan and southern Mayo in Ireland. Much of Lake District, part of Shropshire. Parts of North Wales, Radnor, Brecon, Carmarthen and Pembroke.
CAMBRIAN	Hard, white quarzites and Durness Limestone of North Scotland. In Ireland part of Wicklow and Wexford. East side of Wrekin, Lickey Hills and near Nuneaton. Near Harlech and in Carnarvon in Wales.
PRE-CAMBRIAN	Sedimentary TORRIDONIAN SANDSTONE of North-West Scotland. ARCHAEAN: Large areas of Highlands and Islands of Scotland. LEWISIAN GNEISS. MOINE SCHISTS of North Scotland. Metamorphic Dalradian rocks of SW Highlands, Donegal and part of Connemara in Ireland. Volcanic rocks of Malverns, Longmynd, Wrekin and Charnwood Forest in England and Anglesey in Wales.

Killarney in Ireland there are woods of sessile oak with a rich growth of holly and occasionally strawberry tree. In Herefordshire the rock produces a fertile loam which is widely used for arable land, orchards and permanent pasture. In Caithness the fields, richly stocked with sheep and cattle, are separated from each other by flagstones set on edge and quarried from the deposits of the Old Red Sandstone which once paved many cities in western Europe. Fossil fish remains are common and an example of *Osteolepis* in my own collection is almost perfectly preserved.

Much of the Highland zone is taken up by rocks of the Primary Era. With the exception of those soils derived from the limestones the soils tend to be shallow, acid and liable to turn into podsols. The natural climax vegetation up to 1,000 ft., except in the extreme north, is that of sessile oakwood with birch and pine in the Scottish Highlands and alder in the damper districts. On the limestones the typical tree is the ash with birch at the higher levels. A great deal of the original tree cover has disappeared as the result of human clearance and grazing; in the wet and poorly drained areas of the west peat forms and stops tree development. In Ireland boulder-clay left from the Ice Ages conceals a great part of the central plain formed from the mountain limestone of the Carboniferous Period. The calcareous soil and the damp, not too extreme climate allow the development of extremely fine cattle pastures. Ash grows in amongst the surviving oakwoods and in the west of Ireland there is extensive hazel scrub. In Northern England ash also grows on the mountain limestone "pavements" or terraces, often with hazel and a very varied woodland flora. Above the limestone sediments are the sandstones and shales of the Millstone Grit, with sand grains so sharp and angled that their rock was once used for making millstones. In the Pennines I have seen the ashwoods and grassland of the mountain limestone contrasting strongly with the sessile oakwood and birches of the steep escarpments of the Millstone Grit. In Yorkshire, above the Carboniferous rocks, there is a belt of the softer Permian or magnesian limestone, rich in magnesium carbonate and tending to produce rendzina profiles; here ash is the dominant tree.

Of the Secondary, or Mesozoic, rocks the lowest formation is that of the Triassic and its deposits tend to run parallel to those of the later Jurassic and Cretaceous Periods. The main area of Triassic sediments stretches across the Midlands of England to the Vale of York and to the Cheshire Plain. It is generally separated into two main divisions – the New Red Sandstone with sands and pebbles, including the Bunter Pebble Beds near Birmingham, and the red, fine-grained Keuper Marls. The Bunter sandstone gives a poorish soil which carries oak, birch and heath as in Sherwood Forest; the Keuper Marls form fine grassland. The later rocks of Jurassic age lie mainly in a narrow crescent which sweeps up from Dorset and runs north-east to the coast of Yorkshire. The most important deposits are made up of clays, limestones and occasional sands. On the Oxford and Kimmeridge Jurassic clays the climax vegetation is damp oakwood but over the years this has given way to pastureland. The oolitic limestones of the Cotswolds bear calcareous grassland and sometimes quite extensive semi-natural beechwoods on the hill scarps and valley slopes; here the long dip slope is mainly agricultural land but the north-west scarp is too steep to plough. In north-east Yorkshire the limestones of the Cleveland Hills have heath on their tops and ash and oak in their valleys.

The Cretaceous rocks of the Secondary Era include the Wealden Clays and the sands of Sussex and Kent laid down by three rivers flowing from the north-east, the north-west and the west into what is now south-east England. Today a great deal of the Weald is under pasture but it was originally covered by thick, damp oakwoods – the vanished forest of Anderida. Encircling the Weald and running along the axis of Jurassic deposits stretching north-east from Dorset are the narrow Cretaceous belts of the calcareous Upper Greensand and the clayey Gault. Good arable land can be developed from the former while the Gault, once well covered with oak, is now largely pasture. Below the Gault is the Lower Greensand which rises in places to make an impressive ridge some ninety miles long; it is particularly well shown to the north of the Weald where Leith Hill rises to an impressive 960 ft. – the highest point in south-east England. The climax vegetation of the Lower Greensand is oak wood, but on the sandy, non-calcareous soils this is often replaced by heath on which birch and pine may take hold. The podsolised soils of these woods have been compared with those of the north Yorkshire moorlands. Greensand also occurs, but less noticeably, in the east Midlands and there are quite large plantings of pine on heathland near the borders of Buckinghamshire and Bedfordshire.

Surmounting the Cretaceous layers is the Chalk – a pure, soft, white limestone – forming the North and South Downs, the backbone of the Isle of Wight and a broad band which runs north-east from the Berkshire Downs along the Chilterns and into East Anglia. Farther north other deposits make up the Lincolnshire and Yorkshire Wolds. Some of the Chalk lies concealed beneath layers of boulder-clay or other residues mixed with chalk, such as "clay-with-flints" produced by the processes of leaching. "Clay-with-flints" has a low calcium carbonate content and its vegetation is rather different from that on soils derived from the Chalk itself. Chalk soils are often of the rendzina type and in the south-east

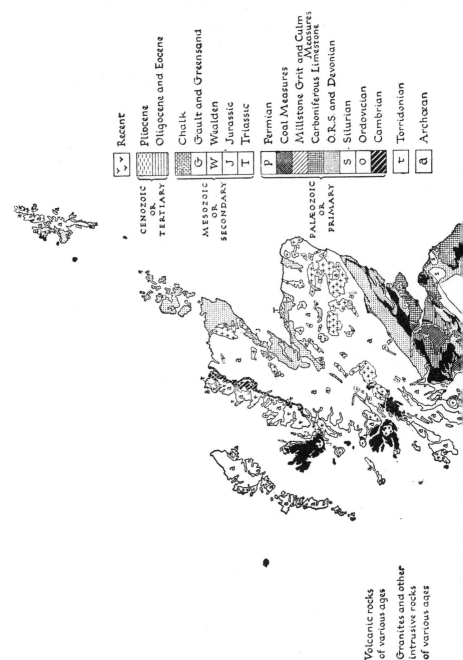

Recent

CENOZOIC
OR
TERTIARY
- Pliocene
- Oligocene and Eocene

MESOZOIC
OR
SECONDARY
- Chalk
- G | Gault and Greensand
- W | Wealden
- J | Jurassic
- T | Triassic

PALÆOZOIC
OR
PRIMARY
- P | Permian
- Coal Measures
- Millstone Grit and Culm Measures
- Carboniferous Limestone
- O.R.S. and Devonian
- S | Silurian
- O | Ordovician
- Cambrian

- t | Torridonian
- a | Archæan

■ Volcanic rocks of various ages

✠ Granites and other intrusive rocks of various ages

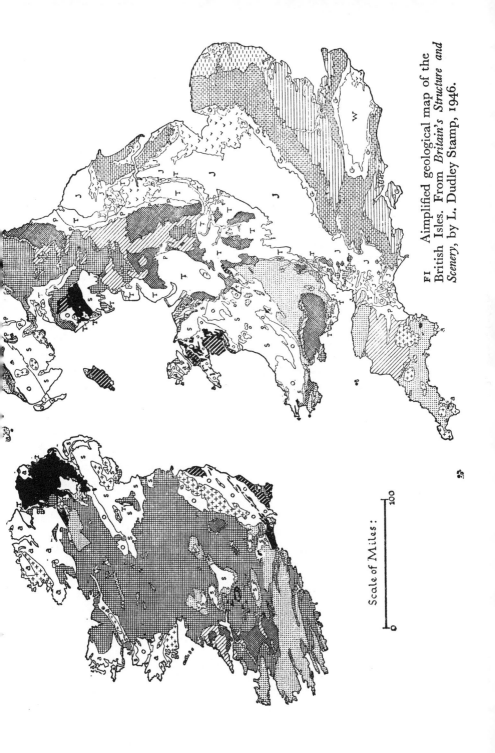

FI Aimplified geological map of the British Isles. From *Britain's Structure and Scenery*, by L. Dudley Stamp, 1946.

Scale of Miles:

0   100

support beechwood but this is replaced gradually to the south-west by ash. On the North Downs it is possible to contrast the two soil types. On the Chalk subsoil the downland consists of grassland with scrub and woodlands of beech, yew and box. Box Hill itself is capped with a layer of "Clay-with-flints" and, although some beeches do occur, the oak is common and well developed, the leaf litter is thick and a loam forms which approaches the Brown Earths in quality. Such land has sometimes grown very fine crops of wheat.

Our journey upwards in time through the most important of Britain's geological outcrops brings us now to the Tertiary Era. In Britain, beds of Tertiary age are almost entirely confined to south-east England and here they occur in two areas – the London Basin which includes much of the Thames Valley and the Hampshire Basin which also incorporates the northern half of the Isle of Wight. There are several other small divisions of the Tertiary but these are disputed among geologists. The Eocene and Oligocene are often considered together and some geologists also bring the Miocene and Pliocene together, but Miocene deposits are not a feature of the British Isles. In the London Basin the thickest of the Eocene deposits are those of the London Clay which breaks down eventually into soils of the Brown Earth type carrying oakwoods. Heath and birch can be found on some of the lower layers of sand and clay. Other Eocene beds include the Bagshot Sands to the south-west of London and isolated patches on the summits of Hampstead and Highgate to the north. These sands often reveal typical podsols and may bear sandy oakwood in places, but they are more usually associated with heaths of birch and sub-spontaneous pine where redpolls and other finches forage for food. Oligocene deposits are to be found only in southern Hampshire and part of the Isle of Wight and are not of great ecological importance. Strata of Pliocene date, composed mainly of sand and pebbles, can be found on top of those of the Eocene in East Anglia and most of them are covered with heathland.

The Quaternary deposits arise from coastal accretion, from river silts, from the formation of peat and from the glacial drift from the Pleistocene ice-sheets which covered much of Britain for many thousands of years. Today in northern Britain moorland covers most of the glacial deposits. The drift of the English Midlands which is now good arable or grazing land was covered up to Saxon times by oak forest. The chalky boulder-clay of Lincolnshire, East Anglia, Essex and the eastern Midlands had a natural forest growth of ash and oak, tiny remnants of which have been developed as coppices and oak standards. In a later chapter we shall look more closely at the period of the Pleistocene with its alternately advancing and retreating ice-sheets and its far-ranging effects on the vegetation and fauna of the British Isles. It was during this period that the early patterns of distribution among woodland birds were laid down while man also appeared upon the scene.

So far we have been considering the way in which physical factors can influence the environment in which trees grow. Now we must examine the biotic factors whereby animals, including man, may change or control the character of the environment. I have already referred to the concept of the ecosystem in which plant development is considered either to be in a state of near equilibrium or moving towards such a condition. Man carries the greatest responsibility for the alteration to ecosystems, and in the extreme case he is capable of destroying them. They are the product of all the factors of the habitat that led to their evolution – soil, climate, associated organisms and so on, and so they tend to reassert themselves if given a chance. Man has often totally destroyed woodland to make way for grazing and arable fields, for houses, roads and reservoirs. Sometimes he has decided to use the ecosystem to his own advantage by altering it to another which depends in the first place on the physical nature of the environment but can be modified by those factors which man brings to bear upon it. It is not always easy to trace the early interference of man and any ecological study should seek to discover what sort of influence earlier and long-ceased activities such as coppicing and thinning have had on the development of a wood.

A great deal of the British countryside has been altered by biotic factors and very little vegetation remains that can be called natural or "virgin". Few woods remain "with a touch of the terror of infinity" (Collett 1940). Forest has given way to farms and grassland. Domestic animals such as sheep and cattle, and wild animals like rabbits have often kept semi-natural plant communities in a state of balance. Severe damage has sometimes resulted from too high a concentration of rabbits but this picture has often changed since the advent of myxomatosis. However, some rabbit populations that I know have made good recoveries from the disease. In broad-leaved woods mice and voles are largely responsible for preventing natural regeneration since they not only destroy the seedlings, but also consume the fruits. Other mammals such as deer and squirrels may do varying amounts of damage to trees. Birds may damage trees during their development, but many species are beneficial and feed on insect and other pests that attack them. Birds may help the spread of tree species by dispersing their seeds by excreting them undamaged or even by burying them in the ground. We shall come back to this interesting aspect of woodland propagation later on.

There are many facets to the ecosystem and vegetation, including that of woodlands, is so important in the lives of birds, that it becomes necessary to examine more carefully the "nature" of woodland. Forest has been described as "the supreme development of nature on land" (Elton 1966), and it is interesting to see how a tree may grow either in association with members of its own species or in competition with those of other species. Woodlands are no more than tight or loose aggregations of trees – plant communities, in fact, which share a common habitat. The concept or idea of plant communities also illustrates the reality of plants which show an interdependence as well as a dependence on their common habitat. To take the argument a stage farther – the study of habitats must go side by side with the study of plants in which it is important to separate the various species from each other. That "ecology cannot precede taxonomy" is an axiom that was propounded in *British Plant Life* – a companion volume in this series.

Simple plant communities may be composed of single *life-forms*, or types of plant. Examples of life-forms are the broad-leaved trees of the European summer forest, the giant evergreens of the tropical rain-forests, the conifers of the colder regions of the north and the mosses growing on the woodland floor. There can be several species all of the same life-form in a community but in the simplest community there may be only one species present. Most plant communities have several, and occasionally many, life-forms. In a community the individual plants may have their shoots or root systems in contact with each other – this is known as a *closed community*. If there is space between the plants which would allow new ones to grow then the community is an *open* one.

Usually inside each plant community there are certain species, generally the tallest, which by the nature of their growth influence and shape the environment in which the other members of the community develop; these are called the *dominant* species. There can be more than one dominant tree species and when this happens they are generally found to be of the same life-form – oak and ash, for example – in a broad-leaved wood. The life-forms of these dominant trees are also characteristic of the general conditions in which the whole plant community evolved. An oakwood can contain not only other species of broad-leaved trees but also a recognisable subsidiary flora typical of oakwoods in general with hazel, primrose, wood anemone and so on.

Plant communities are also made up of units of which the largest is known as a *formation* and consists of a type of vegetation with characteristic life-forms. Each formation is made up of smaller communities dominated, as we have already seen, by one or several tree species. If one species dominates a wood the community is known as a *consociation* but if there are several species of about equal importance then it is called an *association*. Where a wood is dominated by pedunculate oaks *Quercus robur* then this consociation is often described as *Quercetum roboris*: here *-etum* is added to the stem of the generic name while the specific name is put into the genitive case. Since other Latin names are used to describe plants and animals, this system is universally practised and is unambiguous. Consociations of beech are called *Fagetum silvaticae* and of alder *Alnetum glutinosae*. Within a consociation are the plant *societies*; these are local groups formed by one or more species other than that of the dominant one. A small group of ash or birch trees growing inside a large oakwood is an example of a society within a consociation.

Most plant communities can be divided into different layers, zones or formation-types as they are sometimes called; these are important in any study of woodland birds. Four such layers can be seen in an English broad-leaved wood and each contains one, or more than one, dominant species of a characteristic life-form. If you walk through a southern English oakwood it is easy enough to recognise that there are two upper layers above your head. One is formed by the tree canopies and branches, and the other by the shrubs growing underneath. Lower still is a field layer of small plants and herbs, and finally there is a ground zone which, if not covered with herbs, is clothed with mosses and plant and animal debris. In one Midland oakwood I have seen a crow's or wood pigeon's nest in the canopy, a pair of bullfinches foraging in the shrub layer, a marsh tit exploring the field layer and a blackbird assiduously searching the leaf litter of the ground zone for some of the soil fauna. Some bird species may be found in each of the layers in the course of a season, while breeding activities may be confined to just one of them.

Figure 5 shows the distribution of these formation-types and their upper limits of height above the ground. The ground zone of mosses, grasses and small herbs reaches to a height of six inches from the layer of top soil and often carries the largest number of green plant species in the community. The field layer of taller grasses and plants reaches from six inches up to six feet and is sometimes divided again into a low field layer up to three feet and a high field layer from three to six feet. These divisions are at some variance with botanical practice. The low canopy or scrub layer rises from a height of six feet, where the field layer ends, to fifteen feet. Some authorities regard shrubs over fifteen feet as being trees, while others consider that twenty-six feet should be the upper limit of the scrub canopy, but I find that much of the scrub growing in the open tends to be lower than this. If exact heights are given, then there should be no difficulty even with developing plantations and those trees which pass through a scrub stage on their way to maturity. For scrub growing outside there should be some latitude and I have regarded as scrub some growths over the fifteen-foot level. Lastly, there are the canopies of more developed trees and that part of a tree which lies between the canopy and the shrub layer. In a fully mature wood in a severely exposed position, in scrub and along the edge of a wood the canopy can sometimes be as low as six feet; generally, however, the high canopy is regarded as being above fifteen feet. Some species of bird like the heron, rook and wood pigeon may choose the upper canopy for nesting. Smaller species may avoid it and favour the shrub layer below where the more intricate, denser structure of branches and twigs provides a better support for their nests. Canopies are also often exposed and rather wind-swept. Trees in their growth from seed to seedling, sapling and mature tree can pass in turn through the various layers in a wood. Further, as they grow, their root systems occupy deeper layers of the soil underneath.

Scrub and woodland can consist of three main types: these are broad-leaved, coniferous and mixed. It is sometimes difficult to estimate the proportion of each life-form in a wood, but the broad-leaved is important because of the annual shedding of its leaves which has a profound influence on the animal life. Yet the presence of only a few conifers in a broad-leaved forest can attract several insect and bird species. Birds may find more favourable feeding and roosting places in the conifers than in the broad-leaved trees.

Mention must be made here of the boundaries which separate one plant community from another. These have been called tension belts or ecotones and they may contain elements from both communities. It has been said that a true ecotone must occupy a habitat intermediate between those of the two communities on each side. The edge of a wood or a piece of scrubland may be richer in plant and animal species than the centre of each. Clearings and rides are often important to woodland birds while hedgerows (Wordsworth's "little lines of sportive wood run wild") and shelter belts can provide rich havens for birds that have spread out from the forests. We shall take a closer look at these habitats in Chapter 11.

The reader might be misled by this rather short account of plant communities into thinking that they are always static and unmoving. This is not so, since they are dynamic and capable of evolving sometimes slowly but often with considerable speed. Let us imagine that a field that has been long under cultivation is allowed one year to fall into disuse. At first it is colonised by weeds, some of which have been left over from the period of cultivation, and by grasses. Then bushes and small trees follow in a more or less clear sequence of colonisation. This process is called a

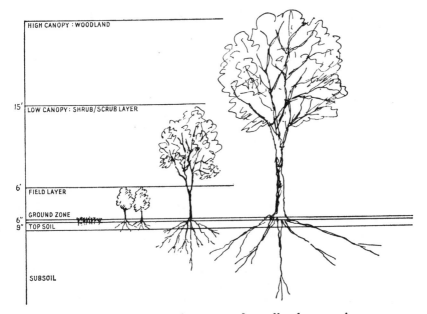

FIG. 5. Four formation-types of woodland vegetation.

succession and there are many different kinds. It is often important to identify the stages of each succession and to look at a wood and decide whether it is at the end of its logical development or is still in the process of evolution. Even inside the same wood it is possible to find different examples of succession since fire, clearance and the natural death of trees can open up spaces to more light, more rainfall and a fresh colonisation by plants. The succession finally ends in most instances in a reasonably stable *climax community* dominated by the largest of the plants able to grow and flourish in the particular environment. In England the climax is broad-leaved woodland. These successions are called *seres* and when development to a climatic climax is reached from a completely bare habitat it is called a primary sere or a *prisere*. Wind scouring, floods, fire and the action of ice can all create new land on which a prisere can begin. After the blitz of 1940 I examined a basement floor in a bombed house in London colonised within the first year by Oxford ragwort, rose-bay, groundsel and Canadian fleabane. All these plants, like the coltsfoot and bracken which came in the second year, were wind dispersed. By the third year elder seedlings had taken hold, probably from seeds excreted by birds like starlings which had been feeding on them elsewhere. The elders were followed by sallows and finally by sycamores which in a few years had become the dominant plants well over twenty feet tall.

The community before the climax is established is usually called the *pre-climax*. On many light soils in the British Isles birchwood is the pre-climax to oak while beechwood may be preceded by ashwood or ash/oak-wood. We shall look more closely at these successions and their bird-life later on. The pre-climax vegetation can sometimes exist as the final form in a nearby climatic region which does not permit the climax dominants to establish themselves. Any seral succession shorter than that of a prisere is often called a *sub-sere*. When the successions or seral changes occur without any change in the environment and are affected only by the activity of the vegetation itself they are called *autogenic*; on the other hand, successions brought about by such changes as leaching are known as *allogenic*. It is possible for both factors to be at work at the same time.

The climatic climax community in a state of balance with its environment normally ends the succession, but many factors can interfere with and prevent the full seral move to the climax. When this happens a very different kind of community can emerge. Extensive grazing by animals on chalkland can stop the growth of woodland and the resulting grasslands form what is called a *biotic climax*. Coppicing and burning can have a similar effect. Soils can sometimes be too wet for trees to grow and climaxes which are in any way dependent on the condition of the soil are known as *edaphic climaxes*.

It can be seen that an ecosystem and its evolution depend upon many different factors. Woodland ecosystems are particularly complex and for future ecologists there remains a vast tangled skein of interrelated patterns waiting to be unravelled. The strands of this skein are numerous and run both laterally and up and down; they may alter according to the season and they are subjected to the subtle influence of climate, geography and history. Their interactions and their stability contribute towards the total synthesis that we call the ecosystem. Some factors may have only a slight effect on the distribution of woodland birds but others, like disease and the age of trees which affect the number of potential nesting sites for hole-breeding birds, may be of supreme importance. By knowing something of the basis to plant communities, their history and structure, it is easier to bring birds more sharply into focus against their shadowy woodland background.

A simple chart drawn up for the pied flycatcher shows some of the influences that brought this species to a particular oakwood in northern England at a particular time. This can be done for other species as well.

TABLE 4. *The Ecology of the Pied Flycatcher – A Demonstration*

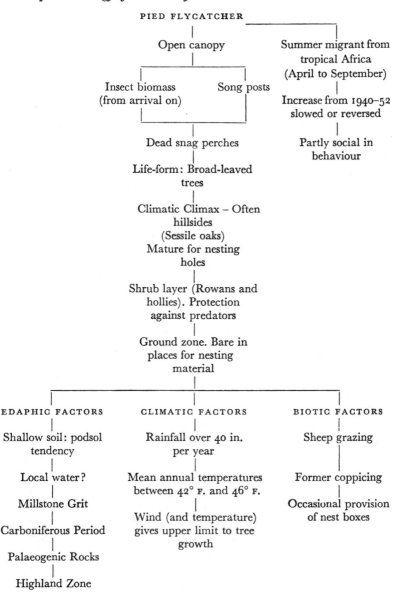

PIED FLYCATCHER

Open canopy

Insect biomass   Song posts
(from arrival on)

Dead snag perches

Life-form: Broad-leaved
trees

Climatic Climax – Often
hillsides
(Sessile oaks)
Mature for nesting
holes

Shrub layer (Rowans and
hollies). Protection
against predators

Ground zone. Bare in
places for nesting
material

Summer migrant from
tropical Africa
(April to September)

Increase from 1940–52
slowed or reversed

Partly social in
behaviour

EDAPHIC FACTORS   CLIMATIC FACTORS   BIOTIC FACTORS

Shallow soil: podsol   Rainfall over 40 in.   Sheep grazing
tendency   per year

Local water?   Mean annual temperatures   Former coppicing
                          between 42° F. and 46° F.
Millstone Grit   Occasional provision
                          Wind (and temperature)   of nest boxes
Carboniferous Period   gives upper limit to tree
                          growth
Palaeogenic Rocks

Highland Zone

THE ORIGINS OF THE BRITISH WOODLANDS AND THEIR BIRDS

T HE earliest forms of birds appeared in the Jurassic Period, while the main orders emerged during the Eocene and the families of perching birds – the passerines – during the late Tertiary. The earliest species began their evolution after the start of what has been called "the long quiet period" of the earth's history when there were no major earth movements or outbursts of volcanic activity. This interval of calm lasted from the Jurassic right through the Cretaceous Period. By the end of the Mesozoic Era (see Table 2) considerable changes in the world's geography took place involving the raising up of the Alps, the Rockies and the Himalayas. Much of the countryside of southern England owes its appearance to the folding and crumpling of the earth that followed the Alpine movements. This can be seen in the chalk folds of the Isle of Wight and the Hog's Back and in the twisting of the Jurassic sediments at Lulworth Cove. By the end of the Tertiary – during the Pliocene Period – the earth's geography had very largely come to resemble that of the present day although the British Isles, Japan and Indonesia were still joined to their mother continents.

During late Pliocene times the climate and the flora of Britain resembled those of today although there were some differences. Near Sheringham in Norfolk there are the Cromer Forest Beds of this period, and the fossil plants found in these deposits reflect to some extent the flora of East Anglia *before* the ice ages. Of these fossils by far the greater number are those of species existing today while only 5% consist of exotic or extinct ones. Among the plants that became extinct were the Water Chestnut (*Trapa natans*) and the Silver Fir (*Abies*). The Cromer fossils included many familiar shrubs and trees including Scots pine, yew, hornbeam, hazel, birch, beech, alder, oak, elm, rowan, blackthorn, hawthorn, maple, alder buckthorn and dogwood. It is likely that many of our woodland bird species were present at this time in some of the habitats suggested by the fossil flora.

The Pleistocene Period lasted roughly a million years during which it is now generally accepted that there were at least four major glaciations with three interglacial periods when some form of temperate vegetation took a hold before being swept away again. This was probably the first real ice age since Permian times and during this period some nine advances and nine retreats of the ice took place. At the height of the glaciations thick sheets of ice covered much of northern Europe and northern North America with subsidiary caps on the Alps, Pyrenees and Caucasus. There is considerable doubt as to how far the ice really extended and about the climatic differences between each period of glaciation and retreat. One argument suggests that the glaciation in the British Isles was so severe that almost the whole of the Pliocene flora was destroyed with only a bare handful of arctic-alpine species managing to survive. On the other hand it may well be that the conditions in some areas and along the glacier fringes allowed many species to persist. Present opinion seems to lean towards the first of these theories and to suggest that the climatic changes of the Pleistocene Period profoundly altered our plant communities. Most of our trees and shrubs and all plants with a southern range were probably wiped out. Yet the similarities between the flora of the Pliocene and of the present day in Britain mean that the greater part of it must have survived in those parts of continental Europe where the ice had no effect; later it returned across the land-bridge between Europe and England in post-glacial times. As each glaciation approached the oakwoods would disappear, then birch and pine would be replaced by the flora of the tundra. As the ice retreated with a rise in temperature the birch, pine and finally the oak would return.

Those parts of the Old World which lay under the arctic conditions of the Quaternary ice ages form what is called the Palaearctic Region; this embraces Europe, North Africa and Asia north of the Himalayas. Although the climate of the region was arctic, the whole land surface was not itself entirely submerged by the ice-sheets which elsewhere made all life impossible as they spread south.

At its peak the huge ice-cap covered the whole of north-western Europe south to the British Isles where it reached roughly to a line drawn from the Thames Estuary to the Bristol Channel. Also under the ice lay Holland and western Europe north of latitude 50° N. and east almost to the Black Sea. Some three million square miles of northern Europe were overborne by an ice-cap whose main centre of dispersal was in Scandinavia with lesser centres in Highland Britain. Ice, too, covered the great mountain massifs of Europe, North Africa and Asia; it also spread over North America beyond the Great Lakes and formed a sheet twice the size of that in Europe. In Scotland the ice was at least 3,500 ft. thick in the hollow in which Loch Maree lies.

During the last glaciation, the ice extended over a slightly smaller area of Europe and reached south in the British Isles only to North Norfolk,

northern England, Wales and Southern Ireland. On the Continent the
edge of the ice swept in a curve from south of the Baltic north-eastwards
(Fig. 6). During this glaciation there were some parts of northern Britain
probably free of ice and the summits of some hills – An Teallach, Ladhar
Beinn and Clisham on the Isle of Harris – may have stood out as nunataks.
It seems likely that the features of this last glaciation were similar to those
of previous ones, especially since all the genera and nearly all the species
of bird known from Pleistocene fossils can still be found somewhere in
Europe. This indicates what Moreau calls "a remarkable persistence and
resilience through great vicissitudes on the part of the European avifauna".

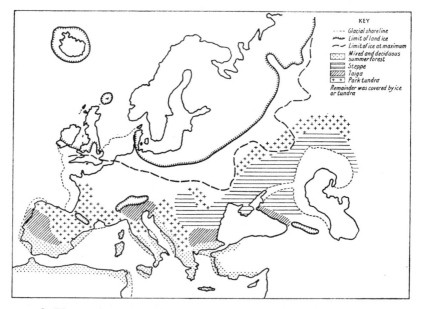

KEY

- - - - Glacial shoreline
━━ Limit of land ice
━ ～ Limit of ice at maximum
Mixed and deciduous summer forest
Steppe
Taiga
Park tundra
Remainder was covered by ice or tundra

FIG. 6. Vegetation map of Europe at the height of the last glaciation.

A list of all the British fossils of this period has been made, but the
evidence is sometimes fragmentary and specific identification is not always
possible. Since birds are adaptable and many are able to change their
habits, considerable caution is needed in any deductions from the fossil
record. For the beginning of the glaciations Fisher (1966) has listed some
typical woodland birds from England, Scotland and Ireland including the
buzzard, raven and crow, from England and Ireland the robin, song
thrush, redwing and greenfinch and from England alone the eagle-owl
and the blackbird. The later record from the Upper Pleistocene reveals an

avifauna very similar to that of the present day; it includes game-birds like the blackcock, capercaillie and the only British record of the hazel grouse as well as kestrel, woodcock, wood pigeon, stock dove, long-eared owl, little owl, redwing, fieldfare, blackbird, mistle thrush, robin, nightingale, wren, great tit, hawfinch, chaffinch, linnet, nuthatch, treecreeper, whitethroat, great grey and red-backed shrikes, rook, jackdaw and jay. In Ireland the great spotted woodpecker and the magpie could be found in Co. Clare. The wren probably entered Asia across the Bering Straits during the Pleistocene Period for all the other species of wren are restricted to the New World.

The overall temperature drop during each glaciation not only forced a retreat on the vegetation but drove the bird populations east, south-east and south. In North America the ice drove many of the forest trees south but, as they were not compressed against lateral mountain barriers in the way that the vegetation was forced up against the Alps and Pyrenees, they moved south. In North America the mountain ranges run north and south so that the trees that retreated south were able to return by the same route. In the Great Smoky National Park in the Appalachians I have visited a rich broad-leaved forest with 131 native species of tree; in Europe the figure is only 85. In Europe, after the final retreat of the ice, many of the birds moved back northwards and westwards – a process which in some places is not finished yet. In the last hundred years or so, more than twenty species have extended their range to the north and west. There are over fifty species that nest regularly in Britain which do not do so in Ireland. The magpie returned to Ireland in 1676 and the stock dove in 1875.

The scenery of much of Britain is that of a countryside once covered by ice. Great masses of ice ground and smoothed the landscape turning old V-shaped valleys into gentle U's and polishing and scoring the rocks below. Softer rocks were scooped out and lakes formed, while other regions became water-logged and marshy like the country of Connemara and the Outer Hebrides. Great drift deposits were left behind and, where the extreme limit of the ice-sheet melted as quickly as it advanced, the debris was left as a moraine or irregular ridge. A glacier retreating in fits and starts could leave behind a whole series of such ridges. Where the ice melted in position great layers of boulder-clay, made up of pebbles, stones and boulders in a matrix of clay, were left behind. Large boulders known as erratics were carried great distances and the London boulder-clay contains a number from Scandinavia. Where some erratics have been traced back to their source research has shown hidden mineral deposits of considerable value.

It is through recent work in palaeobotany that the picture of conditions

during and after the last glaciation have become clearer. The map on
page 32 (Fig. 6) gives a simple guide to the last ice age but it cannot, of
course, show vertical zonation of the vegetation on the mountains. To the
south of the ice-cap lay a strip of tundra from perhaps fifty to three
hundred miles wide. Here the gravelly, rocky ground was frozen for most
of the year; there were no trees and only dwarf shrubs, mosses and lichens
could exist in this hostile environment. Snow showers were frequent and
often heavy. The tundra conditions of southern England at this time have
been compared to present ones in Greenland today, and also to the snowy
wind-swept region of South Georgia. The ground in places may have been
frozen to depths of two hundred feet or more; in the Yukon today the
rocks are full of ice down to 400 ft. below ground. The perma-frost is
thought to have reached as far south as central France. During the last
glaciation, the tundra of what is now the London area probably had a
January isotherm of about 5° F. which rose in July to about 45° F. The
summer was also probably drier with a little more sunshine. The tundra
flora included arctic birch and various arctic willows as well as some
northern and Highland plants. Over fifty species of Arctic mosses from
the Lea Valley deposits near London were collected in 1912; most of
these have been found growing today at Latitude 68° N. in Lapland.
The birds would have been restricted to such arctic tundra species as
ptarmigan, long-tailed duck, knot, snowy owl and the most northerly of
known breeding passerine birds – the snow bunting. Probably musk ox,
elk and reindeer grazed over the tundra as well since their remains have
been found in the Flood Plain terraces of prehistoric London. Park tundra
with low scrub was very much a feature of the Continent and stretched
across northern Spain and southern France and appeared again in
isolated patches in the northern Balkans and central Russia. It is therefore
quite clear that there were at this time no real trees north of the Pyrenees,
the Alps and the Black Sea and correspondingly no woodland birds.

What is now called steppe in Europe bordered on the tundra, and this
has not changed very much since. After the ice ages quite large areas of
Europe became steppe over which roamed herds of bison and wild
horses. The grasslands and bushy parts of the steppes led to the appearance
of many small rodents and Raptores that fed on them as well as wading
birds, buntings, larks, finches, game-birds and bustards. The riverine
plant growth attracted thrushes and warblers. In southern Russia the
steppes form a traditional zone between the south with its deserts and the
north with its forests. Today the wooded steppes are dominated by oak or
birch and here calandra larks, skylarks, whinchats, yellowhammers and
orioles can be found in the areas of steppe which lie like great parklands

inside the wooded regions of Russia. Britain was probably too moist for typical steppes to appear.

Farther south lay the wooded country of the taiga composed largely of forests of northern conifers and birches with some smaller broad-leaved trees such as willow, rowan and alder. The ground was heathy and often water-logged. The taiga could also be found as islands of vegetation in central Spain, in Italy especially in the Po valley, in the southern Balkans and in parts of Russia. In some regions more hilly country rose up above the tree-line while in others the taiga appeared as growth within the areas of park tundra. As the ice-sheets moved south the bird populations were compressed into the shrinking taiga whose area was only one third that of an unglaciated Europe. Some populations became isolated like those of the Iberian taiga while others must have disappeared altogether. The loss of some populations was so great that after the ice ages, when the taiga was re-establishing itself in northern Europe, the surviving bird species in the south were apparently not strong enough to exploit it fully. This might explain the entry into the European taiga of such Siberian species as the Arctic and greenish warblers. It is widely believed that, even at the height of the glaciations, Siberia was not so denuded of wooded tundra that it became unable to repair the losses in the European taiga. The Arctic warbler has moved east to Alaska as well, and the greenish warbler has shown a marked expansion of range in the present century together with the rustic and yellow-breasted buntings. All four species occur in the coniferous forests of the northern taiga. On the other hand the Siberian azure tit seems to be retreating after an expansion to the west. It is therefore difficult to distinguish between birds originating in the east and those which, having survived somewhere in the south-west, came back with the returning vegetation. To what extent movements of population may have been due to short-term climatic changes or to population explosions at a later date must remain a matter of conjecture. The collared dove's phenomenal expansion of range in western Europe took place over quite a short period. The northward movement into Fenno-Scandia and the withdrawal from the Baltic countries of the Siberian jay during the present century is probably due to a gradual rise in the temperatures of northern Europe.

The taiga stretched as far south as Italy, and on its borders the transitional mixed woods of coniferous and broad-leaved trees bounded much of the Mediterranean Sea. Mixed and pure broad-leaved forests were confined to the shores of this sea and to parts of southern Spain, Italy, the southern Balkans and North Africa (Fig. 6). It is difficult to say which species of bird regarded these woodlands rather than those of the taiga as their natural habitat. Man has so interfered with the countryside that he has confused the natural experiment which could have given us the answer. However, if the birds of the broad-leaved woods of today had also been present in Pleistocene Europe in a similar habitat, some of them would have been severely hit by the onset of the various glaciations, particularly the honey-buzzard, tawny owl, green woodpecker, golden oriole, long-tailed, marsh and blue tits, nuthatch, nightingale, hawfinch and warblers such as the blackcap, whitethroat and wood warbler. European orioles migrate either south-east through the Balkans or south-west through Spain. The two groups may thus be derived from birds that survived around the Aegean and in southern Spain and so recolonised the woodlands to the north from two separate directions.

It has sometimes been held that the migrations of some European species can be attributed to the fluctuations of the Pleistocene Period. At the peak of the glaciations most of Europe lay under ice or tundra and could support only a few breeding species; migrants from the tundra would have to pass south over the uncongenial belt of taiga and the broad-leaved woods until they could reach more open areas with a Mediterranean vegetation able to provide winter quarters for them. It is very likely that North Africa and even Arabia were able to offer congenial shelter quite unlike their hostile countryside today and thus were able to attract many of the tundra birds. Their journeys would have been much shorter than those they have to undertake today, and the demands on equatorial and southern Africa would have also been much less. It seems far more likely that migratory journeys were made to find new sources of food than that the birds have a long-held memory of the quiet, settled period of the Pliocene and are seeking to regain their favoured feeding-grounds. The origins of the migration of any individual species must be bound up with its evolution and past distribution as well as those factors of climate and ecology that have worked on it over the years. Some species are becoming less willing to migrate and others, after colonising new areas, seem to lose the desire altogether.

There is not much value, however, in speculating upon the Pleistocene history of each individual bird species. To do so is fraught with dangers since not only is the period so far removed in time, but the recent rapid changes in status and distribution among some bird species seem to have taken place without any apparent great changes in the ecology. We can be sure that some southern species were entirely lost, that those of the taiga suffered reduction and those of the broad-leaved woods were very severely compressed. During each period of glaciation there were sometimes spells of improved climate that would allow some return from the areas of compression. With one inter-glacial improvement broad-leaved trees and their birds were able to move back deep into Russia, but a return of the severe cold killed all the trees north of the Alps. Prehistoric man had also appeared and he would have been subjected to the same climatic changes. During his retreats the presence of caves might well have been decisive for his future.

From about 18000 B.C. to 7500 B.C. there was a general improvement in the climate and the ice-sheets began to recede, at a rate perhaps of about fifty yards a year. It remained cold, and the English countryside to the south of the ice remained tundra with arctic birch, willow and *Dryas*, all of which have been recovered from deposits of this age. The history of the post-glacial period owes a great deal to pollen analysis – a fascinating branch of botany which has set out to date the periods and plot the extent of the various vegetational successions in the British Isles. Most of our forest trees are pollinated by the wind and vast quantities of pollen are scattered through the air at the right season for each tree. Most of it falls to the ground and many grains find their way down to the bottom of lakes or on to the surface of peat-bogs. Peat is formed by the slow decomposition of plant remains and often contains tree roots, trunks, branches, leaves and the seeds or pollen of sub-fossil plants. I expect many people have seen the great bog oaks or pines retrieved from the peat of Fenland. I have a piece of birch branch which I picked out from among several pine roots eight feet down in a peat deposit near Barvas in the Isle of Lewis. Today this part of the Hebrides is quite treeless.

The outer cases of pollen grains – their fatty outer shells – can resist decay and survive in the oxygenless peat for many thousands of years. Some of these pollen grains are as Godwin (1948) so elegantly described "objects of considerable beauty and diversity, some smooth, others corrugated, ridged, or spiny, with pores variable in number, size and disposition." They can be identified by the expert from their characteristic forms (Fig. 7). By taking samples carefully from different layers and then separating out the pollen grains that lie densely packed together, many are found to be from herbs but large numbers also come from forest trees which once grew near the developing peat-bog. Many peat deposits have been investigated and the different proportions of pollen types in a vertical section of the deposit reflect the history and changes of the vegetation in that place. It is usual, within each sample, to count 150 tree-pollen grains and to express the amount of each pollen type as a percentage of this total.

Pollen analysis has shown clearly that certain trees are native while others were later introductions. There are sometimes local differences in peat deposits and it would be unwise to assume that the exact proportions

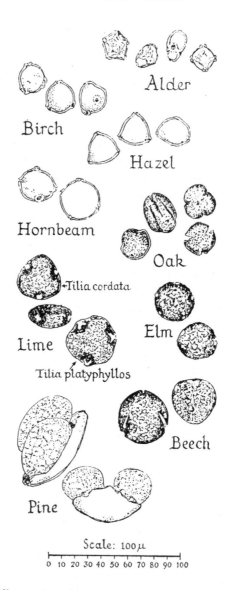

FIG. 7. The pollen grains of those British trees and shrubs most commonly preserved in peats or muds, drawn to the same scale. (1μ=one thousandth of a millimetre). Reproduced from *The New Naturalist, A Journal of British Natural History*, 1948.

of pollen in various samples accurately reflect the proportion of different species formerly growing on the site. Nevertheless there are general implications that are valuable as a guide to the way in which trees returned to Britain after the ice ages and this is useful in any discussion about the origins of our woodland birds. Figure 8 shows a typical pollen diagram. For a fuller account of this kind of analysis the reader should consult the work of Godwin. Table 5 illustrates not only the so-called pollen zones but summarises the whole history of the vegetation of the British Isles from the first glaciation to historic times, which we shall discuss in the next few paragraphs.

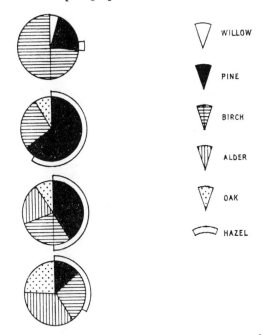

FIG. 8. A typical pollen diagram. The circles represent the composition of a forest revealed by a single sample of peat. From the top downwards they show the progression from the birch forests of the Sub-Arctic Period through the Boreal pinewoods to the mixed oak forest of the Bronze Age. The outside circles illustrate the amount of hazel present and this method of presentation is used to prevent distortion of the proportions of forest trees.

TABLE 5. *Climatic Phases in north-west Europe from the Pleistocene to historic Times*

(largely after Tansley (1949) and Brooks (1951))

Period	Phase	Pollen Zone	Date	Climate	Geographical and Botanical Features
Historic			1000	Milder	Increasing destruction of forests by man
	A.D.		0		
	B.C.				
		VIII	400		
	SUB-ATLANTIC			Colder and	Peat destroys pine and birch in
		VII–VIII		wetter	much of Ireland, Scotland and
			700		northern England
			2000	Mild, drier	Early clearances by neolithic man. Mixed oak forest with elm. Lime
	SUB-BOREAL				decreasing. Spread of beech? Some return of pine.
Prehistoric		VII	4000	Mild Climatic optimum	Establishment of deciduous summer forest – oak dominant.
					Rise of oak, elm and some lime to replace pine
	ATLANTIC			Wetter and milder	Great increase in alder.
			6000		
					Re-opening of Straits of Dover (Ireland separated earlier)
	BOREAL	VI		Dry: warm	Pine replaces birch.
				summers and	Hazel maximum.
				cold winters	Birch and hazel reach Ireland and northern Scotland.
	PRE-BOREAL	V	8000	Dry and cool	Advance of birch and pine.
		IV	11,000	Arctic Sub-arctic	Park tundra. Low growing Arctic
	LATE GLACIAL			becoming temperate	plants such as Dryas, dwarf birch and willow with occasional pine.
	LAST GLACIATION (Phase 3)		20,000	Cold	Extensive ice-caps in Scotland and Wales; smaller ones in Ireland and northern England.
				Mild	
			35,000		
				Cool	
Pleistocene			50,000		
				Mild	
	LAST GLACIATION (Phase 2)		70,000	Cold	Ice covers central Ireland and central Wales, Pennines and much of eastern England.
	LAST GLACIATION (Phase 1)		113,000	Cold	Farthest limit of ice; all Britain extreme south excepted.
			180,000		
	THIRD GLACIATION				
	SECOND INTER-GLACIAL				
	SECOND GLACIATION				
	FIRST INTER-GLACIAL				
	FIRST GLACIATION				
	MINOR GLACIALS		1,000,000		

With improving conditions and a better climate in the later part of the late glacial, or *Sub-Arctic Phase*, it is likely that a number of plant species came into the British Isles by means of the land-bridge to the Continent just as many pushed north into Scandinavia. Successive waves crossed this bridge during the inter-glacials and then were forced to retreat again. These fluctuations could have gone on until the land-bridge disappeared somewhere about 5500 B.C. towards the end of the *Boreal Phase*. It would be interesting to know when Shetland, Orkney, the Outer Hebrides and Ireland were detached from mainland Britain. Some islands including the Hebrides were probably isolated before the ice ages since there are traces there of pre-glacial raised beaches. The final separation of Ireland is thought by some to have occurred during Boreal times. The continental land-bridge may well have been submerged and raised again several times before the final irrevocable break.

With the warmer summers of the *Pre-Boreal Phase*, possibly from about 8000 B.C. to 7500 B.C., the pollen record shows the arrival of birch following up the margins of the retreating tundra. Not far behind came the Scots pine with some hazel, oak and a little elm and alder. Silver Birch (*Betula pendula*) and Downy Birch (*Betula pubescens*) may perhaps have survived the glaciation or come across the land-bridge. Birches are very hardy and some forms reach farther towards the North Pole than any other species of tree. They also reach farther up the mountains of northern Scotland than perhaps any other tree with the possible exception of the rowan. Birches, too, would be the first trees to make any kind of closed woodland. In many places heathy land and swamps persisted. What was this countryside like and what was its bird-life? The nearest approach to it today is the willow scrub of Lapland with small birches, juniper, *Vaccinium* and *Empetrum* shrub-heath. Here the meadow pipit is abundant, as it probably was in Britain, but the bluethroat, which is common enough in Lapland, is an eastern species and was unlikely to have been a member of the British scrub fauna. Other species typical of the northern European birch scrub are reed bunting, redpoll, willow warbler and ring ousel. Brambling occur in the scrub at Kilpisjarvie in Finland at 69° N.; this scrub is similar to that of Sutherland in north Scotland.

Eventually the birchwoods began to grow in size. Species such as the redpoll and willow warbler are typical of many of the close-canopy birchwoods in the north of Scotland and they must have been early colonists advancing northwards with the birches. The northern willow warbler of Lapland is of a different race from the British so subspeciation has been able to take place. The continental race of the redpoll is larger and paler than the redpoll of Britain and Ireland which is often regarded as a relic from the early part of the post-glacial period. The bush-tundra of the Arctic is occupied by the Arctic redpoll (often regarded as a single species with the redpoll). The two forms live alongside each other in the New World without hybridising but hybrids have been found in Norway and Greenland.

The bird communities of the birch forests in the Abisko National Park in Sweden, situated at 68° 21′ N., have been described by Lundevall (1952). At Abisko the woods of downy birch are fairly close or reduced to isolated patches and they contain some examples of rowan, aspen, willow, bird cherry and juniper; the field layer is heathy with *Vaccinium* and *Empetrum*. The birches come into leaf between 15th and 20th June each year about a month after the snow has mainly cleared; the autumn leaf fall is generally over by the middle or end of September. The bird community is made up chiefly of willow warblers, bramblings, bluethroats, redwings, fieldfares and redpolls. There are also a few pairs of pied flycatchers, redstarts, garden warblers, hedgesparrows and willow tits. In these northern birchwoods the brambling is the ecological replacement for the chaffinch; it has occasionally bred in Britain and may well have been a regular nesting species in the past. The bluethroat is a bird of the tundra, boreal and temperate zones and its European range is remarkable for several isolated communities, one of which is in Spain, for I have seen the bird in the Sierra de Guadarrama. The present patchy distribution of the bluethroat is almost certainly due to the shifts of vegetation at the end of the last glacial period. Redwings are common in these northern woods and, although their fossil remains have been found in the Pleistocene deposits of England and Ireland, these may have belonged to winter visitors. They may have been regular in our early birchwoods and today they breed almost annually in Scotland.

Lundevall also noted the occurrence of reed buntings, Siberian tits, ring ousels, wheatears, tree pipits, yellow wagtails, lesser spotted woodpeckers, cuckoos, merlins, kestrels, hooded crows, magpies and willow grouse. Although they are not in Lundevall's list, the bullfinch, waxwing, black woodpecker and osprey may also breed. The yellowhammer is rare at Abisko, but it has been reported in birchwoods in Norway at 69° 13′ N. The kestrels and merlins breed in the old nests of crows in the more mature birch forests. The willow grouse is fairly common but the black grouse does not breed. The latter species has gradually withdrawn from southern England but it was probably an early arrival with our birches. Recently blackcock have increased in some areas as the result of reafforestation. The garden warbler breeds farther north than the closely related blackcap but it is not common in Lapland. I have heard garden warblers singing in eastern Inverness-shire and, although there are records for Sutherland, the species has eluded me during a number of searches in northern Scotland from 1964–67.

At Abisko the time at which the snow melts can be very important. Those species which nest in trees using either the branches or holes in the trunks can begin nesting much earlier than those that breed on the ground. Woodpeckers, tits, crows and magpies breed from about the middle of May while redwings and fieldfares are rather later. The ground-nesting willow grouse and willow warbler show some variation from year to year dependent upon the time the land takes to dry off after the snow has melted. Armstrong (1954), who made many observations at Abisko and on the shores of Lake Torneträsk, found that light appears to be the most important external factor regulating bird activity in the Arctic. He advanced the theory that birds which extend their working day to match the longer daylight in the higher latitudes tend to rear their young more quickly than birds of the same or closely related species farther south. If this is so, then there could be significant differences between the Arctic birchwoods of Lapland and those of Pre-Boreal Britain. In the Arctic, male snow buntings spend rather more time courting, singing and mating than do Scottish birds while the females show differences in their incubation rhythm. Climatic differences between the two regions may be largely responsible, but other factors might be shortage of food early in the breeding season, the intensity and duration of the light, social stimuli and pressure from predators. In winter it must be the length of daylight, the temperature and the snow cover which are the most important factors. Snow (1952), who visited Arctic Lapland in January, recorded the following species as being particularly dependent on birches – redpolls and willow tits which took the seeds, blackgrouse which fed almost exclusively on catkins, hazel grouse which consumed catkins and buds and pine grosbeaks which also ate buds and whose presence in any year was related to the crops of seeds.

During the Pre-Boreal Phase the Scots pine was at first less important than the birch but slowly began to attain dominance. Both pine and birch spread across the uplands, replacing the tundra of Late Glacial times. The pollen analysis also indicates a sharp rise in the amount of hazel towards the end of Pre-Boreal times. At this time large wild cattle such as *Bos primigenius*, red deer and reindeer grazed through the open woodlands, beavers built their dams across the water-courses and bears, wolves and lynxes hunted through the countryside.

From about 7500 B.C. to 5500 B.C., the climate continued to become warmer and drier. This period is called the *Boreal Phase*. Hazel scrub now reached its maximum, spreading with birch to Ireland and the extreme north of Scotland. In early Boreal times the Scots pine continued its forward march while the birch began to decline. In direct competition on equally favourable terms the pine will always become dominant, since its deeper shade can exclude the birch from the ground beneath. In most of England and central Ireland the birch gave way before the pine but the former kept its dominance in Wales, Scotland and northern Ireland. In mid-Boreal centuries oak and elm also made a slow advance from a small bridgehead they had established in the Pre-Boreal Phase, but they remained far below the pine in strength. The conditions of this period enabled large areas of peat and water-logged ground to dry out, and these were soon colonised and then dominated by pine. There may have been a considerable north-west movement of plants, suited to this dry climate, which came up from central and southern Europe and established themselves on the Downs and on the Brecks of East Anglia. Survivors of this migration include Breckland Catchfly (*Silene otites*) and Spiked Speedwell (*Veronica spicata*).

For quite a time a large part of the British Isles was clothed with pine-forest, and the birds of these woods would consist of species best able to meet the requirements of this specialised habitat. Relics of these Boreal pine-forests still survive today along the valley of the River Spey and near Loch Rannoch and Loch Maree and in a few other places in Scotland. The avifauna of these woods can help us to envisage the bird-life of the original Boreal forests or taiga. In Scotland the birds in today's forests are either confined to them or may be found in other habitats as well. The crested tit and the Scottish crossbill are restricted to the forests and probably came with the original pine colonists. Species such as the capercaillie, siskin and goldcrest are very largely but not exclusively birds of coniferous woodland. Other species can be found in the summer pinewoods of Scotland and in broad-leaved forests as well – species such as the long-eared and tawny owls, buzzard, sparrowhawk, four species of tit, tree-creeper, great spotted woodpecker, mistle thrush, redstart, robin, tree pipit, wren, spotted flycatcher, willow warbler, chaffinch, bullfinch and wood pigeon. This third and largest group of species poses a problem. Did these birds originate in the coniferous woods from which they later spread to the broad-leaved, or did they arrive later with the broad-leaved forests and, being adaptable, colonise the pine-forests *after* their arrival? It is possible that the coal tit, redstart, treecreeper, goshawk and great spotted woodpecker, in addition to the specialised birds of coniferous woodland, arrived with the taiga. An interesting suggestion has been made that if some of these species were evolved in coniferous woodland then they are adapted "to the general scruffiness of the woods rather than to conifers as such." In Europe the coal tit is mainly found in the dense taiga but it also appears in beechwoods in the Apennines and the Cantabrian Mountains. In the British Isles it is locally frequent in mixed woods, and it is interesting to note that the coal tits of Japan descend in winter from the coniferous woods into the mixed forests of the lowlands. Perhaps we can see here the origins of the spread to mixed and broad-leaved woods for breeding.

The origins of the treecreeper are more difficult to trace. One theory suggests that the European short-toed treecreeper was once in a community that became isolated during a glacial period – a community adapted to life among the broad-leaved trees of the Mediterranean. In post-glacial times treecreepers from this group made their way northwards with the returning broad-leaved trees. This movement was outstripped by the eastwards migration of the taiga which brought with it another forest avifauna containing the common treecreeper. This latter species went on to win the race to the land-bridge to Britain arriving in the Boreal Phase before the Straits of Dover formed. After making its crossing the common treecreeper slowly adapted itself to the new conditions brought about by the later arrival of the broad-leaved trees. In Europe the two species have rather different habitats and their songs are conspicuously unlike each other. This theory is not capable of proof but it seems reasonable and serves to illustrate clearly the problems left behind by the changing fortunes of the glacial and post-glacial periods.

An increase in moisture and a sustained high temperature mark the *Atlantic Phase* which has been described as "the climatic optimum". This period which lasted from around 5500 B.C. to perhaps 2500 B.C. saw an important change in the vegetation of the British Isles with broad-leaved trees increasing until they became dominant. It was during the Atlantic period that deciduous summer forest was established. Elm (probably wych elm), pedunculate and sessile oak spread widely, bringing with them some small-leaved lime which became quite common in places, but did not, in fact, reach Ireland. Oak became the dominant tree of the Atlantic woodlands and remained so up to a certain altitude in most of the English, Welsh, Irish and southern Scottish forests except on the poorer heathlands, limestones and in the wetter areas. Elm was much more frequent in England and Ireland than it is today. Alder began to succeed pine and remained an important constituent of our flora up to historic times; it still frequently occurs in the oakwoods of the wetter, more western areas. Hazel never again matched its early Boreal distribution but it has survived as dominant scrub on the limestone of Co. Clare in Ireland and on some of the hillsides of Argyll. Very little is known about the distribution of either ash or beech. There are some traces of the former in Atlantic times and it must have increased at a later date.

The change from the Boreal climate to that of the wetter Atlantic one was an important one. Sir Dudley Stamp attributed this indirectly to the final cutting of the land-bridge with the Continent some 7,500 years ago. This caused a fundamental change in the circulation of water around the British Isles and consequently in the air movements as well. Whether this is so or not, the Atlantic Phase saw the oak-forest become the most important climatic type in a vegetation which, had it not been for the activities of man, would have survived unaltered to the present day. Together with the early broad-leaved colonists, that is the oaks, elms, alder, lime, ash and hazel, came hawthorn, blackthorn, rowan, various willows, wild cherry, aspen and the broad-leaved evergreen the holly. Later still others which were held back by conditions of climate or merely late arrivals made their way into Britain. These late-comers are only found in a natural state in Lowland Britain and include beech, hornbeam, whitebeam, wild service, field maple and poplars. The Grey Poplar (*Populus canescens*) is believed to be native in Ireland.

The climate became drier again in the *Sub-Boreal Phase*. On the English clays and loams dense forests of oak with occasional elm and lime gave shelter to wolves and bears. Neolithic man and the discovery of metals soon after 2000 B.C. made possible the first cultivation of the drier uplands of chalk and limestone as well as the pasturing of sheep and cattle. Early man settled on the chalk of Salisbury Plain, on the Downs and Wolds, on the oolite of the Cotswolds and the mountain limestone of the Pennines. From now on the biotic factor was to affect our landscape more and more. On the thin chalk and limestone soils oak does not grow well and is often replaced by beech, ash or the native conifer, yew. It is not clear when beech first came to Britain and its pollen was not found in quantity before the late *Sub-Atlantic Phase*. The beech spread during the dry Sub-Boreal period farther than its present native range, even perhaps to the south-west and Wales. Beech becomes the dominant tree of the chalk uplands if left to itself; otherwise the climax is ash or yew. It may be that many of the old beechwoods were cleared from the hills to permit cultivation and pasture, and then a combination of climatic and biotic factors prevented a return. The later Bronze Age peoples extended the clearances and from this time man began to fashion the landscape on an ever increasing scale. In the Sub-Boreal Phase pine and birch staged a recovery in the drier conditions and a belt of pine-forest was even established along the west coast of Ireland.

PLATE I. Chaffinch pair at nest. These are the most widely distributed of all woodland birds, but may have evolved in marginal woods.

Somewhere about 700 B.C. to 550 B.C. the British climate became again wetter and much cooler. With this change vast swamps and marshes formed and began to overwhelm many of the birch- and pine-forests which were the climax communities of Highland Britain. In this way the peat-bogs of northern England, Scotland and Ireland began to take shape. This phase has continued with some fluctuations up to the present time. The weather of today certainly bears a closer resemblance to that of the *Sub-Atlantic Phase* than to any of the other post-glacial climates. Table 5 summarises the more important developments in British vegetation and gives a series of useful though unavoidably approximate dates for the chief phases. The general sequence – tundra, park tundra, coniferous forest and broad-leaved woodland – is fairly clear.

The return of our flora is therefore comparatively recent and this is underlined by the scarcity of endemic plants in the British Isles. There has not been enough time for speciation or subspeciation to take place except among a few apomictic groups such as the Hawkweeds (*Hieracium spp.*) and Whitebeams (*Sorbus spp.*) in which reproduction takes place by the seed, developed without fertilisation. Ireland's native trees do not, of course, include those that failed to spread beyond south-east England, but there is one – the arbutus or strawberry-tree – which is absent from the rest of the flora of Britain. This is a Mediterranean evergreen which grows in Portugal, but it is not uncommon at Killarney where another evergreen, holly, appears in the oakwoods. The arbutus behaves very much as it does in its Mediterranean home, but the cool, wet summers of Ireland allow it to make a richer growth. Perhaps the holly/arbutus type of vegetation was once more extensive than it is now and could have revealed a close link in Atlantic times with the Mediterranean and Spain. However, no sub-fossil remains of any other species of evergreen typical of such a flora have yet been discovered in Britain. On the other hand, the Irish fauna and flora show marked absences as a result of the early separation from Britain; these missing species range from snakes to the willow tit and the Milk Vetch (*Astragalus glycyphyllos*). There are also some fifty-one species of bird breeding regularly in Britain that do not occur in Ireland.

What then are the species that might have come into Britain with the returning broad-leaved forests? Some birds, as we have seen, whose original home was in the taiga may have adapted themselves later, and there are probably some twelve species at least which came in with the broad-leaved trees – hawfinch, great and marsh tits, wood warbler, garden warbler, blackcap, nightingale, kite, wryneck, green and lesser spotted woodpeckers and nuthatch. The hawfinch perhaps originated in the broad-leaved forests of south-eastern Asia, and in Great Britain it keeps its preference for deciduous woods. On the Continent the hawfinch also prefers broad-leaved trees but has made small penetrations into coniferous areas. The great tit occurs so rarely in coniferous woodland, unless nestboxes are provided, and the marsh tit is so partial to broad-leaved that both species are likely to have come in with the later forests. The wood warbler also avoids conifers preferring woods of sessile oak, beech, birch and mixed tree species but it does sometimes occur on the Continent in sub-alpine spruce forests. Both garden warbler and blackcap have very similar habitats in woods of mixed broad-leaved trees but the former seems to need a dense deciduous undergrowth while the latter has song-posts in the higher levels of the shrub layers and tree canopy. The nightingale is regular in oak and beechwoods with a shrub layer in south-east Britain at heights of less than 500 feet. It is decreasing in parts of Europe as the result of reafforestation with coniferous trees. The kite is also a bird of broad-leaved woods – the relict population in Wales prefers those of sessile oak – but most of the nests in Scotland before the kite became extinct there were in pines. The wryneck and the green woodpecker in my experience are more birds of parkland but both must in the past have been associated with the open patches and discontinuous sections of the old broad-leaved forests. The lesser spotted woodpecker I have found in oak and beechwoods, alder carrs and roadside ashes and willows. The British nuthatch is rarely seen in conifers but in Siberia is a bird of the taiga. It has been suggested that the nuthatch came into Scandinavia by the same route and nearly at the same time as the oak, both coming to a halt at about the same northerly limit. The restriction in range in the British Isles to a northerly breeding limit about the 60° F. July isotherm may not be solely due to climate as there are some gaps in its distribution south of this line. Of the twelve species I have mentioned only two appear in Ireland – the garden warbler which is local and the blackcap which is scarce.

From about A.D. 400 to A.D. 1200 northern Europe enjoyed a rather milder climate during which vineyards were cultivated in southern England. This was followed by a colder, stormy period about A.D. 1200 to 1300 with an increase in peat-bogs. For the 300 years from about 1550 the climate has been uncertain and sometimes very cold and wet. There has been some improvement again in the twentieth century and the rise in the decadal mean temperature of the summer months in central England has been 1° F. between 1900 and 1950. This has caused wetter summers and, according to some accounts, a shortage of large flying insects which are the food of certain bird species now rather low in number. The rise in temperature has also coincided with the penetration into north-west Scotland of such species as the chaffinch, tree pipit, garden warbler, wood warbler, whitethroat, chiffchaff and great spotted woodpecker. However, in the last two decades the average January temperature has fallen more than 1° F. below that of the mild spell of the 1920s and 1930s. There seems to have been a recent and general lowering of temperature in the whole North Atlantic area – perhaps the start of a long-term tendency.

So far we have traced some of the fluctuations in fortune undergone by our woodland birds from the beginning of the Pleistocene. Throughout this long period the climate had a profound effect on the vegetation and bird-life of the British Isles. Then man began to dominate the scene. From the Belgic settlements before the birth of Christ until the present day it is the biotic factor, with man at the centre, which has had the greatest effect on our woodland avifauna.

CHAPTER 3

THE WOODLANDS IN HISTORIC TIMES

A T their greatest extent the forests of Britain covered more than half of the land area. This was during the most favourable period after the ice ages when oak was the common tree, when birch and Scots pine dominated the lighter soils and those of the upper hillsides, when ash crowned the lime-stone outcrops and when alder and willow flourished in the marshes and along the river-banks. Elms and limes established local strongholds and hornbeams and beeches grew well in parts of the south. There were probably also some pure woods of yew, whitebeam and field maple. Large carnivores such as bears and wolves helped to keep in check the many deer, boars and wild cattle that grazed the regenerating tree seedlings. At this time the bird species of inland Britain were those of woodland and woodland ecotones, and moorland and heath with a few fenland species as well; these are, in fact, the typical bird communities of the Palaearctic fauna. The British Isles lie on the very edge of the Palae-arctic zone and here species tend to be at the outer limit of their distribu-tion; their hold may be rather precarious, but we can assume that the once extensive forests provided sanctuary for a number of species now lost or in the process of being lost to us. Recent changes in climate may have contributed to the decline of such species as the wryneck and the red-backed shrike, but the destruction by man of birds' preferred habitats may have accelerated the decline. Today woodland covers only 6% of the British Isles which means that from Neolithic times onwards man has successfully cleared 90% of our native forests.

It has been suggested that early Neolithic man chose the hills of chalk and limestone for his early settlement as the tree-cover was slight and the light soils were easy to cultivate. At this time the lowlands below the level of the hills lay largely under a dense cover of damp oak-forest often with big areas of swamp and fen, all of which early man found rather un-attractive. Many of the hills may have been covered by beech-forest since the downs are quite well wooded today and revert easily to woodland as soon as grazing is stopped. The early Neolithic settlers perhaps ring-barked the beeches with their stone axes, so killing the canopies of the trees and allowing light to reach the ground, which was then cultivated for a few seasons before the settlers moved on to another area of untouched forest. It was much easier to clear beechwood than oak-forest or scrub and it was this, rather than the absence of trees, which led early man to the hills. Since H. L. Edlin describes in *Trees, Woods and Man* in this series the clearance of the forests by man, it is not my intention to do more than give a short account and to bring up to date the figures for woodland distribution in the British Isles.

At the beginning of the Bronze Age Ireland possessed a great wealth of alluvial gold and easily mined deposits of copper. England, astride the lines of communication from Ireland to the Continent, began to acquire the first flat metal axes. By the late Bronze Age – about 1000 B.C. – socketed axes were quite common in England and these would have been valuable tools for felling or ring-barking trees. About this time and during the early Iron Age, the light Mediterranean plough appeared to supersede the old hand-held hoes and, although it did not result in the kind of tillage we expect to see today, it marked a great step forward. Restricted as it had to be to the lighter, poorer soils of the uplands, it yet allowed a method of settled farming with permanent fields. Into these areas of cultivation came the skylark and the lapwing while from the woods came starlings, jackdaws and carrion crows to take advantage of the open, tilled ground. Timber was also being taken from the forest for farm-buildings and fences, and to provide charcoal for smelting metals – man had now embarked on the long process of deforestation that has continued ever since.

When the Belgae settled Britain in about 100 B.C. they brought with them a heavy wheeled plough needing four oxen to draw it and for the first time making possible the cultivation of heavier and richer soils. This plough brought a sharp increase in the growing of cereals in south-east England and farmers soon began to cast covetous eyes on the lowland forests with their fertile brown earths. During the Roman occupation the heavy plough was largely restricted to work on the farms while the "scratch" cultivation of the uplands persisted on the poorer land. Settlements were frequent on the southern chalk plateaux and, according to Crawford and Keiller, "in Romano-British times practically the whole of Salisbury Plain, Cranborne Chase and the Dorset uplands were under the plough." The settled period of the Roman occupation brought some increase in arable land and an extension of sheep-grazing on the existing grasslands. Iron was extensively smelted in the Weald of Kent and in the Forest of Dean. Charcoal remains of the period show that the Romans used oak, ash, birch and hazel for this purpose. There were still thick forests of oak, elm and alder on the clays dating from the Triassic and Jurassic periods. Oak then grew to a greater height on the hills than it reaches today and in the Lake District the high-level oakwoods reached 2,000 ft. or more. The relics in Cumberland now do not occur above 1,700 ft.

Sixteen Romano-British sites that have produced bird-bones have been recorded. From these the following woodland birds have been identified: pheasant and black grouse from Corstopitum (Corbridge-on-Tyne); buzzard from Camulodunum (Colchester); thrush, jay and carrion crow from Calleva Atrebatum (Silchester); jackdaw from Verulamium (St. Albans); rook from Rutupiae (Richborough) and hedgesparrow from Venta Silurum (Caerwent). This gives a small but useful guide to the bird fauna of Roman times.

After the departure of the Romans the forest clearances began to accelerate. In the fifth century A.D. Anglian and Saxon tribes from Europe, formerly only daring raiders, now began to appear as conquerors and settlers. The civilised part of Britain once occupied by the Romans was almost certainly devastated before their arrival. The details of the actual conquest are not clear, but it seems that these new invaders were also drawn towards the lighter soils of south-east England. The little principalities of the Celts were destroyed and their inhabitants driven westwards. The old arable fields on some of the chalk plateaux were abandoned and reverted to forest, which on part of the Wiltshire Downs survived until the twentieth century. Late in the sixth century the English advance continued. The battle of Deorham brought the Saxons to the Bristol Channel and in 613 a battle near Chester gave the inhabitants of Mercia their first access to the Irish Sea. Two centuries of conquest resulted in the establishment of many farming settlements in the forested parts of the Midland Plain.

With the invading Saxons came a special method of land cultivation called the Open Field System. The township was often no more than a clearing in the middle of a large tract of woodland or heath. The normal practice in lowland England except in the east and south-east was for each township to have three common fields of great size – one sown with wheat, one with barley, oats or beans and the third lying fallow. In some districts two common fields, one arable and one fallow, were the rule. The fields were unfenced but were divided up into a number of compartments each of which was divided again into strips separated by balks of unploughed land. The villager did not hold all his strips in one convenient block but, for reasons of equity, had them allocated to him in various parts of the open fields. Each year a fresh field was allowed to lie fallow. After harvest the fields became common grazing-ground for the sheep and cattle of the township. The open field system began to disappear after the

Middle Ages but at Laxton in Nottinghamshire there is still an almost complete field system with 560 acres of open field now belonging to the Ministry of Agriculture. When I walked these fields in April and May, 1963, the commonest large animals were skylarks and hares in that order – a fauna that has remained unchanged since Saxon times. Then foraging starlings and rooks would have flown in from the surrounding woodlands, but today there are no nearby forests or intersecting hedgerows and so the skylark is the dominant bird of the Laxton fields. With their axes and eight-ox ploughs the Saxons turned more and more of the forests into cultivated land. Some regions of the south remained under dense forest like that of Anderida in the Weald which was described in about 731 by the Venerable Bede as "thick and inaccessible" and a haunt of wolves, swine and deer. According to the Society of Irish Foresters, many of the old Irish township names date from the seventh and eighth centuries and from the evidence of these names elm and yew, now rare in the wild state in Ireland, were widespread species.

The Danes carried on the clearances so that by the time of the Norman Conquest the woodlands of England, Wales and Scotland had probably shrunk from their former 40 million acres to about 10 million acres. The forest clearances in Scotland and Ireland may have varied in different localities but it is clear that the burning of heather and grazing of the open moors prevented the regeneration of tree seedlings. In Ireland the westerly winds, heavy rainfall and poor drainage tended to retard tree growth in any case, and land grazed in a favourable climate was likely to change into grassland.

The Norman Conquest brought the introduction of a code of forest law as well as the setting up of royal forests which were put outside (*Foris*) the common law. It is now impossible to know the real number and extent of these forests in the eleventh century and later, but they may have occupied as much as one third of England. The Domesday Book mentions five forests, including the New and Windsor Forests, but there were certainly others such as Sherwood, Arden and the Forest of Dean. In 1228 there were some 23 English counties which still had Royal forests. Not all these forest lands were wooded and some may have borne very few trees indeed. Within these areas some of the enclosed land that had been "afforested" may well have reverted to the wild and so augmented the overall amount of woodland. This attempt by the Norman kings to preserve the land was doomed to eventual failure. In the manorial woods sheep, cattle, horses and goats grazed under the trees – the common of pasturage – and effectively prevented tree seedlings from surviving. Swine entered the woods in the autumn – the common of pannage – and, although they may have trodden some acorns and beech nuts safely into the ground they also consumed vast quantities of these tree-seeds. The increase in the pasturing of animals in both royal and manorial forests together with the demands on timber for house building, fences and fuel would result, if they were to continue indefinitely, in the ultimate destruction of the forests.

From 1250 to 1350 there was an increase in Britain in the growing of corn, which was now being exported, and in the pasturing of sheep. As early as the twelfth century the Cistercian monks had set up huge sheep farms on the drier, eastern slopes of the Pennines. By the thirteenth century Yorkshire, the Cotswolds, the Chilterns, Hereford and the Lincolnshire Wolds were important wool producing areas. By 1350 there were some eight million sheep in Britain – four times the human population. These advances could only be made at the expense of the woodlands and such was the shortage of timber in north-eastern England that it became necessary to import oak and pine from Scandinavia. Because of this shortage there began the medieval practice of producing timber by the "coppice" and "coppice-with-standards" methods. In an oakwood a number of the trees were felled to allow more light to penetrate the roof of the wood. Certain trees would be left as "standards" to develop normally; the others were coppiced and cut near the ground at intervals of from, say, ten to fifteen years. When a tree has been cut down in this way a number of shoots spring up from the remaining bole or stool; these grow into pole-shaped "coppice-shoots" of small diameter which never reach the size of mature trees but are useful for poles, fence-posts, hurdles and firewood. The "standards" would be felled on reaching maturity at perhaps a hundred years old but because of their wide separation from each other, which led to short trunks and big canopies, they were not very highly regarded. Their timber was sometimes useful, however, in ship-building when curves were needed in the beams. Coppicing was usually carried out among broad-leaved trees such as oak, ash, alder, hornbeam and hazel and later, sweet chestnut. The practice of coppicing was undertaken on a rotational basis so that at intervals, according to the species, the young shoots were cut right down to the stumps. The coppices had to be protected from cropping by domestic animals and so hedges were planted and this was authorised in 1483 by a statute of Edward IV. Man-made coppices can be recognised by their purity of species, regular shape and simple internal system of rides and paths. The field layer in an oak/hazel wood was very much affected by the process of coppicing. Just before cutting dense shade inhibited most of the flower growth, but a couple of years after coppicing the ground would blossom and be rich in primroses, wood anemones and bluebells. Most coppice was in southern England and

PLATE 2. Great spotted woodpecker. A hole-nesting species primarily of woodlands but it also occurs in parks and gardens.

Wales but much of it is now being turned into high forest plantations. Coppices are very attractive to certain birds which demand a shrub layer in woodland, such as the nightingale and garden warbler, but the birds would disappear for a short time while the wood recovered from the effects of coppicing. Some broad-leaved trees such as oaks, beeches, hornbeams and willows were pollarded and their heads lopped off so that they would put up a crown of small upright shoots, useful as small timber for fencing or firewood and sufficiently far above the ground to be safe from cattle. The hornbeams of Epping Forest and the beeches of Burnham Beeches are classic examples. Trees pollarded in this way are sometimes used for breeding by such hole-nesting birds as tree sparrow, redstart, stock dove and pied wagtail.

By the twelfth century, the southern part of Scotland had lost much of its forest, and in the Highlands woodland was only able to survive after a great deal of hill-grazing and valley clearance in some of the more sheltered glens and on their steep sides where it maintained a precarious foothold. The trees growing in these sites could provide some resources and many were coppiced irregularly and degenerated into "coppiced scrub": the Forestry Commission's Census of 1947 calculated that there were a quarter of a million acres of this kind of scrub in Britain. Ireland was once rich in primeval forests and in 1183 Giraldus Cambrensis found the country "well-wooded" with "vast herds of boar and wild pigs". However, the coming of the Normans and the years before the Tudors brought vast clearances to Ireland. So much so, that Fynes Moryson in 1603 found himself "deceived in the common fame that all Ireland is woody." The Civil War brought more deforestation so that wood ceased to be a domestic fuel and turf firing had to be substituted for it. By 1700 the area of forest in Ireland had been reduced to almost nothing.

Eventually, the growing loss of woodland came to be recognised. This happened first in Scotland, where an Act was passed in 1457 requiring and charging tenants of the Scottish king to plant trees. In England the drain on the forests continued, especially during the Civil War. Plot, speaking of Oxfordshire in 1677, complained "The hills, 'tis true, before the late unhappy Wars, were well enough beset with woods, where 'tis now so scarcy" (Aplin 1889). Timber was imported from the already vastly reduced Irish resources or from North America, for the end of the seventeenth century very nearly saw the end of our native timber. In England and Wales woodlands, forest, parks and commons covered only 16% of the land surface. Attempts were made to awaken opinion to the seriousness of the situation and to encourage new planting, but the results at first were small. The Irish Statute Book from the Restoration to the close of the eighteenth century contained many measures to encourage planting. Some of the Irish landlords carried out planting on their estates from 1700 to 1850, particularly in counties Dublin, Kildare and Wicklow, but there were many evasions of the planting Acts.

One other development that had been occurring for some time was the enclosure of many of the medieval open fields. Enclosures had been made ever since the Black Death in 1348 when arable land was turned into sheep pastures. It is unlikely that the rate of enclosure in the sixteenth century was much faster than two hundred years before. By 1700 more than half of the agriculture was still being carried on in open fields but a hundred years later nearly all the remaining fields had been enclosed by quick-set hedges usually of hawthorn, blackthorn, crab-apple, elder and holly. Ash, oak, beech and elm were often left to develop into mature trees and it was always thought unlucky to cut back a holly. This practice has left an indelible and characteristic mark on much of our countryside today. Other shrubs were often cut back and "laid" to form a close barrier. The hedges themselves were commonly planted along the old field margins, lanesides and other boundaries and so helped to preserve something of medieval Britain for posterity. Excluding urban and suburban districts, there are perhaps about 616,000 miles of hedge in Britain. The Forestry Commission's Census Report No. 2 (1951) noted that the trees of good size growing in hedgerows probably numbered 73 million and that these contained one fifth of the country's timber resources. With the coming of these hedgerows many birds of woodland and woodland ecotones found habitats similar to those of scrub and the shrub layer in forest. Blackbirds, thrushes, robins, chaffinches, wrens, hedgesparrows, whitethroats and yellowhammers are very typical of the hedgerows. However, there has been a tendency in recent times to pull up the hedges in favour of larger fields but this reduces the shelter from wind and may lead to erosion of the soil. One other effect of the enclosures was to leave many small woods and belts of trees dotted about the land which, at a distance, gives the false impression of heavy afforestation when farming is its main use.

The eighteenth century is noteworthy for the increase of planting in England, Scotland and Ireland. Private landowners not only planted specimen and rare trees but some even began to put in plantations of native broad-leaved trees such as oak, ash, beech and sycamore as well as exotic European conifers such as spruce, larch and silver fir. The Norway spruce is not native to Britain but it grows wild in northern Europe and north-east Asia. The European larch is native to the Alps and the European silver fir originated in the mountain ranges of central Europe.

Pine was also planted, and in 1705 some 800 acres were afforested in Scotland by Lord and Lady Hamilton and from 1716 onwards Sir Alexander Grant planted at least 50 million trees. Financial inducements were offered to landowners and as a result of such factors as "sport, shelter, timber production, scenic values and scientific interest", many fine stands of trees appeared in the parks and policies of some of the great houses. In Ireland most of the older woods are to be found on private demesnes; at Tollymore Park in Co. Down the Earl of Clanbrassil planted from 30,000 to 60,000 trees a year. Not so much planting went on in Wales where there were rather fewer landowners. The plantations had the advantage of reproducing the conditions of high forest with a canopy density of more than 20%. A large number of trees, growing competitively together, causes the trees to be drawn up and so produce long, straight trunks. Some thinning is necessary but the canopy remains close and so suppresses any coppice shoots that might develop.

In the meantime, animals grazing among many of the trees prevented the natural regeneration of existing woodlands. Lord Nelson, after staying on the edge of the Forest of Dean in 1802, said in a letter: "Nothing in it can grow self-sown, for the deer bark all the young trees. Vast droves of hogs are allowed to go into the woods in the autumn and if any unfortunate acorn escape their search and takes root, then flocks of sheep are allowed to go into the Forest, and they bite off the tender shoot." In the Forest of Dean these biotic factors have continued their work until modern times.

The great wave of planting began to lose its momentum in the nineteenth century. More timber was imported, iron began to replace oak and new chemical methods were applied to the processes of tanning leather. The Industrial Revolution also saw men of means invest, not in timber, but in the new railways, in mining projects and in industry. Woodland was often looked upon as solely a sporting amenity with an attractive amount of cover for game whose preservation took pride of place over forestry itself. Gamekeeping also resulted in a sharp decline in the numbers of some predatory birds. Unfortunately the growth of the purely sporting estates coincided in the early nineteenth century with the production of a new and damaging weapon – the shot-gun. This had far-reaching effects; in three years from 1837 to 1840 the keepers of one Scottish estate, on the direct orders of the lessee, killed no fewer than 462 kestrels, 285 buzzards, 275 kites, 63 goshawks, 35 long-eared owls, 18 ospreys and 3 honey-buzzards in addition to many other species of bird and mammal. We shall consider the effects of gamekeeping later on. Private planting did not stop altogether. In Scotland plantations of Scots pine on the drier, sandier soils and of Norway spruce on the damper, flushed ones were soon followed by those of two western American conifers – the Douglas fir and the Sitka spruce. The Douglas fir, whose seed was sent to Britain in 1827, does well on good ground, especially cleared woodland in sheltered places. There are some fine examples in the Bolderwood arboretum in the New Forest, and it is also Britain's tallest tree with an individual at Powis Castle in Wales reaching a height of 181 ft. The Sitka spruce from British Columbia and Alaska grows well on poor, peaty soils and is hardy and windproof. The fast-growing Japanese larch was introduced in 1861 and makes a valuable hardy pioneer. The grand silver fir came from British Columbia in 1832 and the western hemlock in 1851. Other alien species of conifer such as the Corsican and maritime pines, the lodgepole pine, the noble fir and the western red cedar were introduced later. The Forestry Commission's booklet "Know Your Conifers" is a useful guide to these softwoods which so often confuse the layman.

The growth in industrialisation and town building during the late nineteenth century accelerated the already sad toll of forest destruction. In Northern Ireland the system of land tenure was altered so that farmers could buy the land they formerly held as tenants. The new owners did not have the resources to look after the surviving woodlands, and it was recorded that "a mushroom growth of sawmills sprang up and travelled round the country clearing one wood after another". Game was heavily preserved and in Surrey "the woodpeckers, the owls and the nightjar suffer without cause; the harriers and the buzzards are gone; the magpie is getting rare; the jay, the sparrowhawk, the carrion crow and the kestrel all share their more just burden with them" (Bucknill 1900). Yet to a small extent these losses were being balanced by the new plantations which, maturing in what were once open areas of moorland and heath, brought back a succession of woodland birds missing for centuries from these parts of Britain. In 1900, most of the woodland was in private hands and the Crown's share had fallen very greatly.

The severely strained resources met further heavy blows when Britain's timber supplies were again drained during the Great War of 1914–18 due to the clear felling of 450,000 acres of trees to meet the German U-Boat campaign. In an attempt to make up this grave deficiency, the Forestry Act of 1919 established the Forestry Commission whose task was to devise and implement for Britain a proper forest policy. It was given the authority to set up and maintain its own forests, to encourage the proper management of woodlands and private estates and to promote research and education in forest science. Its chief task at the outset was to reafforest the devastated areas and the targets, envisaged by the Acland Committee whose report preceded the setting up of the Commission, were the replanting of 200,000 acres within ten years and 1,770,000 acres within eighty years. Replanting of the privately owned woodlands did not materialise in the way that had been hoped and, in fact, thirty years later much of it had still not been afforested. On the other hand, the Commission, by the outbreak of the Second World War, had already set up over 200 new forests with half of their total of 655,000 acres actually replanted. Yet the area of high forest at the end of this war was only 77% of that immediately before the First World War in spite of the Commission's planting activities. During the Second World War private landowners clear felled more than 373,000 acres of woodland. The Forestry Commission's Census of Woodlands of Five Acres and Over (1952) showed that 18% of the woodlands of Britain were in State ownership, while 52% of the country's coniferous high forest was also owned by the State. According to this Census the total woodland area in relation to land surface in England was 5.8%, of Wales 6.2% and of Scotland 6.6%. These figures mean that just over 6% of Britain is wooded, while those for Northern Ireland and Eire show just over 3%. For a time the Forestry Commission took over the work of the Irish Forestry Department but after the political settlement of 1922 forestry became solely an Irish concern. In Northern Ireland, where the forests are administered by the Forestry Division of the Ministry of Agriculture, replanting is carried out at the rate of 5,000 acres a year. In the Free State, later to become the Republic, 1,000 acres were planted in 1923 and by 1961 the annual figure had risen to 26,000 acres. In Eire, forestry is the responsibility of Roinn Tailte – the Department of Lands.

Table 6 provides a guide to the approximate areas of forest, both privately and State-owned, in relation to the total land area in the British Isles.

TABLE 6. *The Forest Areas (in Acres) of the British Isles*

	State	Private	Total
Great Britain	1,344,200 (2.4)	2,066,377 (3.7)	3,410,577 (6.1)
Northern Ireland	80,600 (2.4)	29,300 (0.8)	109,900 (3.2)
Eire	428,359 (2.5)	90,000 (0.5)	518,359 (3.0)

The figures in brackets show the percentage of the total land area.

Mr A. W. Simpson has shown that there is a present objective for forest area in Northern Ireland of 150,000 acres of State forests. He has compared this figure with those in the Post-War Forest Policy Report

(1943) for Great Britain and in the F.A.O. Forestry Adviser's Report (1951) for Eire. I am grateful to him for permission to reproduce Table 7. To achieve the target of producing one third of Britain's timber requirements there will have to be some 7 million acres of managed woodland by A.D. 2000 or about 12½% of the total land area.

TABLE 7. *The Forest Area Objectives of Great Britain, Eire and Northern Ireland*

	Thousands of Acres Unofficial objective	Per million population	Per million acres land area	% of land area
Great Britain	5,000	97	89	8.9
Northern Ireland	200	140	59	5.9
Eire	1,100	390	65	6.5

The present distribution of woodland between various parts of the British Isles is very uneven. The greatest density can be found in the north and east of Scotland where the following counties have more than 8% of their surface under woodland: Moray, Nairn, Kincardine, Aberdeen, Inverness (without the islands), Clackmannan, Banff, Perth, Fife and Angus. Of these Moray and Nairn both exceed 19%. The second high density region of Britain lies in the south-east with Sussex, Surrey, Hampshire, Kent, and Berkshire with more than 8% of their area under woods. Hereford is the only other English county with a similar figure. In Wales the only county with a high density is Monmouth. In Northern Ireland Fermanagh carries the most woodland with a percentage of 6.5 while Londonderry with 4% is followed by Tyrone, Antrim, Down and Armagh with from 2%–3%. The situation in Eire is unclear since figures kindly made available to me by the Irish Embassy in London exist only for the areas of State woodland (Table 10) and not privately-owned woods. From Table 10 it appears that Co. Wicklow is the most heavily wooded with some 10% of its area under trees followed by Waterford, Laois and Tipperary. The statistics are based on State forests the limits of which may sometimes cross county boundaries, so that the figures may not exactly match the true county figures although they are nevertheless an invaluable guide.

The lowest density in England is in a group of midland and eastern counties and these in descending order are Rutland, Chester and Essex with just over 3%, Warwick, Lincoln, Huntingdon, the East Riding and Leicester with just over 2% and Cambridge, Middlesex and London with less than 2%. In Scotland the lowest density is on the north and west

TABLE 8. *Areas of Woodland under Major Tree Species in Great Britain*

High Forest Areas under Major tree species (as at 30/9/67 but allowance for windblown January 1968 included)
Pine and Mixed Stands Combined
Forestry Commission Woodlands

	ENGLAND			SCOTLAND			WALES			GREAT BRITAIN		
		PERCENTAGES			PERCENTAGES			PERCENTAGES			PERCENTAGES	
	Area acres	(a) of category	(b) of all species	Area acres	(a) of category	(b) of all species	Area acres	(a) of category	(b) of all species	Area acres	(a) of category	(b) of all species
Scots pine	105241	23	19	163366	21	21	11598	4	4	280205	19	18
Corsican pine	63980	14	12	7114	1	1	8311	3	3	79405	5	5
Lodgepole pine	24001	5	4	93274	12	12	14783	5	5	132058	9	8
Sitka spruce	104727	23	19	306736	40	40	128602	46	44	540065	36	34
Norway spruce	61383	14	11	83493	11	11	38229	14	13	183105	12	11
European larch	13792	3	3	18774	3	2	2763	1	1	35329	2	2
Japanese and hybrid larch	28639	6	5	66487	9	9	42128	15	14	137254	9	9
Douglas fir	32994	7	6	16579	2	2	19025	7	7	68598	5	4
Western hemlock	8726	2	2	2577	—	—	6855	2	2	18158	1	1
Red cedar	4807	1	1	471	—	—	1217	—	—	6495	—	—
Other conifer	9244	2	2	10750	1	1	8700	3	3	28694	2	2
Total conifer	457534	100	84	769621	100	99	282211	100	96	1509366	100	94
Oak	31712	36	6	1296	27	—	3422	30	1	36430	35	2
Beech	37064	42	7	939	19	—	5170	45	2	43173	41	3
Other broadleaved	19523	22	3	2623	54	—	2789	25	1	24935	24	1
Total broadleaved	88299	100	16	4858	100	1	11381	100	4	104538	100	6
Grand Total	545833	—	100	774479	—	100	293592	—	100	1613904	—	100

coasts where climate and the nature of the soil tend to inhibit tree growth, particularly Wigtown, Sutherland and many of the islands. In Eire the counties least well endowed with State forests are Louth, Limerick, Roscommon, Mayo and Kerry.

The map in Fig. 9 shows the relationship between the total area of woodland in Britain and the total land area. Each circle is plotted to the area of the map and shows therefore the actual land area occupied by woodlands in each county. It has been specially prepared for this volume by the Forestry Commission.

The acreages of the woodland areas of Britain under particular species of tree are shown in Table 8. I am again grateful to the Forestry Commission for these new, unpublished figures. The Ministry of Agriculture provided me with figures for Northern Ireland for woods of over 5 acres at 31st March, 1966, and these include estimated State forests, the estimated area of local authority and water-board woods and the area of privately owned woods based on the agricultural figures for 1959; these figures can be seen in Table 9.

TABLE 9. *Areas of Woodland over 5 Acres in Northern Ireland in 1966*

	Antrim	Armagh	Down	Fermanagh	Londonderry	Tyrone	Total
Total of woodlands	19,000	6,000	14,400	27,100	20,800	22,600	109,900
Mainly coniferous	14,000	4,400	8,900	22,900	17,300	17,800	85,300
Area of State forests							
at 31.3.56	3,900	1,100	5,900	6,900	12,900	10,000	40,700
at 31.3.66	12,700	4,000	7,000	22,600	17,100	17,200	80,600
Total Land area	699,931	309,877	604,518	413,810	510,780	775,184	3,314,100

(The total of land area does not include the County Boroughs of Belfast and Londonderry)

The Forestry Commission Census of Woodlands gave some interesting figures to show the differences between the amount of woodland in Britain and that in a number of other European countries. These figures have been slightly amended and can be seen in Table 11.

According to this census there is slightly more coniferous forest in Great Britain than broad-leaved – a difference that has grown with the planting of more coniferous trees. The decision to plant with conifers was largely influenced by the poor quality of much of the ground available for planting, by the wide use in Britain of softwoods and the need to replenish timber stocks as quickly as possible. Figure 10, supplied by the Forestry Commission, shows the classification of woodlands into mainly coniferous or mainly broad-leaved types. More than half of the high forest of Scotland, Wales and Northern Ireland is coniferous while that of England is predominantly broad-leaved.

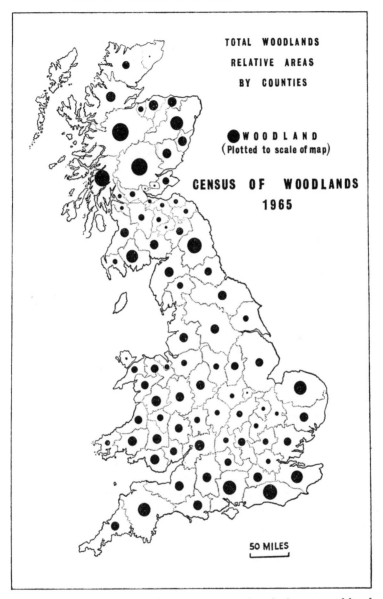

FIG. 9. Map to show total woodland area in relation to total land area in Britain (total woodlands relative areas by counties).

England therefore is noted for its broad-leaved trees, some of which are confined to the country. Figure 11 shows the distribution of oak in Britain, but it does not separate sessile oak from pedunculate. It is clear from the map that oak predominates on the heavier soils of the south Midlands and is well distributed in several Scottish counties as well as Kent, Cornwall and several other counties. In Northern Ireland the only oakwoods of any size are in Co. Antrim and Co. Down, but there are many new young plantations of oak mixed with conifers although the exact areas of these are unknown. In Eire, sessile oakwoods are frequent in Co. Kerry, near Lough Derg and in the Vale of Clara and there is a wood of pedunculate oak near Tullamore in Co. Offaly. In all, there are about 6,500 acres of oak in Eire belonging to the State.

The distribution of beech in Britain is shown in Fig. 12 and falls roughly into two zones. The first is in the south where the beech is native, and includes the woods of Oxfordshire and Berkshire that run along the Chilterns and those growing on the chalk of southern England. The second zone is in the midland and eastern counties of Scotland where the beech has been widely introduced. In Northern Ireland woods of pure, or nearly pure, beech do not exceed two or three acres in size. In Eire, beech can be found in the Vale of Clara and the Powerscourt Estate in Co. Wicklow and there are some 14,000 acres in the State forests. It is also a common hedgerow tree.

Ash is generally distributed, and is typical of the limestones of Yorkshire, Derbyshire and south-west England. There are few ashwoods in Wales while in Scotland Wigtown and Kirkcudbright are the only counties with a fair amount of ash. Of these woods very few are pure and the ash is often mixed with oak. In Eire good ash can be found in Meath and Westmeath. Birch is also widespread in Britain but good woodlands are common only in Shropshire, Norfolk, Yorkshire, Cumberland and Perth and in some of the counties of south-east England such as Kent, Surrey and Sussex. In Ireland birch is regular as a pioneer species of bare ground and newly felled woodlands and there are a few stands in Eire including a good one on bog near Carrick-on-Shannon. Sycamore, which became very popular during the plantings of the eighteenth century and was brought from Central Europe, occupies nearly 100,000 acres of woodland. It is an important tree in Lancashire, the West Riding and Derby and also occurs widely in northern England, North Wales and the Scottish counties of Midlothian, Fife, Lanark and Ayr. Sycamore is common in Ireland, especially on soils with a fair amount of lime.

The ornithologist who is interested in woods and woodland birds may also come across other broad-leaved trees which are of less economic

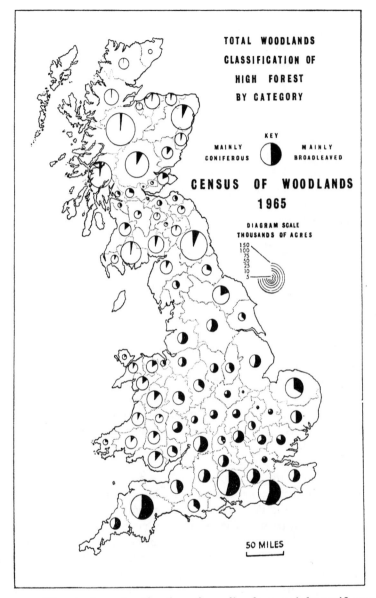

FIG. 10. Map to show classification of woodlands as mainly coniferous or mainly broad-leaved (total woodlands classification of high forest by category).

importance. There are several species of oak such as the serrated-leaved Turkey oak which has become naturalised in the south, the evergreen holm oak of the South Coast and the Isle of Wight, and the widely planted North American red oak with russet foliage. Alderwoods occur in damp places in East Anglia where they are known as "carrs", in Glamorgan, the western Highlands and near Lough Neagh. Alder is perhaps best known as a riverside tree. Several foreign alders have been grown here in an experiment to cover colliery tips and dumps. The field maple is commonest in the south and east, and although individuals may reach 60 ft. in height it is often a member of the shrub layer of woods of other tree species including beech. The native hornbeam is largely confined to Kent, Essex, Hertfordshire and Middlesex where, if left alone, it can grow to almost 90 ft. in height. The native small-leaved lime grows wild in some parts of England and Wales and the large-leaved lime is perhaps native in Wales. The hybrid common lime is often planted in avenues, gardens and streets. The sweet, or Spanish, chestnut is not uncommon in Norfolk, Nottingham, Gloucester, Kent, Surrey, Sussex and Hampshire and it is regularly coppiced. Horse chestnut, whose original home was in the Balkans, is often grown in mixed woods and can sometimes be found in fairly pure stands. The wych elm of the Highland zone is common as high forest in the Pennines, in Wales, Lakeland, West Lothian, Fife and Lanark. The lowland or field elm is essentially a tree of the hedgerows and small spinneys of southern and eastern England.

The census taken by the Forestry Commission showed that of the 29 trees classified individually 14 accounted for 98% of the high forest area. Among the broad-leaved trees the most important species were oak, ash, beech, birch, sweet chestnut, elm and sycamore, while among the conifers the most significant were Scots pine, Corsican pine, European larch, Norway and Sitka spruce and Douglas fir. Scotland has the largest individual share of the coniferous high forest as well as of Scots and lodge-pole pine. This latter pine from western North America is suited to the poorest soils, and the Forestry Commission have been planting it at the rate of 10 million trees a year. Scots pine has been widely planted as a forest crop in eastern and southern Scotland, on the lighter soils of East Anglia and Lincoln and on the heaths of southern England where it has increased with a lessening of grazing by animals. Corsican pine is frequent in Nottinghamshire, Stafford, East Anglia, the North Riding, Lincoln, Hampshire, Dorset, Somerset and Devon and it has also been used to stabilise sand-dunes in the Moray Firth, Anglesey, Carmarthen, Glamorgan and Lancashire. Two other pines – the maritime from the Mediterranean and the Monterey from California – can also be found, particularly

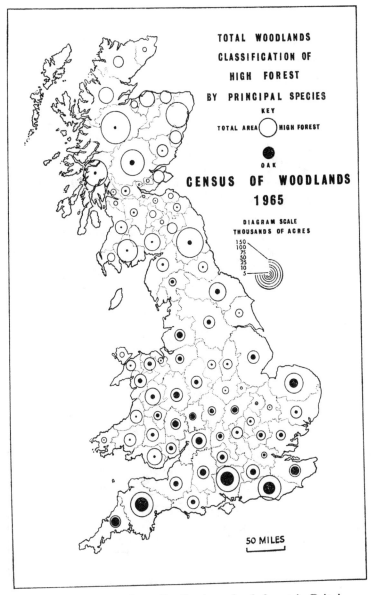

FIG. 11. Map to show distribution of oak forest in Britain.

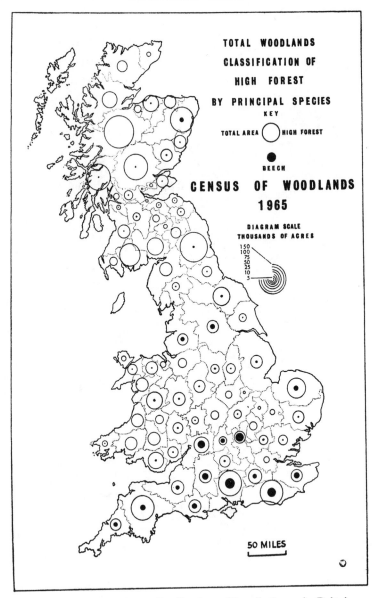

FIG. 12. Map to show distribution of beech forest in Britain.

TABLE 10. *The Areas of State Woodland in Eire by County*

County	Total Area (in acres)	Area owned by State under woods and plantations (in acres)
Carlow	221,485	5,962
Cavan	467,162	6,235
Clare	787,704	14,298
Cork	1,843,322	61,284
Donegal	1,193,621	31,187
Dublin	227,754	3,819
Galway	1,467,670	43,700
Kerry	1,161,706	13,903
Kildare	418,644	6,928
Kilkenny	509,431	11,498
Laois	424,892	20,390
Leitrim	376,764	11,985
Limerick	663,654	8,418
Longford	257,936	3,044
Louth	202,806	2,085
Mayo	1,333,940	16,537
Meath	577,824	—
Monaghan	318,985	5,995
Offaly	493,636	7,880
Roscommon	608,540	7,053
Sligo	443,806	8,467
Tipperary	1,051,292	36,036
Waterford	454,128	29,731
Westmeath	435,606	5,522
Wexford	581,061	15,572
Wicklow	500,328	50,829
Total	*17,023,697*	*428,359*

in some south-western coastal districts. The European larch is common in the Highlands, North Wales, the Welsh Marches, Somerset, Devon and some Midland counties. Japanese larch has been planted on poorer sites in the same localities as the European but it is most regular in areas of high rainfall in Devon, Wales and south-west Scotland. Sitka spruce from North America grows on the wet grass-moors of the western Highlands and the Irish blanket bogs and is commoner than the Norway spruce which has a more eastern distribution and flourishes on lower slopes and on less acid flushes. Because Sitka spruce is so well suited to damp climates and peaty soils, it comprises 64% of the trees planted in Northern Ireland compared with 12% each of Norway spruce and larch. The deep ridges

TABLE II. *The Woodlands and Land Area of 11 European Countries*

Country	Total Woodland in Millions of Acres	Percentage of Land Area
Great Britain	3.40	6.1
Germany	32.25	26.8
Portugal	5.75	25.8
Norway	19.00	23.8
France	26.00	19.1
Belgium	1.50	18.2
Spain	12.00	9.7
Denmark	1.00	9.3
Netherlands	0.50	6.1
Northern Ireland	0.10	3.3
Republic of Ireland	0.42	3.0

and furrows produced by the deep ploughing that precedes planting has scarred many hillsides, but the growth of trees gradually hides the wounds. Douglas fir is not uncommon in Inverness, Perth, Argyll and Kirkcudbright in Scotland, in Caernarvon, Merioneth, Montgomery and Radnor in Wales, in Somerset and Devon in England and on the mountain slopes of Counties Wicklow, Wexford, Waterford, Tipperary and Louth in Eire. The grand, silver and noble firs and the western hemlock have been planted in Scotland in small amounts while the western red cedar is more regular in England and Wales. The native yew forms natural woodlands in England in Hampshire, Sussex and the Wye Valley and in Ireland at Killarney, but it also forms a secondary tree in many beechwoods and sometimes in oak and ash as well. Table 8 summarises the proportion of the major broad-leaved and coniferous tree species in Britain. Figure 13 shows the areas in acres that have been planted in Great Britain, Northern Ireland and Eire between 1922 and 1962.

The Forestry Commission's later census of 1951 was devoted to hedgerow and park timber and to small woods under five acres in size. It was found that only 5% of the total woodland area of Britain could be found in these small woods of which 63% occur in England, 21% in Scotland and 16% in Wales. Oak was the most important species and accounted for about a third of all the woods. Another third was represented by the combined total of beech, ash and sycamore while other broad-leaved trees such as birch, alder, hazel, hornbeam, sweet and horse chestnuts, lime, poplar, willow, elm, hawthorn and elder together with conifers such as Scots pine, larch, spruce, Douglas fir and sequoia made up the final third.

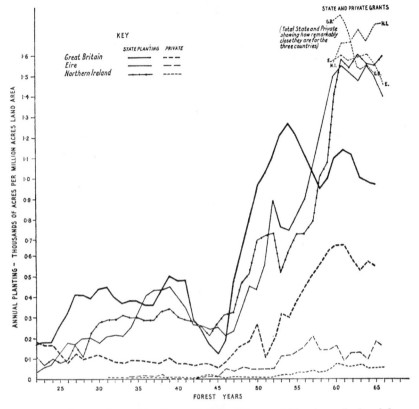

FIG. 13. Areas planted in Great Britain, Eire and Northern Ireland from 1922-66. Reproduced from *Quarterly Journal of Forestry* by kind permission of A. W. Simpson (who has brought the graph up to date for 1966).

These small woods are often surrounded by quite different types of countryside – heath, parkland, farmland, fen, built-up area and so on.

The theme of this chapter has been the increasing activity of man. Forests have made way for his farming, his towns, roads and reservoirs and his operations have given England its characteristic appearance of a vast patchwork quilt. In more recent years new plantations have begun to restore some of the losses and have carpeted the once bare slopes and hills. Private landowners are seeking to redress the balance, and when farmers begin to consider the possibility of including the practice of forestry in the management and planning of their farms we shall come even nearer the vital target of replacing a significant part of our lost heritage of trees. The new woodlands have restored lost woodland birds to areas they abandoned a long time ago, but they have not yet produced any great revolutionary changes among our birds. There has not been any mass movement south of the typical birds of the old Caledonian Forest. How do we sum up the present position? I cannot do better than quote one of the Forestry Commission's conclusions: "British woodlands are characterised by relatively small size, multiplicity of ownership, and by the diverse character of individual blocks, scattered over a countryside which, although predominantly agricultural . . . is frequently broken up by urban and industrial development."

CHAPTER 4

A WALK THROUGH THE WOODS

"To shape a landscape is to shape its bird-life," wrote E. M. Nicholson in *Birds and Men*. Yet, in spite of the change from woodland to more open conditions, the land bird fauna of the British Isles has remained very largely a forest one. Of the fifty or so bird species found commonly on farmland with its mixture of fields, small woods and hedgerow strips about 80% are birds originally of forest or scrub. Many of these species also moved successfully into the parks, orchards and gardens devised by man and some also became the typical birds of suburbia. We know that very few birds characteristic of steppe still remain on farmland. Undoubtedly the widening of the range of habitat open to woodland birds has increased their numbers, for birds are fewer in a mature forest than in the shrub layer or along the woodland edge. The Common Birds Census, organised by the British Trust for Ornithology, mapped in 1965 some 12,000 bird territories over 35 square miles of farmland and 3¾ miles of woodland. They found that among the song-birds the blackbird was the commonest bird on farmland, but in woodland it just took second place to the robin. Chaffinch and hedgesparrow took second and third places among the farmland birds. Hedgerows are important to species such as these and their destruction would profoundly affect their numbers. There is about an acre of hedge to every 100 acres of crop but in the last twenty years we have lost nearly a fifth of our hedgerows.

Woodland birds have been faced with many changes in their environment. Some have adapted themselves well but others have not. Some species can be found not only in woods but also in a variety of marginal and often different habitats. This chapter is an attempt to codify the habitats in which we find our woodland birds, to define what we really mean by a "woodland" bird and to consider the various ways in which estimates and counts of populations can be made. This is a difficult task, and some of my judgments may not agree with those of others who feel that their local situation is different. After all "Men that undertake only one district are much more likely to advance natural knowledge than those that grasp at more than they can possibly be acquainted with." Gilbert White's warning is important, and this book itself would not have been possible without the exacting and meticulous work of ecologists who examined small areas with infinite patience.

Along the edges of woodlands it is possible to find several types of ecotones which resemble areas of open, grassy woods and parkland. Other habitats such as scrub, young plantations, orchards, farmland, gardens and towns may all contain species whose density is higher in these areas than in woodlands. The Forestry Commission in its Census No. 2 observed, after a small sample count, that "it does appear possible that the density of hedgerow, park and garden timber may be at least as great in some built-up areas as it is in rural ones." Ecotone birds will be the subject of later chapters, but it may be of interest here to point out that a species may have arisen in an early ecotone or may have penetrated from another rather like it; other species may be typical of either one or the other of the two habitats between which the ecotone occurs. Some birds can appear in all the possible habitats but show a preference for one or two of them. The blackbird is undoubtedly in origin a bird of woodlands and it prefers woods on the better soils. I have found blackbirds nesting in woods of sessile, pedunculate and hybrid oak, of ash, beech, birch, alder, sycamore, pine, larch, spruce and yew. It is also common in scrub, in plantations up to a certain age, in parkland, hedgerows, orchards and gardens. I have found blackbirds nesting in stone walls and in byres in Skye and Shetland, on clocks in workshops, on ladders and against drain-pipes in north-west London, and even on the ground; yet four nests at Dollis Hill were more than 25 feet above the ground. The blackbird is therefore an extremely adaptable species that ranges widely through the ecotones which it successfully invaded from its woodland home. The starling also breeds in many woods that I have visited, but it feeds chiefly outside them on grassland, and is therefore rather more a bird of parkland than woodland. It also breeds around and in our houses, in quarries and church towers, while the island races use stone walls in Fair Isle, Shetland and the Outer Isles. Some mainland starlings will also enter woods to feed on caterpillars in the summer or to roost in winter. The heron feeds along river-banks and lakesides but often breeds socially in tall trees in woods. And to mark the greatest restriction in range the crested tit is confined to mature Scots pinewoods in the Highlands of Scotland. Indeed we can deduce that in earlier times our woodland birds would have been sharply divided in many cases from those of other habitats.

These examples illustrate some of the hazards accompanying any attempt to separate habitat from habitat and species from species. Already we can see that some species may satisfy their needs in woodlands while the heron has in fact only one demand – that of nesting. It is possible too that pure woodland has not always been the most important source of evolution of our forest birds. Some groups – the buntings (*Emberizinae*) and leaf warblers (*Phylloscopi*) – may have evolved in ecotones, but some of our ecotones are fairly recent and could have had no real effect. When land has been abandoned by man we have seen that its vegetation undergoes a regular succession in its growth; this is matched by the bird-life as some species appear only in the early stages and others in the later stages of development. As the vegetation approaches its optimal stage for a particular species of bird its numbers will begin to increase. At this point the marginal habitats may be important since they are able to absorb the overflow when, under population pressure in the optimal habitat, the birds begin to spread out. I have recorded about a hundred different species of bird in woodland and woodland ecotones in Britain, but this is some thirty fewer than I have observed in western Continental woods, and their ecotones. Limiting factors at work here may be rather complex, and it is not necessarily the variety of the flora which has the most effect on numbers. Density and type of foliage, thickness and height in the shrub layer and the development of the trees may be important. A habitat composed of all sizes of a single tree species can support more kinds of bird than a wood composed of many tree species, but it is rare to find a pure broad-leaved wood of this kind in Britain.

The distribution of birds can be regulated by the vegetation, climate, food, presence of nesting sites and predators, disturbance, pollution; these are factors which we shall look at again later. Each species also tends to settle in a habitat like its ancestral one, and indeed there is often a preference for certain habitats which may prevent the birds breeding elsewhere. This was called "the psychological factor" and was mainly supported by the absence of a species from habitats apparently "well-suited in essential but not in superficial appearance" (Lack 1937). I have always been intrigued by the patchy distribution, for example, of the corn bunting in the South Midlands where many apparently suitable areas hold none at all. It was thought that the presence or absence of a species was controlled by food supplies but it is possible that some species may be restricted to certain foods because their habitats are so limited. Lack cited the examples of the reed bunting and the yellowhammer of which the former eats mainly insects and the seeds of marsh plants and grasses, while the latter prefers the insects and seeds of drier situations. Yet this case has been weakened by the recent spread of reed buntings into dry, yellowhammer-type countryside.

The type of twigs in a particular kind of tree may be an important limiting factor. For instance, certain species of North American woodland birds may have been confined to oak-forests or maple and elmwoods because of the differences in the branch and twig structure of the tree canopies. It may well be that this restriction is due rather to structural adaptation than to habit. The twisted beak of the crossbill is an adaptation to a particular food that will restrict its range in the breeding season to coniferous trees. Among finches there are thought to be indications sometimes that a structural change was necessary before a new behaviour pattern and feeding habit could evolve. Any preferences in food or habitat were developed in a very different environment from that of today; these preferences often separate closely related species from each other. Modern habitats are in a state of change and the redpoll has switched in some parts of England from birch seeds to those of farmland weeds and is now in some parts a resurgent species. Other finches have been forced to change their feeding habits through the effects of herbicides. Some differences in feeding behaviour among the finches still exist that cannot be attributed to structural differences, and Newton is of the opinion that some psychological factor is present in the growth of these patterns of behaviour.

The study of animals in a truly natural environment has become almost impossible in our twentieth-century world. Once, as we have seen, the greater part of the British Isles was under woodland, evolved and adjusted to the climate of the Sub-Atlantic but modified by man. Natural or near natural vegetation has been able to survive only on some of the higher mountains, on a few parts of the sea-coasts, in a mere handful of bogs and in a few patches of relic pine-forest in Scotland, of sessile oakwood in south-west Ireland and perhaps of some high-level woods. Nearly all the communities of native plants are the result of man's activities. When we talk of original habitats we must remember that those that appear to be of this kind are really "semi-natural".

Before looking more closely at the factors which influence the range and distribution of our woodland species it might be useful to draw up a simple method of classifying various types of woodland and ecotone; this system then can be used throughout the remainder of the book. Since the presence of birds may depend on the area, shape, situation and species composition of a wood, on the age and height of the trees, on the existence, nature and stability of the shrub layer, on the character of the transitional zone between the wood and other habitats and on the degree of intervention by man, it is essential to employ some system of classification. Previous methods of tabling information and describing woodland have been drawn up by Tansley (1949), the Forestry Commission (1952), Yapp (1955) and Emlen (1956). I have drawn rather heavily on the second and third authorities for the method which I have used during the course of my research and the terms adopted will be maintained in this volume.

The following system of classification is designed to embrace all areas of trees, mature and developing woodlands irrespective of their exact composition:

GROUPS OF TREES

Wood   A tree-covered area, consisting usually of a community dominated by one, or several species, of five acres or more in size. The term "forest" derived from the old place-names, such as New Forest (see page 53), is still widely used for the older forests although a large area may be without tree cover. The Forestry Commission also use the word "forest", as in "The Queen's Forest", to denote the larger areas of plantation which they have set up. Both "wood" and "forest" have wider and looser meanings as large and fairly continuous aggregations of trees.

Grove   A small wood of from ½ acre to five acres in extent. Woods of this kind are frequent on farmland and on private estates.

Clump   A group or cluster of trees covering less than ½ acre. This may include the small, often circular groups of trees planted on the Downs and other hills.

Belt   A strip of trees less than 22 yards wide but of indefinite length. This is often a shelter-belt planted to protect fields, farms and houses from the wind.

Line   A single or double line of trees with their canopies touching or nearly so.

Stand   Any area of woodland, one acre or more in area, which is uniform for the purposes of description. Many individual woods can be subdivided into stands.

Plantation   An area of artificial woodland, composed usually of coniferous trees, or mixed species, mainly of uniform age and planted in straight lines. At first planting trees may number from 1,000 to 5,000 per acre. Before thinning is carried out the dead side branches are cut away from the stem to a height of about 6 feet from the ground; this process is called "brashing". Thinnings are carried out at intervals depending on the age and species of the trees. Some plantations may have trees of two age groups if lost seedlings are replaced.

Compartment A unit of about 25 acres inside a plantation and used as a unit of management.

Thicket A young plantation before "brashing" when it is usually impenetrable.

Scrub This is composed of bushes or trees of woodland type rising to not more than 26 ft. in height. Although the shrub layer of a wood is often described as scrub and contains birds typical of scrub, it is more convenient to restrict the term "scrub" to young, regenerating woodlands, to bushy growth that will not develop farther into woodland and to tree growth inhibited by climate or altitude to a stunted form. The term "shrub layer" is reserved for the secondary growth from 6 to 15 ft. high inside a wood.

Spinney An area of thorny plants, pure or mixed, of hawthorn, blackthorn or bramble. Often planted or allowed to develop for fox and game coverts.

Carr A fenwood of alder or buckthorn with extensive shrub growth often of sallow, hawthorn, spindle, privet and currant.

MAIN TYPES OF WOODLAND

1. *Broad-leaved Woods* with the following principal trees – sessile and pedunculate oak, ash, beech, silver and downy birch, sweet chestnut, sycamore, alder, hazel, hornbeam, poplars, limes, elms, willows, Norway maple, cherry and other minor species. These woods include broad-leaved with conifer mixture, or standards, if these form less than 20% of the crop in terms of the canopy.

2. *Coniferous Woods* with the following principal trees – Scots pine, Corsican pine, lodgepole pine, European, Japanese and hybrid larches, Norway and Sitka spruce, Douglas fir, western hemlock, Lawson cypress, grand, common silver and noble fir, western red cedar and other minor species. These woods include coniferous forest with broad-leaved mixture, or standards, if these form less than 20% of the canopy.

3. *Mixed woods* Include all mixtures of conifers with broad-leaved trees where either category forms 20% or more of the crop.

4. *Coppice (Simple)* Areas in which all trees are cut at intervals so that shoots spring up from the stumps with a rotation from open ground to scrub. It is made up chiefly of hazel, oak, sweet chestnut, ash, hornbeam, birch and alder but can be mixed. Represents 34% of all coppice.

5. *Coppice-with-Standards* Areas in which most of the trees are cut but more than six are left to the acre. Composed chiefly of sweet chestnut, hazel and oak. Represents 66% of all coppice.

6. *Scrub*

7. *Devastated Woods* Stands, usually of broad-leaved or mixed woods, from which the best timber has been removed leaving a scattered remnant of the original crop. 92% of these are in private ownership.

8. *Felled Woods* Represents land which once carried high forest, usually of conifers, which has been clear felled.

9. *Disafforested or Lost Woods* This is woodland converted to other uses such as farming, airfields, roads, houses and gardens.

In describing a bird's habitat we can now use these more exact terms as well as giving information about the geological and climatic background, the situation, slope and soil characteristics and so on. A woodland bird can often be watched in several of the layers and zones in a wood and it is helpful to divide the tree itself into zones. Dr. Yapp has drawn up a structural classification but, as he did not state the size of the standard bird to meet all the requirements, I have included the dimensions suggested by Gibb (1954) which seem to be apposite.

The Structure of a Tree

1. *Trunk and Major Branches and Limbs* Those parts, exceeding 3 inches in diameter, which a bird cannot grasp.

2. *Branches* Those parts, between $\frac{1}{2}$ inch and 3 inches in diameter, which a bird can grasp.

3. *Twigs* Small branches, less than $\frac{1}{2}$ inch in diameter and those not strong enough to support the bird's weight except when it hangs from them.

4. *Leaves*

5. *Flowers*

6. *Fruits*

We have seen something of the complex environment in which a bird of the woodlands may live. But what is a woodland bird? This is not easy to answer. A bird such as the tree pipit may need only a single tree as a launching pad for its song flight and a kestrel require only an old crow's nest in an isolated tree. But one tree is not enough for the blackcap or the great spotted woodpecker. Lack and Venables considered as woodland birds those "that occur regularly when there is more than one tree". This is not exact enough, I feel, and the definition given by Campbell seems nearer the mark – "a species which, during all or part of the year, can fulfil all the demands of its life within a woodland habitat." The type of woodland may be very important. It is most instructive to walk through a southern summer oakwood and compare the number of birds to those in a yew-wood. Redstarts, pied flycatchers and nightjars prefer more open woods in which to hunt their aerial insect prey while jays, bullfinches, long-tailed tits, garden warblers, nightingales and hedgesparrows demand a thick shrub layer. The blackcap likes the shrub layer but also seems to need fairly tall trees as song-posts. Robins feed and may nest on the ground zone, often forage in the field and shrub layers and sing in the canopy. The treecreeper's view of the world is largely from the fissures which run up the trunk and main boughs and branches of the trees. Some woodland birds, such as the woodcock which often nests near its favourite feeding swamp and the willow tit which likes elders for nesting, often prefer the damper corners of the woods. Many birds select the edges of the forest and the distribution of many is dependent upon the age of the trees which to provide nest-holes have to be mature and past their best. Other birds which we would expect to see in other habitats may spend part of their time in the woodlands. Moorhens may wander from their pool and explore the forest floor in the dusk while black-headed gulls often forage during the hours of daylight in the wooded areas of the New Forest and the Scottish pinewoods. In the broad-leaved woods there is often a diversity of environment within the habitat, and it is here where "relationships and population pressures exist in their most elaborate form" (Elton 1966).

I have attempted to classify the birds of woodlands and woodland ecotones in Table 12. The groups represent what I feel are the most convenient ecological niches for the different species, but they are not mutually exclusive. A species like the blackbird can fit, as we have seen earlier, into several niches besides its original one and ecotone birds can appear in woodlands as well. The tree/water ecotone represents a mixed habitat now greatly reduced but suitable for the reed bunting or for the grey wagtail which can often be seen feeding and nesting along burns inside the Scottish pinewoods. The osprey builds in a tall pine but quarters the lochs and rivers for fish. Herons search for food along the rivers but like tall trees in close-canopy woods for nesting in Britain, although I have found heron nests in reed-beds in Spain, and on Welsh cliff-faces where trees are scarce. In Ireland I have seen herons' nests in scrub. The heronries themselves may be from five to twelve miles from the nearest feeding place. The tree/heath ecotone is composed of scattered trees and heath, dominated by ling and *Vaccinium*, and is common in the Highland Zone as well as appearing less frequently in parts of southern England. All the twelve species that I have put into this category favour heathland with not too many trees. I have seen black grouse, cuckoo, whinchat and yellowhammer in quite dense woodland although this is not their typical habitat. The parkland ecotone is made up of trees and grassland, sometimes with shrubs and I have used this ecological group to include hedgerows, parts of farmland, orchards and gardens. Another kind of ecotone is the forest-edge which I have indicated in Table 12 and this draws a number of species like the magpie from the main table. It is an ecotone generally richer in birds than the centre of a wood.

The placing of each species in its niche is my own responsibility and is based on my own observations. There may be some objection to my

TABLE 12. *A List of the Birds of Woodlands and Woodland Ecotones*

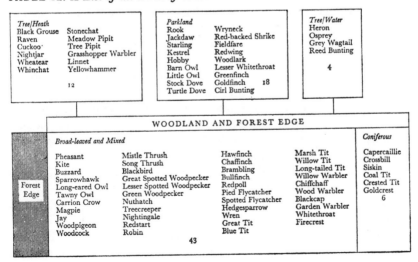

Tree/Heath		Parkland		Tree/Water
Black Grouse	Stonechat	Rook	Wryneck	Heron
Raven	Meadow Pipit	Jackdaw	Red-backed Shrike	Osprey
Cuckoo·	Tree Pipit	Starling	Fieldfare	Grey Wagtail
Nightjar	Grasshopper Warbler	Kestrel	Redwing	Reed Bunting
Wheatear	Linnet	Hobby	Woodlark	
Whinchat	Yellowhammer	Barn Owl	Lesser Whitethroat	4
		Little Owl	Greenfinch	
	12	Stock Dove	Goldfinch 18	
		Turtle Dove	Cirl Bunting	

WOODLAND AND FOREST EDGE

	Broad-leaved and Mixed					Coniferous
	Pheasant	Mistle Thrush	Hawfinch	Marsh Tit		Capercaillie
	Kite	Song Thrush	Chaffinch	Willow Tit		Crossbill
	Buzzard	Blackbird	Brambling	Long-tailed Tit		Siskin
Forest Edge	Sparrowhawk	Great Spotted Woodpecker	Bullfinch	Willow Warbler		Coal Tit
	Long-eared Owl	Lesser Spotted Woodpecker	Redpoll	Chiffchaff		Crested Tit
	Tawny Owl	Green Woodpecker	Pied Flycatcher	Wood Warbler		Goldcrest
	Carrion Crow	Nuthatch	Spotted Flycatcher	Blackcap		6
	Magpie	Treecreeper	Hedgesparrow	Garden Warbler		
	Jay	Nightingale	Wren	Whitethroat		
	Woodpigeon	Redstart	Great Tit	Firecrest		
	Woodcock	Robin	Blue Tit			
		43				

placing of particular species, and a good example to discuss is the haw-finch. Mountfort described the habitat of the hawfinch as "moderately hilly country, interspersed with patches of mixed woodlands, coppices, thickets, orchards and hedges" while Yapp regarded it as a bird of ecotones – "land with scattered hawthorns, orchards or large gardens". According to *The Handbook of British Birds* the habitat in the breeding season for the hawfinch is well-grown deciduous woodland or mixed woods, wooded gardens, parks, bushy places and orchards. The late Commander A. W. P. Robertson and I spent many days in the field together and found that the majority of colonies were in mixed woodland – "oak, birch and sycamore and wych elm, with hawthorn scattered round the edges and in the rides" (Robertson 1954). Although I have also seen nests in orchards and thorns the true woodland habitat seems the more fitting to me. Other species have been put in their groups according to similar lines of reasoning. I think it is of some value at this stage to list the more important species of woodland and marginal habitat, since these are the main subjects of the book. The birds of woodlands and their ecotones, according to this list, number 78 species from 51 genera. Seventy-eight species were found from 55 genera in some of the lowland forests of Slovakia.

Some of the densest populations of birds are to be found in woodlands, parks and richly varied built-up areas. Although the untouched northern forests of Europe without clearings or rides may support under 100 individuals to the 100 acres, normal woodland may support from 100 to 1,500 and exceptionally even 2,000 birds per 100 acres. The pattern in different countries tends to be similar with low densities in purely coniferous woods – in Finland 150–200, in central Europe 100–500 and in northern America 190–660 – while higher densities can be found in broad-leaved forest, ranging from 430 per 100 acres of Finnish birchwood to 640–1,200 in some of the central European forests. For comparison, the density of breeding birds in an English wood in the Midlands is just over 400 per 100 acres and in the suburban area of Dollis Hill in London it is from 520 to 530 per 100 acres. Since many Continental figures for bird densities are given in hectares it may be useful to remember that there are some 2.47 acres to the hectare.

Table 13 gives some of the national averages for the breeding densities of birds per 100 acres from a number of different habitats.

To know the numbers of a species in an area is essential for a better understanding of its ecology since such numbers provide the basic material for much wider studies. There are two ways in which this can be done – by census making and by taking counts. A census is usually an estimate of the breeding population of an area while the term "count" is more generally applied to a method of finding out the number of individuals present in an area at a certain time. To know the numbers of birds present at different seasons is important since in this way light can be thrown on the ecology and status of any species as well as on the effects of climatic change, alterations in land use and the application of chemicals.

TABLE 13. *Some Breeding Densities of Birds in Britain* (largely after Fisher 1940)

Area	Density of Breeding Birds per 100 acres
Rough grazing	70
Permanent grass	200
Coniferous woodland	200
Broad-leaved woodland	400
Mixed woodland	500
Built-up areas	500
Parks	1,000

Any method of assessing numbers is subject to some error, and its validity can be shaken by mistakes and inconsistencies in the observer, by the comparative inconspicuousness of some birds according to size and time of day and by the thickness of the cover. Areas in which censuses are made have to be revisited a number of times to reduce the margin of error. Most woodland birds are territorial, and repeated visits will soon reveal the breeding birds present including usually the most secretive ones.

For more than twenty years I have carried out censuses in both woodland and suburban areas during the breeding season by counting the number of singing males and then by plotting their territories. Every morning from spring onwards I move along a fixed route in each section of my study area until the census is complete and the district fully covered. The counts are repeated a number of times throughout the breeding season. Every count begins before dawn and is continued until the dawn chorus begins to die away. I do not begin to move until the chorus is at its height and the count may not last for more than twenty-five minutes. Since the counts begin when the territories of most species are being established and continue throughout the season I can soon distinguish paired from unpaired males; further periods of daylight can be used to plot the nest sites for each pair. The counts must be made in the early morning when song is at its height and they must be repeated regularly, which calls for a certain amount of self-discipline. This technique I applied over five years in a Northamptonshire oakwood and over eighteen years in suburban north-west London. As a result I have been able to compare breeding densities from year to year and to examine the consequences of severe winters such as those of 1947, 1955, 1961–2 and 1962–3. A single observer can amass quite a bit of information in this way, but a team can cover a bigger area altogether or a smaller area more quickly. It has been claimed that the static singing male in a territory provides the most important unit of measurement in census work. However, for some species it is not easy to determine the precise population in the time available, and the Common Birds Census has as its declared aim the study of population changes with the aid of an index of population.

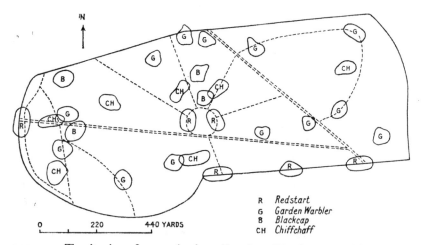

FIG. 14. Territories of 4 species breeding in a Northamptonshire wood, 1949.

Figure 14 is a species map for Badby Wood in Northamptonshire for 1949 showing the territories in that year of four species of bird. In practice, as a result of my census methods I drew up maps for every species in relation to topography and vegetation, but the map shown here is for the territories of redstart, garden warbler, blackcap and chiffchaff in that year. Badby Wood consisted then of just over 200 acres of mature pedunculate oakwood with a little Scots pine, larch, beech and ash with a shrub layer of occasional sweet chestnut, hazel, holly and rhododendron and a considerable amount of bramble and honeysuckle. The field layer was typical of a lowland pedunculate oakwood. There were one or two small clearings and these were extended in later years by felling and replanting with conifers; considerable portions of the wood are now very different from what they were in 1949.

The way in which censuses were carried out over many years in an oakwood on Bookham Common in Surrey is a classic study of bird populations. Observers walked about the wood and recorded on a map the approximate positions and numbers of all species encountered. Different sections of the wood were worked by various members of the observing group. An area might be covered more than once by the same or a different observer, but birds of species already noted were not included again unless it seemed likely that there were more than were first counted. This made a thorough search possible and the various maps were all amalgamated. The counts of singing males were generally made from 11 a.m. to 2 p.m., and despite this disadvantage, it was felt that the census figures would give "an indication of the breeding season population which can be compared from year to year" (Beven 1963). Figure 15 shows the number of territories in Eastern Wood, Bookham Common, of singing males from 1946–56 and 1958–63; no census was made in 1957. Territories were recorded as half-territories when they extended beyond the confines of the wood, but the maximum number of these was only three. The letter code at the top and bottom should be interpreted as a guide to the nature of the winters: vc (very cold), c (cold), fc (fairly cold), fm (fairly mild), m (mild) and vm (very mild). The classification of the winters was based on the monthly average minimum night temperatures at Kew, which is also in Surrey.

A mapping technique for the birds of the 44 acres of Bagley Wood near Oxford has been described by Williamson. He did not employ the fixed route method used by Enemar and myself and concluded from his study that it was not essential and that "an observer with limited time can make an effective census in woodland provided that he does not choose an area which is too large to be covered sufficiently fully and often in the time available". Williamson suggested that the size of the area should be regulated by the number of visits that can be made; 12–15 visits mean a wood of 40–50 acres and 8 visits one of only 20–25 acres. The visits should be spread through the whole breeding season and take place on days of good weather when song is not inhibited. Such censuses may produce "surplus" observations of birds passing through on migration, just wandering without owning territories or occupying them only briefly.

There is an American cruising method of taking a census in woodland which I have employed to ensure a proper coverage of an area. In this, the observer follows conveniently spaced parallel tracks that effectively cover the area of a wood in the form of a grid. Every bird seen or heard is mapped according to its approximate position in the wood. The observer may need to use several ways of fixing his place in the wood – compass, tape-measure and so on. Some of the records may apply to the same bird, or to members of the same pair, but experience and repeated visits will soon enable individuals to be distinguished from each other. The Common Birds Census, which was started in 1961 to obtain information on population fluctuations, has as one of its requirements a minimum of six well-spaced visits to the survey area through the breeding season. The results of this census are also being plotted on species maps. Repeated visits are helpful in obtaining a fuller picture of a bird community, and twenty minutes spent in a wood of ten acres could reveal all of the birds except the most secretive. The percentage of nesting birds in a pinewood in the Sverdlovsk district varied from an average of 48.8% for a single transect to 100% for one repeated only five times.

There may not always be either the opportunity or the time for an observer to carry out repeated censuses in some woods, but it would nevertheless be valuable to have at least an estimate of the densities of birds in woods visited only infrequently or perhaps on a single occasion. Here it is possible to apply sampling methods. One of the most straight-forward consists of making an exact count of the birds in a part of the wood, then multiplying the total for this by the number of times the acreage of the surveyed area will divide into the total acreage of the whole wood. However, the type of woodland has to be uniform for this kind of treatment and small topographical variations can make the tree development not at all uniform.

Another and widely used method of sampling is that of the line transect. Transect counts were used to estimate the total numbers of different bird species in Finland, and totals were reached of about $5\frac{1}{2}$ million each for willow warbler and chaffinch – the two commonest birds in a country 65% of which is under forest and only 8% under cultivation. The theory behind the line transect has been expressed in an equation which I shall not reproduce here but which has been resolved by Dr. Yapp. Transects can be used for comparative purposes between species of about equal conspicuousness and between habitats, and I have carried out many such transects in British and Irish woods. They cannot solve the problem of absolute densities. Some authorities believe that line transects should be applied only to static objects like plants, but in the absence of any more convenient kind of sampling method this system does have some value. The observer carrying out a line transect travels alone at a speed of about 2 miles an hour along as straight a line as possible and records the birds

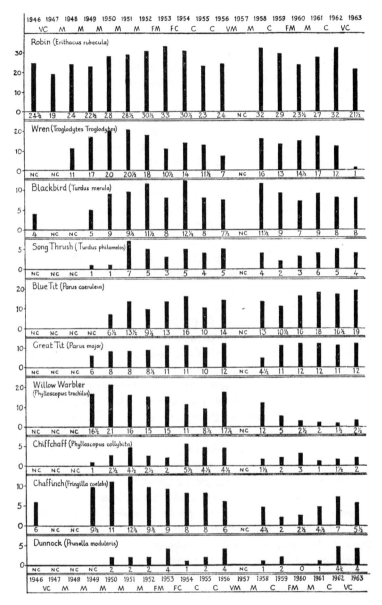

FIG. 15. The numbers of territories of singing males in Eastern Wood, Bookham Common, Surrey, 1946-56, 1958-63. Reproduced from *British Birds* by kind permission of Dr Geoffrey Beven.

he sees or hears. He does not have to concern himself with his own position or that of the birds. This technique will not work in woods with a very dense shrub layer and no tracks, or in those with a rocky ground zone. The 2 miles per hour speed is one at which few birds will be missed and is also capable of being maintained for a long time. In the conditions of woodland, auditory contacts are obviously more important than purely visual ones and the proportion will be higher in the denser plantations and woodlands. It is imperative that the observer is expert in the recognition of bird-songs and calls. The line transect is valuable for territorial passerines and the bigger the sample the better the result. The relative abundance which gives some guide to bird populations can be calculated by converting the number of records or contacts for each species into a percentage of the total records. These relative abundance figures will often be quoted in this book and the abbreviation RA, followed by a number such as 5, indicates that out of a total of 100 records a particular species has scored only five contacts. Some of the more conspicuous species may come higher in the list than they should, and conversely the less conspicuous may appear lower than they should. I have sometimes resorted to my own bird imitations to elicit responses from particularly elusive species such as goldcrests in conifer plantations and treecreepers in broad-leaved woods. A list of contacts per hour with the species listed in order can provide a clear record of the birds of a habitat and a guide to their absolute density.

Another counting method involves the percentage frequency. For each area of woodland a large number of sample plots, sometimes called "quadrats", is worked out and the species to be found in each plot is recorded. It is not necessary to record the number of individuals. Then the number of plots in which a species appears is expressed as a percentage of the total number of plots; the result is the percentage frequency. This method works quite well if woods can be found in natural plots or in the artificial compartments of many coniferous plantations. It is a useful and speedy way of comparing different species in woods of different types. Numbers acquired by this method are very close to those obtained from line transects. It is important to know in what proportion of woods certain species appear as this is a guide to their frequency as opposed to their abundance.

Some authorities believe that the only correct way in which to express abundance is by means of the biomass – the total weight of all the individuals in the community – since it is the biomass "which consumes, produces, stores and exchanges energy." The true dominants are considered to be those with the highest biomass. From figures for the spruce forests of Slovakia the relationship between the number of individuals and their biomass has been worked out. In the four food groups of herbivores, insect-eaters, mixed feeders and carnivores it is possible to work out the biomass for each group by multiplying the number of individuals by their average weights and then adding them up. This number can then be compared to the number of individuals in each of the four groups. Turček found that the numerically dominant species in descending order were coal tit, chaffinch, and song thrush and the biomass dominants chaffinch, song thrush, coal tit, wood pigeon, carrion crow and hazel hen.

Counts are not only valuable as comparative material in themselves, but can also give an indication of population trends which in themselves provide the basis for modern conservation studies. Although observers may differ in their keenness of vision and hearing and in their speed and methods of recording information in the field, the errors in the results should not be too great provided that the observer's standards do not vary from year to year. The Common Birds Census, which involves numbers of observers, has maintained an adequate year to year consistency. I have found that the maintenance of the same system from year to year has great practical advantages in observing and recording. Some counts have been made to find out which species occupy various zones in woodland and how long certain species spend in these zones. With an increase in these counts and the gathering of more information we shall move nearer to a better and more complete understanding of the structure of bird communities in the different types of woodland.

CHAPTER 5

THE BIRDS OF THE SUMMER OAKWOODS

WITHOUT any doubt the commonest and most typical of the forest-forming trees of the British Isles are the oaks. From late Boreal and early Atlantic times the oaks have established themselves on most of the soils at the lower altitudes to become the climatic climax community of many parts of England and in the valleys of Wales, Ireland, the Scottish Uplands and central Scotland. Although only a few fragments of what may be natural oakwoods survive in the British Isles, many of our semi-natural woods are dominated by the oak. Many people must have had their first experience of woodland birds in an oakwood of some kind. Many of the mature oakwoods of the south with their open canopies, old trees and rich shrub layer are as rich in bird-life as any type of woodland.

In the British Isles there are two native species of oak, but there are also certain hybrids and intermediate forms which are often difficult to separate. Before taking a closer look at the birds of the summer oakwoods it is important to distinguish between the two species of oak, since they tend to occur in different areas and to have differing shrub and field layers and often bird populations as well. Of the two species the pedunculate oak (*Quercus robur*) is dominant in much of the Lowland Zone of Britain. It can be recognised by its stalked flowers and acorns which are carried on peduncles. Its leaves are without stalks, or occasionally on very short ones, with small lobes known as auricles at their base. The acorns are of a good size with rather blunt, rounded ends. The sessile or Durmast Oak (*Quercus petraea*) is more characteristic of the Highland Zone. It has unstalked or sessile flowers and acorns. The leaves are often larger than those of the pedunculate oak, of a rather darker green, glossy and with tapering, unlobed bases; they are also carried on stalks at least half-an-inch long and the mid-rib on the underside of the leaf has a line of longish hairs. The acorns are often smaller than those of the pedunculate species and have sharper points. These differences may seem clear enough, but there is a great variety of forms some of which may prove quite baffling to the ornithologist who will then require expert advice. Sessile oaks in the Scottish Highlands often show divergences from the features just given. Both species also grow together on some of the damper soils of south-eastern

PLATE 3. Greenland ice cap. This photograph shows how Europe might have looked at the close of the ice ages with nunataks in the foreground and melting ice beyond.

PLATE 4. The biotic effects of man on woodland. *Above,* sweet chestnut in Kent coppiced on a rotational basis, often a haunt of nightingales and garden warblers; *below,* pollarded hornbeams in Hertfordshire; the tree in the foreground is a nest-site for tawny owls.

England, as well as the Highlands. About 40% of our oakwoods are almost pure, that is, they consist of more than 90% oak.

The pedunculate oak is especially typical of deeper soils derived from the softer rocks of the Midlands and south-east of England – the silts, clays, loams and marls and the brown earths derived from the Secondary, Tertiary and Post-Tertiary rocks. Oaks of this species can also be found in the west and north, although rarely in Ireland, and here they grow only on the valley soils formed from the softer rocks and alluvium. Pedunculate oaks may also grow on poorer and more acid soils provided that they are not too dry. In a close-canopy forest with a deep, rich soil this oak may grow to more than a hundred feet in height, but on Dartmoor on poor granitic land in an exposed situation it fails to make any really good growth. It can also tolerate a wide range of climatic variation and reaches north to 63° N. in Norway and south to Africa and Asia Minor. It is rare to find an absolutely pure piece of pedunculate oakwood and other trees such as beech, ash, Scots pine, downy and silver birch, wych elm, alder, poplar, hornbeam, aspen, field maple and sycamore may grow up through the canopy. Subsidiary smaller trees may include holly, rowan, yew, crab-apple, wild cherry and wild service. Some trees are regularly coppiced and hazel and sweet chestnut are two of the best known of these. The shrub layer is often luxuriant, and this is particularly important since many of the birds of pedunculate oakwood are essentially shrub-nesters. Hazel is abundant while hawthorn, blackthorn, dogwood, guelder rose and pussy willow are regular. I have also found privet, sallow, spindle tree and rhododendron, while the presence of elder often gives away the site of a badger sett. Ivy can be found both as a ground layer and a climber while honeysuckle and bramble often mat the shrub layer together to form a dense barrier inside the wood and a hazard to census-makers! The shrub layer is dependent for its light and subsequent growth on the nature of the canopy so that the spacing of the trees will influence the development of the lower layer. In a young oakwood full of competing trees there may be no shrub or field layers to speak of but, as some of the trees die or are thinned out, the wood will gradually be occupied by other societies at the lower levels. A mature oakwood with a close canopy can have a poor shrub layer whereas open-canopy and coppiced woods allow more light in and therefore a richer shrub growth. The field layer is a varied and exciting one which annually draws thousands of visitors to admire the flowers of a woodland spring.

The countryside of Britain can offer nothing more beautiful nor more satisfying than a lowland oakwood in spring and early summer. Just before coppicing time in a mixed oak/hazelwood the lack of light has inhibited most of the field layer, except for a few shade plants. Then two or three years after coppicing the sleeping roots and seeds wake up and bring back to the oakwood floor a fresh beauty of petal and leaf. The societies of the field layer come into leaf and flower at different times, so there is a progression of growth beginning with what has been called the "pre-vernal" flowering of dog's mercury, lesser celandine and anemone in March and April when sunlight reaches the woodland floor without difficulty, then follows the "vernal" flowering of bluebell and ground ivy in April and May and finally the "aestival" flowering of pignut from June onwards. On lighter, non-calcareous soils under moderate shade bramble is often dominant, as in Sherwood Forest, and there may be fewer shrubs; the herbs may include bluebells, wood anemones, primroses, wild straw-berries, wood sage and wood soft grass. On more acid, sandy soils where pedunculate oaks often grow with birches the shrub layer is sparse and the field layer includes heather, *Vaccinium* and tormentil. On heavier soils, dog's mercury, which is also common in beechwoods, wood sanicle and enchanter's nightshade are common in the field layer with bugle and yellow pimpernel flourishing along the damp rides. Oakwoods growing in very moist conditions, sometimes in association with alder, often have creeping buttercup, meadow sweet, nettle and pendulous sedge in their field layers. In the more open parts of many English pedunculate woods rosebay willowherb and red campion are locally abundant. Early morning in a summer pedunculate oakwood is full of charm with the rich flora and varied and impressive chorus of bird-songs.

It is possible that the sessile oak came to the British Isles before the pedunculate and we know that the latter has been widely planted in many places. Unfortunately pollen analysis cannot yet distinguish between the two species in the fossil record. It looks as if foresters have had a greater liking as well for the pedunculate species. Professor M. L. Anderson put forward a theory that the pedunculate oak is an alien introduced in the Middle Ages which spread gradually north and west. Hybrids exist in the Scottish glens and most planted oak is of pedunculate or hybrid origin. Pedunculate oak has also been planted in Ireland. The sessile oak is the dominant species of the older siliceous hills and rocks of the north and west where it often grows on hillsides, but it can also be found in the Midlands and south on soils with a relatively high acidity. It grows on metamorphic rocks in Co. Galway, on rocks of the Ordovician Period in Cumberland, Wales and Co. Wicklow, on Silurian soils in Herefordshire, on the Old Red Sandstone in Ireland and western England, on the Pennine Millstone Grit and the Coal Measures of the Carboniferous Period. Quite extensive sessile woods can be found near Killarney and Lough Conn, on the

Malvern Hills, in the Forest of Dean and the Towy Valley, and in Cumberland. It has been suggested that the dominance of the sessile oak could be correlated with a relatively high acidity in the soil and that its presence in the more westerly regions had resulted from the extreme leaching of the soils, the growth of acid humus in the wetter parts of the west as well as the tree's development on the older siliceous rocks rather deficient in bases. The reasons for the distribution of the sessile oak have not yet been fully resolved, but its occurrence on acid soils in midland and southern England is of interest; it can be found on the Bunter Sandstone of Sherwood, the Lower Greensand of Surrey and Kent, the London Clay, the Bagshot Sands and the sands and gravels of Hertfordshire where it grows with hornbeam. The sessile oak can tolerate almost the full range of climate in the British Isles, but in Norway it can reach only 60° N. It really likes lighter, drier and less acid soils and is less common than the pedunculate on heavy clays and loams. The soils it flourishes on in the west are formed in a wet climate, but they are generally well drained. The Atlantic sessile woods of Killarney experience a high annual rainfall of about 54 in. and their mean atmospheric humidity is high as well. Both species can grow to good heights, but the sessile trees tend to grow more in close canopy. Some sessile woods are on valley sides and hill slopes up to 1,200 ft. or more, but at these heights the trees are retarded and small. In some parts of Wales, north-west England and elsewhere the sessile oak was regularly coppiced, leading to the development of multiple stems. Some of the upland woods contained 98% or 99% sessile oak. The trees most commonly associated with sessile oaks are downy and silver birch, rowan and wild service while alder and holly are uncommon but characteristic. Yews sometimes occur and in damp areas inside the oakwoods ash, wych elm and wild cherry can sometimes be found. In some parts of Ireland sessile oakwoods have been underplanted with conifers and one I visited in Co. Galway had spruce and pine trees growing up under the oak canopy.

The shrub layer of a sessile wood is not as luxuriant as that of a pedunculate wood and sometimes it is completely absent. This has a profound effect on the bird-life. In some places hawthorn, sallow, alder and buckthorn may occur. Many field layer plants are common to both kinds of oakwood, but in the sessile woods the colonies tend to be smaller and the layer more heathy and grassy. On the Pennine uplands, in the Killarney woods and in western Scotland the field layer is often rich in *Vaccinium* and heather with bluebells, bracken and wood soft grass on the less acid soils. In the Scottish woods I have found bramble, cow wheat and yellow pimpernel. It is interesting to note how some of the typical plants of the pedunculate woods appear in the sessile woods only along the damper paths and rides. Here there is more light and I have found bugle, water starwort, enchanter's nightshade, herb bennet, wood sorrel, ground ivy and annual meadow grass. Some of the sessile woods that I have visited in Ireland are very rich in ground plants, while others are without a field layer, this being replaced by liverworts and bryophytes that flourish in the damp, shaded conditions under a closed canopy. Where woodland contains both species of oak growing side by side the shrub layer is often poor and the field layer heathy or grassy. In Sherwood Forest, where both oaks flourish together with occasional downy birches and rowans, the shrub layer is almost entirely missing while the field layer is composed largely of bracken with a certain amount of foxglove, tormentil, wood soft grass and wavy hair grass. These mixed woods so closely resemble one type of sessile oakwood that they can best be regarded as such.

To what extent does the bird-life of the two types of oakwood differ in the summer months? I have visited a large number of oakwoods of both types in the British Isles and have either obtained figures for the number of breeding pairs or, more regularly, made sample counts in the breeding season. My records are based on visits to 153 woods of which 88 were of the pedunculate species and 65 of the sessile; of the latter 19 were in Ireland and 10 in Scotland. I visited only one pedunculate oakwood in Ireland. From lists obtained by the transect method from April to June I have obtained what I think is a fairly clear picture of the distribution and frequency of birds in the two kinds of wood. Although the work was often repetitive the confirmation of earlier discoveries and patterns was encouraging. Separate records for pedunculate and sessile oakwoods were first published in 1962 by Dr Yapp; tables for oakwoods had been produced earlier, but without differentiating between the two species of tree. It is my intention to compare those figures with mine where this is possible, but statistics for Ireland were not included. I am very grateful to Dr Yapp for his permission to reproduce his figures for relative abundance.

Table 14 lists the dominant species of bird, in order of relative abundance in the two kinds of oakwood based on my figures and those from Dr Yapp. It will be remembered that the relative abundance is expressed as a percentage of the total contacts made. It becomes clear that the most important species in the English pedunculate woods are chaffinch, robin, wren, blackbird, willow warbler, blue tit, great tit and wood pigeon. The five species at the top of my list and that of Dr Yapp were also the top five in the records of Lack and Venables. In the English and Welsh sessile woods the dominant species are chaffinch, pied flycatcher, willow warbler, wood warbler, robin, wren, redstart and tree pipit. The sessile woods in

TABLE 14. *The relative abundance of Bird Species in British and Irish oakwoods*

Pedunculate Woods

(England)

Simms (*88 woods*)		Yapp (*13 woods*)	
Chaffinch	13	Chaffinch	12
Robin	11	Willow Warbler	9
Wren	10	Robin	7
Blackbird	8	Wren	7
Willow Warbler	7	Blackbird	7
Wood Pigeon	6	Blue Tit	4
Blue Tit	5	Great Tit	3
Great Tit	4	Redstart	2
Garden Warbler	3	Song Thrush	2
Song Thrush	3	Chiffchaff	2
Hedgesparrow	2	Mistle Thrush	2
Blackcap	2	Jay	2
Redstart	1	Tree Pipit	1
Tree Pipit	1	Garden Warbler	1
Great Spotted Woodpecker	1		

Sessile Woods

(England and Wales)   (Scotland)   (Ireland)

Simms (*36 woods*)		Yapp (*32 woods*)		Simms (*10 woods*)		Simms (*19 woods*)	
Chaffinch	17	Chaffinch	18	Chaffinch	16	Chaffinch	15
Pied Flycatcher	7	Pied Flycatcher	8	Wren	10	Blackbird	11
Willow Warbler	7	Wood Warbler	8	Blue Tit	8	Robin	11
Wood Warbler	6	Willow Warbler	6	Starling	8	Wood Pigeon	10
Wren	6	Robin	6	Willow Warbler	6	Willow Warbler	7
Robin	5	Wren	5	Robin	6	Wren	7
Redstart	5	Wood Pigeon	4	Song Thrush	6	Blue Tit	5
Tree Pipit	5	Redstart	4	Tree Pipit	5	Chiffchaff	4
Coal Tit	5	Coal Tit	4	Wood Pigeon	4	Mistle Thrush	4
Crow	4	Tree Pipit	4	Pheasant	4	Song Thrush	3
Wood Pigeon	4	Great Tit	3	Blackbird	3	Great Tit	3
Blackbird	4	Crow	3	Redstart	3	Goldcrest	2
Great Tit	3	Blackbird	3	Hedgesparrow	3	Coal Tit	2
Blue Tit	2	Buzzard	2	Jackdaw	3	Treecreeper	2
Starling	1	Blue Tit	2	Treecreeper	2	Bullfinch	2

Scotland are dominated by chaffinch, wren, blue tit, starling, willow warbler, robin, song thrush and tree pipit and in Ireland by chaffinch, blackbird, robin, wood pigeon, willow warbler, wren, chiffchaff and mistle thrush. The British oakwoods of both kinds, therefore, have three dominant bird species – chaffinch, robin and wren – and these are some-times numerically superior members of the communities of other types of tree. The wood pigeon did not qualify for Yapp's list of birds of pedun-culate woods. It is interesting to note that the blackbird is low down in the lists for English and Scottish sessile woods where the shrub layer is poor or absent, but high in those for English pedunculate and Irish sessile woods, where the layer is often rich and varied. The tree pipit is missing from the Irish sessile woods, but the chiffchaff is not uncommon. The redstart appears in all the lists except that for Ireland where I have found it in only one sessile oakwood in a sheltered valley in Co. Wicklow. The bullfinch is a characteristic bird of Irish woods. In the English pedunculate woods and the sessile woods of Scotland and Ireland the blue tit is the dominant species of tit whereas in the sessile woods of England and Wales the great tit assumes that role. I have found small numbers of starlings breeding in all the types of wood and this species came fourth in the list for Scottish sessile woods. Starlings will often invade pedunculate woods during cater-pillar plagues and after this may penetrate the woods in bigger numbers to breed. Caterpillars of *Tortrix viridana* are eaten by many species of bird and not only starlings but also redstarts, tits and tree sparrows have been recorded.

I came to know the birds of pedunculate woods earlier than those of the sessile woods since I was born in the south of England and began to investigate the woodlands there first of all. In 1940 I paid my first visit to a large oakwood on the Upper Lias of Northamptonshire near Daventry – the same wood to which I referred briefly in the last chapter and for which I also gave a description. From 1946–50 I was able to explore this wood very thoroughly each breeding season and the results can be seen in Table 15. I have laid out in this table not only the numbers of pairs of each species breeding each year but I have also given the density of birds per 100 acres. The table is useful for showing the effect of the severe weather of early 1947. The total of species in Badby Wood varied from 32 to 34; these figures can be compared with that of 35 found in summer oakwoods by Lack and Venables (1939). At Bookham Common in Surrey a total of 28 species was recorded for 40 acres of semi-natural pedunculate oakwood, and it was shown that the population in the breeding season was probably greater than 320–500 birds per 100 acres. The figures for Badby Wood are 286–388 and these are close to the 400 per 100 acres given for broad-leaved woodland in Britain. A figure of about 300 was given for oak stands in the Russian forests, while a high figure of 830 was produced for Slovakian oak/hornbeam forests.

Of the 36 species that have bred in Badby Wood, 18 normally select holes, crevices or the forks in trees, 12 nest in the shrub layer, 2 in the tree canopy and 4 on the ground. The bird community of this wood is very dependent on the maturity of the timber and the richness of the shrub layer which flourishes well under a largely open canopy. This is one reason why a sessile oakwood without shrubs will lack such species as the jay, bullfinch, garden warbler, blackcap, hedgesparrow and long-tailed tit but can retain hole-nesters like the pied flycatcher, wren, redstart and coal tit, ground-breeding birds such as the tree pipit, wood warbler and willow warbler or canopy nesters like the crow, buzzard, sparrowhawk and long-eared owl.

The chaffinch comes at the top of all the relative abundance lists and is the most widely distributed of all our woodland birds. It is a hardy and most adaptable species with perhaps a slight preference for oakwoods for breeding, but in the winter most chaffinches are found on farmland. In the last few years there seems to have been an overall decrease in England. The population in Badby Wood has shown fluctuations and the work done on the Bookham Common oakwood also seems to indicate that natural population swings have been occurring (see Fig. 14).

The robin was second in relative abundance in my list for pedunculate woods, and is also frequent in the sessile oakwoods. The robin is essentially a ground feeder using low twigs and stumps as vantage points from which to spy out its prey. It sings from high song posts, nests in holes and on or near the ground, so that the nature of the shrub layer may not be so important in regulating its distribution. The population is much more seriously affected by cold winters than by local changes in the vegetation. This is a subject we shall look at again when we come to discuss the influences at work on woodland populations. The wren is also found in almost all the oakwoods of both types, although the evidence I have suggests that it is slightly less common in the English and Irish than in the Scottish sessile oakwoods. Since it relies much more on an animal diet outside the breeding season than the robin does, it is more likely to experience population crashes when the autumns and winters are especially severe. It is a difficult bird to observe, but seems to obtain a great deal of its food in the shrub and field layers; it is essentially a prier and an explorer. The hedgesparrow has an RA of 2 in my list for English pedunculate woods and, rather surprisingly, 3 for Scottish sessile woods.

The willow warbler is adaptable and fairly undemanding in its choice

TABLE 15. *The Numbers and Density of Breeding Birds in a Pedunculate Oakwood, Badby Wood, 1946–50*

Species	Number of Pairs Breeding				
	1946	*1947*	*1948*	*1949*	*1950*
Carrion Crow	3	2	2	2	3
Jackdaw	5	5	5	4	5
Jay	2		3	1	3
Starling	14	12	14	13	14
Bullfinch	2	1	1	1	2
Chaffinch	28	22	29	30	34
Tree Pipit	1	1	1	1	1
Treecreeper	15	12	13	14	14
Nuthatch	3	2	3	3	3
Great Tit	23	16	19	20	22
Blue Tit	35	25	29	34	34
Coal Tit	2	2	2	2	2
Marsh Tit	6	4	5	6	5
Willow Tit		1			2
Long-tailed Tit	3		1	2	2
Spotted Flycatcher	3	3	2	3	3
Chiffchaff	5	5	5	7	6
Willow Warbler	20	21	20	16	20
Wood Warbler		2			
Garden Warbler	12	11	11	13	12
Blackcap	4	3	5	4	5
Mistle Thrush	2	1	2	2	1
Song Thrush	12	8	10	12	12
Blackbird	30	27	30	30	36
Redstart	2	3	6	6	5
Robin	58	46	64	65	69
Hedgesparrow	11	8	10	11	8
Wren	40	28	39	38	42
Green Woodpecker	3	1	1	1	3
Great Spotted Woodpecker	4	2	4	4	4
Lesser Spotted Woodpecker			2	2	2
Cuckoo	2	3	1	2	1
Tawny Owl	5	3	4	4	4
Woodpigeon	25	21	20	27	25
Stock Dove	3	2	3	3	3
Pheasant		1	1		
Total of Species	32	33	34	33	34
Total of Pairs	383	304	367	383	407
Total Birds per 100 acres	365	286	334	365	388

of habitat, like the chaffinch, robin and wren, but it seems to have a special liking for birches. Where woods of oak and birch occur the bird is often very common indeed. Since my original survey of Badby Wood the willow warbler population has dropped from about 20 territories to 12. At Bookham the number of territories dropped from 21 in 1950 to 2 in 1963 (Fig. 15). Similar changes have taken place in some oakwoods in the Severn Valley with a gradual drop in numbers from 1939 to 1960. Figure 16 illustrates the general decline compared with the more recent drop in the numbers of nightingales and the steady state of the chiffchaff population. Willow warblers tend to outnumber chiffchaffs in the oakwoods and it is only in some of the Irish sessile woods that the latter species is comparatively common. The willow warbler also outranks the chaffinch in some of the northern oakwoods in Scotland.

Of the thrushes the blackbird is the most frequent in the oakwoods. It feeds extensively among the leaf litter in grassy woods as well as in those with rich field layers. The blackbird is very much a bird of the woods on the better soils and is less common in the sessile woods of England, Wales and Scotland. In Ireland I found it in all of the nineteen sessile woods I visited and it ranked second with the robin in relative abundance. It was the commonest bird in the oakwoods at Rostrevor, Upper Lough Erne and Woodford and shared first place with the robin in one heavily moss-grown wood at Glengarriff. In the Badby summer oakwood the blackbird outnumbered the song thrush 2 or 3 to one. At Bookham Common this proportion was also found at the start of the survey, but by 1951 the numbers of the two species were about the same. Figures of from 2 to 4 to one were found to be fairly accurate, but a separate observation revealed twice as many blackbirds on one Surrey estate. The song thrush is often scarce in the sessile oakwoods of England and Wales, but tends to re-establish itself in those of Scotland and Ireland. It often favours woods with richer shrub layers, but its clear dependence on snails and worms suggests a preference for land with a good lime content. The smaller, shyer and less adaptable song thrush seems more vulnerable than the blackbird which is of a confiding nature in many places and makes a most wide choice of nesting sites. In dense, remote woodland the blackbird, of course, is extremely shy and wary. The larger mistle thrush is, in my experience, very thinly scattered through the pedunculate woods and is much scarcer in all the sessile woods except those of Ireland where its numbers often exceed those of its smaller relative. In some parts of Ireland the mistle thrush is much the commonest member of its family.

The redstart was literally one of the brighter gems of the Badby bird community, but it tended to appear either on the edge of the wood adjoining parkland or in an area of open canopy woodland in the centre. This bird is almost completely absent from Ireland and in the rest of the British Isles it is very much a bird of sessile woods. Its distribution is in part influenced by the availability of nesting sites since it uses holes in trees and walls and crevices in rocks. In the Lake District its breeding sites are often similar to those of the coal tit. I have found the redstart commonly in Lakeland, the Pennines and some of the Welsh hillside woods like those of Gwenffrwd.

The wood pigeon came sixth in my list for pedunculate woods and could be found in nearly all of them. It is plentiful in most of the sessile oakwoods and is especially common in Ireland; in late May I have found it to be the commonest bird in the sessile woods at Glendalough in Co. Wicklow, at Roosky in Co. Leitrim and in two of the Killarney woods. The densest populations are usually in woodland in regions of intensive arable farming. Three pairs of another dove – the stock dove – nested in Badby Wood in most of the years. It is rather a scarce bird of pedunculate woodland. In recent years it has spread to north Scotland and southern and western Ireland, but from 1957–63 it suffered a serious setback in parts of eastern and south-eastern England, almost certainly as a result of the use of seed-dressings. The only summer records I have in sessile oak-woods are from the River Don in Scotland, on Upper Lough Erne and at Mossbrook in Co. Mayo. The turtle dove is also a visitor to some pedunculate woods, but it seems to have a distribution limited perhaps by temperature since its range coincides with the 67° F. July isotherm and includes part of south-east Ireland through which the isotherm also runs. One suggestion is that its range is regulated by the distribution of the plant fumitory.

Two other species which rank high in both the Badby list and the table of relative abundance are the great and blue tits. In the pedunculate woods and the Scottish and Irish sessile ones the blue tit is the commoner of the two species but this situation is reversed in the English and Welsh sessile woods. The two species have different feeding ecologies and the great tit feeds much less in the canopy and more in the shrub layer than the blue tit. The smaller blue tit has a special preference for oak, and it has also been demonstrated that the blue tit feeds largely on the insects of oak twigs, buds and leaves as well as scale insect larvae and pupae. "The British oak," wrote Connold in 1908, "is the abode of a vast concourse of dependents," and 227 species of herbivore especially associated with oak have been noted, including various species of bugs, thrips, mites, aphids, beetles and moth caterpillars. At Wytham near Oxford, it was found that the breeding seasons of both great and blue tits were linked to the period

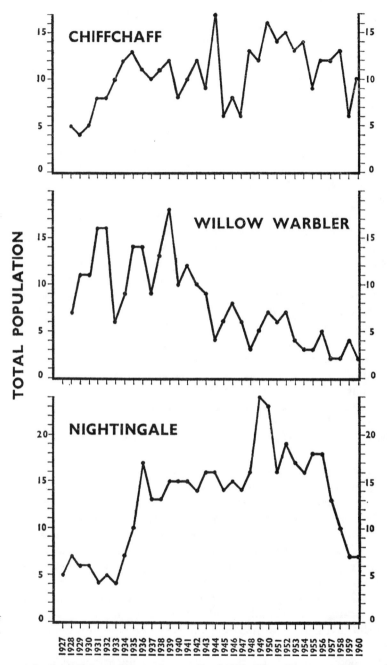

FIG. 16. Population fluctuations of chiffchaff, willow warbler and nightingale near Gloucester, 1927-60. Reproduced from *British Birds* by kind permission of M. Phillips Price.

of abundance of the larva of *Cheimatobia brumata* and *Hibernia defoliaria*. The coal tit is scarce in pedunculate woods but may become dominant in some of the sessile including parts of the Wyre Forest, in Coille Mheadonach in Glen Creran and at Breen in Northern Ireland. In summer the coal tit feeds very much in the canopy of the trees. The long-tailed tit is not a common bird and it qualifies for my lists of relative abundance only in the Irish sessile oakwoods. However, some one to three pairs bred in Badby Wood each year nesting in the forks of boles or branches and feeding in the canopy and upper shrub layer. This was not a high density since nine pairs were found nesting on about 65 acres of Wytham Wood in 1957 and this was considered an optimal habitat for the species. The marsh tit was represented at Badby by from 4 to 6 pairs. This species of tit occurs only in England, Wales and a few places in southern Scotland. It is regular in small numbers in pedunculate but very scarce or absent in sessile woods. The closely related willow tit has bred in Badby Wood and occurs, sometimes alongside the marsh tit, in other woods in England, Wales and southern Scotland. Since the willow tit excavates its own nesting site in rotten timber it is dependent on the presence of old or soft trees and particularly favours elder, birch and willow. Oakwood sometimes gives way to alder in damp situations and these too are often used for nesting by willow tits. Each of the tit species tends to use different feeding sites and so can live together for most of the time without direct competition and the four species – the great, blue, marsh and willow tit – also spend different proportions of their time in the various parts of the habitat. Table 16 is intended to provide a general guide to the feeding habits of the birds of oakwoods as well as an indication of where the males of territorial species may have their song posts.

Table 17 gives the numerically dominant birds in the various habitats in dense oakwood at Bookham Common in Surrey.

The sessile oakwoods, except for some of the Irish ones, lack those species which need a thick shrub layer for feeding and nesting, and it is possible that the bird communities of pedunculate woodland are really those of scrub rather than a tree habitat. Irish sessile woods are of several kinds. Those at Breen in the north have bracken, rushes, bramble, wood sorrel and no real shrub layer; here there are no scrub birds and the mistle thrush outnumbers the blackbird six to one. The woods at Pontoon have heather and *Vaccinium* while others in Counties Fermanagh and Leitrim have hazel, hawthorn and ash and a rich field layer similar to that of an English lowland oakwood with bluebells, violets, bugle, wood sorrel and wood anemones. Of the warblers the chiffchaff is widely spread through the pedunculate woods and its presence in Scotland would seem to depend on the presence of rhododendron to give shelter. In Ireland the willow warbler is regular and the chiffchaff is common in sessile woods although in general it is absent from other woods of this species in Britain. The wood warbler is not common in the pedunculate woods, but ranks very high in the sessile lists; it extends to the exposed fellwoods with their twisted trees and I have found it at over 1,100 ft. Wood warblers are common in the oakwoods of Deeside in Aberdeenshire, in parts of Wales, and in May, 1968, they were the commonest singing birds in the sessile woods at Beasdale, near Morar, on the west coast of Scotland. The wood warbler seems to prefer a field layer not overshadowed by shrubs but its appearance in Badby Wood in one year only cannot be explained by a change in habitat such as the rampaging bramble which clogged up the oakwoods near Gloucester and prevented willow and wood warblers from finding nesting places. The wood warbler is very rare in Ireland.

At Badby there were roughly four times as many garden warblers as blackcaps but this is a high proportion compared with that for the rest of the English pedunculate woods. In Scottish sessile woods the blackcap is the more frequent species but is rare in Ireland. I found blackcaps most regularly in two areas of Ireland – in Co. Wicklow and near Upper Lough Erne where the commoner garden warbler seemed to favour shrubs and scrub near water. For the garden warbler in Ireland a habitat near a lake seems imperative. The garden warbler, unlike the blackcap which favours high song posts, can dispense with trees altogether. In some woods the blackcap may outnumber the garden warbler, but their positions in a common habitat remain something of a mystery since their liking for similar cover, food and feeding stations suggests some competition between them. The whitethroat did not appear in the early Badby lists, but I have later records for it and it seems, like the lesser whitethroat, to be an occasional bird of pedunculate woods and sometimes sessile woods as well. The tree pipit ranked lower in the Badby list than in the national one, but after the canopy was opened in several places by felling the number of pairs rose from one to eight in 1952. For the tree pipit the areas of highest density are north-west of the Humber–Severn line, and it is very much a bird of the northern sessile oakwoods, close-canopied and without many shrubs, since, like the wood warbler, it is a ground nester. Its cheerful song is one of the delights of many remote sessile woods. In the Wyre Forest the tree pipit is second, after the chaffinch, in the transect lists. It is missing as a breeding species from Ireland.

The tree pipit, redstart, wood warbler and coal tit are very typical birds of sessile oak forest and they are joined by one other species – the pied flycatcher. This is a bird of the foothills of the upland areas of England and

TABLE 16. *Some Ecological Aspects of Birds in Oakwoods*

Site for nest	Food preferences			Feeding stations		Song post
	Summer Adult	Young	Winter	Summer	Outside Breeding Season	
High Canopy (HC)						
Crow	O	O	O	D	D	
Buzzard	C	C	C	E	E	
Wood Pigeon	V	V	V	D.E	LC.G.E	HC.LC
Mistle Thrush	O	I	O	G	LC.G	HC
Holes in Trunks and Boughs (T)						
Jackdaw	O	O	O	D	E	
Starling	O	O	O	D	LC.FL.G	HC.G
Green Woodpecker	O	I	O	T.G	T.G	
Great Spotted Woodpecker	O	I	O	T.	T	
Tawny Owl	C	C	C	LC.G	LC.G	HC
Treecreeper	I	I	I	T	T	T
Nuthatch	O	I	O	T.G	T.G	HC
Great Tit	O	I	O	LC	LC.G	HC
Blue Tit	O	I	O	HC.T	HC.T	HC.LC
Marsh Tit	O	I	O	LC.FL	LC.FL	HC.LC
Willow Tit	I	I	I	LC.FL	LC	LC
Pied Flycatcher	I	I		D		HC
Redstart	I	I		D		HC
Stock Dove	V	V	V	E		HC.LC
Low Canopy and Shrub Layer (LC)						
Jay	O	I	O	D	D	
Sparrowhawk	C	C	C	D	D	
Song Thrush	O	I	I.V	D	D	HC.LC.FL
Blackbird	O	I	I.V	G	LC.G	HC.LC
Chaffinch	O	I	V	D	G	HC.FL
Long-tailed Tit	I	I	I	HC	LC	
Spotted Flycatcher	I	I		LC		
Blackcap	O	I		HC.LC		HC.LC
Field Layer (FL)						
Chiffchaff	I	I	I	D	FL	HC.LC
Bullfinch	V	I	V	LC.FL	LC.FL	LC
Wren	I	I	I	T.FL	T.FL	LC.FL
Hedgesparrow	I	I	V	G	G	LC.FL
Cuckoo	I	I.V		FL.G		HC
Garden Warbler	O	I		LC.FL		LC.FL
Ground Zone (G)						
Willow Warbler	I	I	I.V	D	FL	HC.LC
Wood Warbler	I	I	I	HC	LC	HC.LC
Nightingale	I	I		FL.G		LC.FL
Robin	I	I	I.V	FL.G	FL.G	HC.FL
Tree Pipit	I	I		G		HC
Coal Tit	I	I	O	T.HC	T.HC	HC
Woodcock	I	I	I.V	G	G	
Pheasant	O	O	O	G	G	

Key:
O = Omnivorous tastes   HC = High canopy of tall trees   G = Ground zone
I = Mixed invertebrates   T = Trunk and boughs   D = Range of zones from HC to G
V = Vegetable matter   LC = Lower canopy and shrub layer   E = Feeds outside wood
C = Meat eating   FL = Field layer

TABLE 17. *The Distribution of Bird Species in Dense Oakwood, Bookham Common, Surrey*

The numerically dominant birds in each habitat in dense oakwood									
Canopy (1023)	%	Shrub (634)	%	Trunk (177)	%	Herb (44)	%	Ground (236)	%
Blue Tit	44.8	Long-tailed Tit	27.4	Treecreeper	31.1	Wren	50.0	Blackbird	51.3
Long-tailed Tit	25.5	Blue Tit	22.2	Blue Tit	16.5	Robin	15.9	Robin	29.7
Great Tit	6.8	Great Tit	11.5	Nuthatch	14.7	Goldcrest	11.4	Blue Tit	4.7
Coal Tit	5.4	Goldcrest	8.0	Coal Tit	8.5	Great Tit	9.1	Wren	3.4
Marsh Tit	4.9	Marsh Tit	7.6	Marsh Tit	5.1	Marsh Tit	6.8	Jay	2.5
Nuthatch	3.0	Robin	5.7	Robin	4.5	Other Species	6.8	Great Tit	2.1
Goldcrest	2.9	Wren	4.1	Great Spotted Woodpecker	4.5			Other Species	6.3
Chaffinch	1.8	Nuthatch	3.5	Long-tailed Tit	3.9				
Other Species	4.9	Other Species	10.0	Great Tit	2.8				
				Other Species	8.4				
	100.0		100.0		100.0		100.0		100.0

The total observations in each habitat are analysed to show the proportion of records of different species feeding there throughout the year. The figure in brackets is the total number of records for each habitat.

Reproduced from *The London Naturalist*, No. 38, by kind permission of Dr. Geoffrey Beven.

Wales, but it is less frequent in the Scottish Highlands. The slowing down since 1952 of an earlier phase of expansion has been traced, and in the English Midlands where old timber has been extensively felled it has been forced to retreat. From 1953–62 the pied flycatcher bred in 39 British counties; it does not appear as a breeding species in Ireland. The ideal habitat has been described as one containing over-mature trees in high forest with little shrub layer, but what is present should provide good cover; in this way the pied flycatcher will have nest holes available as well as high display and song posts. It will probably be an area close to water since the bird requires plenty of invertebrate, largely aerial prey in late April and early May. Its needs are most easily fulfilled by the sessile oakwoods of the highland areas even where water is absent. In Scotland a slow spread may have followed in the wake of the great spotted woodpecker whose activities increased the number of possible breeding sites. The range of the pied flycatcher in Scotland seems to resemble that of the woodpecker a half century before. It is singularly attracted by nestboxes and local populations have been increased in this way. The pied flycatcher is second in number to the chaffinch in the sessile woods of England and Wales. The related spotted flycatcher was always present in the summer at Badby, and I have found it in small but regular numbers in pedunculate woods, but it is not uncommon in the sessile woods of the Highlands and Ireland.

In Badby Wood the commonest woodpecker was the great spotted and this situation has continued although it is at variance with one survey which showed that where this species appeared with the green woodpecker it was less numerous, but that its range extended farther to the north. However, the green woodpecker has increased in northern England and the Lowlands of Scotland while the great spotted woodpecker breeds in every mainland county except perhaps Caithness. The lesser spotted woodpecker was less regular in Badby Wood, but I have often seen birds in quite dense pedunculate woodland. These woodpeckers normally excavate their own holes and the sessile woods are not rich in woodpeckers since the trunks are often of rather small diameter, and many of the woods are outside the range of the two species of woodpecker anyway. The nuthatch was also present in small numbers at Badby and, although there may be some ecological links with the woodpeckers, its present distribution would seem to be influenced by other factors. It is frequent in the upland counties of south-west England and Wales, but is missing from similar areas in north-west England and Scotland. Its range may be influenced by climate or perhaps by the distribution of trees. The treecreeper explores the trunks of both kinds of oak-tree and is widely distributed. It is often overlooked in both kinds of wood and its higher relative abundance in the sessile list may be due to its greater conspicuousness there.

Like the nuthatch, the nightingale has a restricted geographical range in the British Isles and is confined to a lowland distribution in the south-east. There is an interesting correlation between the limits of the nightingale's range and the 66° F. June isotherm. There is a possible link between temperature and population density so that the greatest number of birds appears where the higher temperatures in June will ensure an abundance of food at the time immediately after the young have hatched. The nightingale did not appear in Badby Wood where the height above sea-level is too great. It is very much a bird of pedunculate oakwoods under five hundred feet above sea-level especially those with a rich hazel layer. There is also a certain critical amount of shade and density of cover, and I have known birds desert previously favoured haunts when the cover was opened up or the shrubs reached a height where they began to grow more sparsely and let more light through. At its western limit in Britain the nightingale is on the very edge of its range and here small changes in the environment may prove of greater effect than in Europe. In southern France nightingales behave in a very different manner from their more retiring relatives in the north.

Two other woodland species that did not appear in the Badby list were the woodcock and the nightjar. The woodcock, which sometimes visited

PLATE 5. Hillside afforestation. *Above*, conifers growing in Dovey Forest,
Merioneth; *below*, mixed conifers and broad-leaved trees in the
Lledr Valley near Bettws-y-Coed, Caernarvonshire.

PLATE 6. Canopy nesters. *Above*, carrion crow in willow; *below*, heron in mixed broad-leaved wood.

the wood, appears in woods of several different types. I have seen it in damp oakwoods of both kinds often with open glades and rides as well as good cover from bracken and brambles where the sitting hen can rely upon her wonderful camouflage. The woodcock does not qualify for any of my lists of relative abundance but as a species it often rises up from one's feet and so draws attention to itself. It is widely distributed in woodlands over much of the British Isles but is scarcer in parts of the south-west and west. I have found it in the highest numbers in some of the sessile woods of the Borders and in Ireland. The nightjar is primarily a bird of the woodland/ heath ecotone, but I have seen it in the heathy field layer of both sessile and pedunculate oakwoods. Although the nightjar is common in the south and south-west there has been a decrease in thirty of the fifty-four counties in which it was reported in 1957–8. The thinning of oakwoods, which brings them nearer to a woodland ecotone, can bring a local increase in numbers.

Of the larger species certain members of the crow family can be found in the summer oakwoods: they do not occur in large numbers since they are often birds of ecotone and forest edge. The carrion crow is regular in both kinds of oakwood, but the hooded crow is rather more common in the sessile woods of the north and west. Since the carrion crow can be found in woodland when its food demands are most pressing, this suggests that woods are its natural niche. In the wilder highland areas crows may often have escaped the persecution that has befallen their kind in the more heavily keepered southern areas. The raven was once to be found regularly in lowland oakwoods and Gilbert White described how a pair bred in the centre of an oak grove "for such a series of years, that the oak was distinguished by the title of The Raven Tree." In recent years the raven, once exiled to the mountains and rocky sea-cliffs, has begun to return to the woods to breed, especially in north-west and south-west England, in Wales and south-west Scotland. Rooks also use trees for nesting, especially high ones, but the species is one of parkland ecotones. Although there were no nests in Badby Wood there were nearly a hundred in an oak-grove a quarter of a mile away. I have found rookeries in many pedunculate woods in England and in sessile woods in the Highland Zone and in Ireland. Rooks prefer groves, belts and lines of trees along roads and hedges to very extensive woods, but they quite frequently come into the oakwoods to feast on the leaf-eating caterpillars of early summer. The jackdaw scored 1 in my list for pedunculate woods and 3 for the sessile woods of Scotland but there were sometimes cliffs and exposed rock-faces in the latter. As a species the jackdaw is unevenly spread throughout the British Isles and although it breeds in oakwoods with over-mature timber its colonies tend to be bigger in ruins, quarries and on cliffs. I have seen jackdaws nesting in sessile oaks from the Midlands to the Borders, in central and western Scotland and in central Wales, but in the nineteen Irish woods I visited there was only one record for a single wood. The jackdaw is a bird of parkland like the carrion crow and the rook. The magpie often appeared on the margins of Badby Wood, but it did not breed in the wood itself. Its food and feeding habits are much like those of the crow and although it does occur in woodland it is not typical. The jay is present in small numbers in most pedunculate woods and in some sessile ones as well, provided that there is a reasonable shrub layer. Its occurrence in Europe matches very closely the distribution of oakwoods. The jay has increased slightly in northern Scotland where the magpie has undergone a decline, but it would seem from one report that the jay's increase is due to a lessening in game preservation and to the planting of new forests. Jays have been recorded at over a thousand feet in some sessile woods in England and Wales. In Ireland the bird is widely distributed except in the west and I found it common in the sessile woods of Co. Wicklow. The jay is undoubtedly a true woodland species.

The cuckoo is not really typical of oakwoods although birds appeared at Badby in each year of the survey and victimised robins and hedge-sparrows. In rural England the hedgesparrow is the commonest host, but it may be that in earlier times it was the robin which was a common victim in the broad-leaved forests of Europe. In Ireland the cuckoo was present in about half of the sessile woodlands and was missing from the Glengarriff and Killarney woods although it was a common and very tame bird in the surrounding heathy country as far south-west as Mizen Head.

Larger species such as the crows and cuckoo appear in smaller numbers in the woods than do those of lesser size, and this applies to the predators such as the owls and the birds of prey. The tawny owl appears in oak-woods of both kinds, but is totally absent from the Irish woods where the long-eared owl is the commonest member of the family, and hunts by day in the sessile woods of Ulster. The barn owl and the little owl are not birds of woodland, but I have twice found barn owls roosting by day in haw-thorns in open-canopy pedunculate woodland in East Anglia.

The kestrel sometimes hunted over Badby Wood and I have records in many oakwoods in the British Isles. Its numbers have gone down in eastern England in recent years and this decline has been attributed to the use of toxic chemicals on the land and to a lowered breeding success. The sparrowhawk is very much a bird of broad-leaved forests, including those of oak, but I have never recorded it at Badby although I have seen birds in other Midland woods; it, too, has suffered a catastrophic decline in eastern parts of Britain. There has been some drop in numbers in eastern Ireland, but in 1967 I found many Irish oakwoods with their resident pair of sparrowhawks and this was a refreshing sight for an observer who had seen only two in south-eastern England in the preceding decade. The larger buzzard has also undergone changes of fortune in recent years including a decrease in south-west England after 1954 of up to 50% or more. The buzzard is very rare in Ireland, but is not uncommon in the north and west of Britain where its numbers have shown some recent improvement. One survey showed that the breeding densities of the buzzard are higher in agricultural or mixed moorland areas with agricultural land than on moorland or in forests. The handsome kite is now really confined to the hanging sessile oakwoods of central Wales where there are about twenty breeding pairs. In 1964 there were seventeen known nests of this bird whose eyrie could once be found in Hyde Park. The peregrine sometimes hunts over sessile woods and I have seen hobbies chasing insects over pedunculate oakwood. The rare honey-buzzard likes beech trees for nesting, but has been known to use oaks as well.

During visits to different woodlands it soon becomes clear that other less familiar species of bird may turn up – greenfinches, goldfinches, goldcrests and yellowhammers in pedunculate woods and meadow pipits, ring ouzels, whinchats, wheatears and linnets in sessile woods. Since 1950 there has been one interesting addition to the fauna of Badby Wood. The tree sparrow has come into the wood and by 1967 the breeding population had reached eighteen pairs all nesting deep inside the wood. Since I was curious to find out whether this phenomenon was confined to Badby I also visited other pedunculate woods, formerly without tree sparrows, some two or three miles away at Mantles Heath and Everdon Stubbs; here in that same year were seven and eleven pairs respectively. It would be interesting to know if similar changes have taken place in other Midland woods. The goldcrest was a winter visitor to Badby, but it scored 2 in the Irish sessile woods. The pheasant sometimes appeared in Badby, but was regular in many of the Scottish sessile woods; there has been an increase in pheasant numbers in England, Scotland and Ireland.

These then are the birds of the British oakwoods. At Badby 47½% of the birds are omnivores, 45% are insect eaters, 7% are vegetarians and 1% are carnivores. Table 16 on page 104 is an attempt to show simply some of the ways in which the members of a woodland bird community and their activities fit together in space and time. There is overlap in food and feeding range and the table is a guide rather than a definitive statement.

Lowland pedunculate woods seem to be full during the summer months with birds whose choruses are rich, varied and powerful. To rise early on a May morning and go out into these oakwoods to listen to the dawn chorus is a unique and rewarding experience. This I have done many times, often with recording apparatus as well. It is during the dawn chorus that one realises the size and variety of the bird population. I remember one such chorus from a Midland oakwood. The morning was still and cold with white patches of mist clinging to the stream-sides that fringed the great expanse of oaks. In the far darkness a skylark began to rise in song and then at four o'clock a whitethroat sang a rapid little phrase and fell silent once more. A few minutes later a mob of carrion crows in the wood woke up in a frenzy of raucous caws and wild gobbled notes. This set off the rooks which with softer, conversational notes began to stir nearby. A cuckoo called in the distance and a plaintive "tic-tic" from a robin brought a full song phrase from his neighbour. At eight minutes past four two redstarts started singing almost simultaneously and were followed by blackbird song, wood pigeon coos and the "ki-wik" of a still active tawny owl. As the dawn gradually rose the chorus reached its magnificent peak of song. The songs of a song thrush, a garden warbler and a blackcap from a tree above could all be distinguished. By five o'clock wrens, chiffchaffs, chaffinches, tree pipits, nuthatches, marsh, blue and great tits could be heard, and their songs echoed through the wood. Gradually the chorus began to die away, leaving only a treecreeper and a stock dove in song, with the drumming of a great spotted woodpecker. With the dawn the colours of the bluebell glades brightened, and I saw a grizzled dog fox pick his way through the wet bracken and a mud-bespattered boar badger trundle back to his sett on a slope in the wood. The sun was beginning to rise and as the birds began to feed and set about the affairs of the day the chorus died away.

In the sessile woods of Wales, the Forest of Dean, the Wyre Forest, the Lake District, Yorkshire, the Borders and southern Scotland one can also hear the pied flycatcher, the tree pipit and the redstart in song, yet these woods seem much poorer in birds than the pedunculate forests. But are there more birds in these lowland forests? On a subjective basis it might seem that this is true, but what do the counts reveal? For the 88 pedunculate woods in England for which I have figures my contacts per hour vary from as low as 48, for one Hampshire wood with little shrub layer, to as much as 200 for a luxuriant wood in the Midlands. My average figure is 120, but my woods have a strong southern and Midland bias. The only Irish pedunculate wood I have visited – at Tullamore – gave a figure of 92. My average figure for the sessile woods of England and Wales is 62 which is closer to Dr Yapp's figure of 56. The Scottish sessile woods have figures sometimes as low as 35 for Coille Mheadonach and 36 for Ariundle but rising to 64 as at Glentanar. Altitude does not seem to have any appreciable effect on density in the sessile woods. In Ireland the sessile woods are more densely populated. The sessile wood at Breen in Northern Ireland, with a slight admixture of birch, rowan, bracken and rushes and no real cover, gave as high a figure as 96 while the richer woods of Fermanagh, Leitrim and Wicklow produced figures of around 200 – comparable to those for some English pedunculate woods. In short, whereas the density of English pedunculate was matched by many of the Irish sessile oakwoods, it was generally greater than that for the sessile woods of England, Scotland and Wales. My details for the woods of Ireland have added support to the general belief that, if all other things are equal, it is not so much the species of the oak but the actual structure and formation of the wood, the distribution, age and height of the trees and the composition and richness of the shrub layer that regulate the size and nature of the bird community to be found within it. In pedunculate woodland the number of robin territories may be as much as six times more densely packed where the undergrowth is thicker.

The population of oakwoods tends to be at its lowest in February and early March when winter mortality has most affected the numbers, when some species have become widely dispersed and before the summer visitors have arrived. In March and April the chaffinches return from their winter foraging in the more open country while the warblers begin to arrive from their southern winter-quarters. We have seen that about half of our woodland birds are essentially insect-eaters and they tend to come back in time for the first flush of insect life. In the following month young birds begin to appear and rooks, crows, jackdaws and starlings may feed extensively on the defoliating caterpillars on the oaks. Robins and redstarts may pick them from the leaves while ground-feeding birds such as blackbirds and song thrushes retrieve many of the larvae that fall down from the trees in order to pupate. The importance of this food supply is shown by jackdaws near Wytham which fed their young on these caterpillars; in two years these larvae represented from 63% to 66% of all foods brought to the young. At this time the density of birds in an oakwood may be at its height and some species will often crowd together in the same feeding-site when there is an abundance of food.

The younger oakwoods have a poor selection of bird-life. There are no holes available for those species that are regular hole-nesters and only the provision of nestboxes can redress this disbalance. With a closed canopy the lower layers of vegetation are poor or absent. We shall look at these young woodlands again in Chapter 10. We shall also return to a more detailed study of some of the ecological problems of oakwoods when we have examined the bird-life of other types of woodland. In this way it will be possible to make comparisons between the breeding biology and the populations of different species, but as oakwood is the climatic climax for so much of the British Isles it was logical for it to come first.

CHAPTER 6

THE OAKWOODS IN WINTER

THE month of June in the pedunculate oakwoods marks the end of the breeding season for most of the woodland birds and the bird-chorus tends to die away. With the coming of the foxgloves some of the young birds begin to leave the woods and this dispersal is sometimes achieved very rapidly indeed. Colour-ringing 248 juvenile blue and 191 great tits at Wytham in Oxfordshire revealed that an explosive dispersal can take place within a week or two of the young birds leaving the nest; from then on the birds continue to move away. Some of these family parties begin to absorb young from more than one brood, but the juveniles wander more than the adults. Flocks of mixed tit species begin to form in July and are maintained until the following January; these parties move about a good deal and the overall number of birds in a wood in winter can fluctuate very much. Chaffinches and some of the warblers abandon the lowland oakwoods in June and July and do not return until the spring. Chiffchaffs, however, can often be heard singing in Midland woods in September. Some of the robins also begin to move away from the woods, often towards human habitations. When autumn comes wood pigeons, long-tailed tits, crows and bullfinches start coming into the woods and they are joined by some of the winter visitors such as goldcrests, redwings and fieldfares. Some wood pigeons seem to use the oakwoods solely for resting. The characteristic bird activities of the pedunculate woodlands in winter are those of the nomadic bands of tits foraging with goldcrests, treecreepers and occasional nuthatches and woodpeckers through the bare branches of the gaunt, black oaks.

In the pedunculate wood at Bookham Common, it has been observed how the tits inflate the population from July to September; then there are fluctuations with a noticeable drop in February or early March, a rise in April and May and a decline in June. How do the winter population totals compare with those of summer? At Badby from 1946–50 the summer population ranged from 280 to 380 birds per 100 acres while quadrats taken in each of the winters gave figures of 160 to 300 per 100 acres. At Bookham in 1951 and 1952 the breeding population was thought to be between 130 and 200, giving a density of 320 to 500 birds per 100 acres; the winter density was estimated at 200 to 380 birds per 100 acres. Thus the overall winter population is lower than that of the summer. Carrion crows and thrushes may increase the numbers at night by using parts of a wood for roosting.

The onset of severe weather can influence the numbers of certain species in the following spring. It can be seen from Table 15 that there was a reduction in the number of breeding pairs in Badby Wood after the severe cold of early 1947. Of the nineteen species so affected chaffinches, great and blue tits, robins and wrens suffered badly. From Figure 15 it is clear that the robin at Bookham Common also declined in numbers between 1946 and 1947. Unlike the robins, nearly all the wrens seem to remain in the pedunculate woodlands throughout the winter. Even in favourable winters more robins leave the woods towards the end of the year because of a shortage of food. They start to return in March, and transects I have made in the middle of that month in southern and Midland pedunculate woods show that the robin is generally first or second in the lists of relative abundance. At this time the chaffinch is still in the process of coming back. Cold winters may also affect blackbirds which tend to remain in the woods and numbers will drop if the weather is very bad.

Blue and great tits rank high in the lists of relative abundance for the winter months. I have made frequent winter visits to Badby Wood along the slippery, water-logged rides and the most regular sounds have been the various contact notes of the different tit species as the mixed flocks foraged through the oaks. Blue tits are the most important species of tit in the winter oakwoods. Their main source of food from September to December is among the dead branches. From November to January they begin to move gradually towards the leaf-buds and are seldom seen on the ground. Gibb also found that at Marley Wood in Oxfordshire – an artificial 66 acre wood with 17% of its area under pedunculate oak – coal tits also feed chiefly in oaks, searching the leaves in the early part of the winter and then moving on to the limbs and both live and dead branches. Marsh tits feed less among oaks than other tits both in Oxfordshire and at Badby in Northamptonshire. The great tit spends a lot of time feeding on the ground and I have seen birds for up to twenty minutes at a time feeding on hazel nuts; it also likes beech-mast. According to one report great tits in winter collect many ground-living insects and spiders, including the *Lycosa* wolf-spider. Long-tailed tits which start the winter searching hawthorns for food switch to the twigs of oaks from December to April. Competition for food can be acute in winter. It has been shown that blue and great tits rob each other in about equal amounts, but both these species dominate marsh and coal tits. A society ranking has been drawn up beginning with the great spotted woodpecker and descending through nuthatch, great, blue, marsh and coal tit. As yet no one has quite determined the relative positions in this hierarchy of the long-tailed tit, goldcrest and treecreeper. The tit species have similar behaviour patterns but they have succeeded in evolving what Gibb called "characteristic methods of feeding, with corresponding structural adaptations" – in particular of the bill – and these allow the six species of *Parus* to live together and occupy distinct feeding niches. Similarly I have watched several species of vulture all with different bill and skull structures share the same zebra in the Serengeti and exploit all parts of it to the full. Among the woodland tits there is sometimes an overlap in food, and actual fighting can occur which may ensure the survival of a higher proportion of one species than another.

After studying some thirty acres of pedunculate wood near Oxford Colquhoun and Morley drew up a zonal distribution plan for the birds recorded there in the winter of 1941–2. The purpose was to show the ecological niches occupied and exploited by each species. They began by defining five zones:

1. The upper canopy; above 35 feet
2. The tree; 13 to 35 feet
3. Shrub; 4 to 15 feet
4. Herb; 3 inches to 4 feet
5. The ground

Although there is no need to adopt this structural system in preference to the one described on page 27, it provides a framework for their observations. It was found that the tits generally fed in an ascending order of height – great, marsh, long-tailed, blue and coal; these results were later confirmed by Hartley and Gibb. Great tits feed lower than coal tits in winter but at similar heights to marsh tits from October to the end of the year. Blue tits feed lower than coal tits during the first part of the winter and then at a greater height from December to March. Blue and coal tits prefer higher feeding stations than marsh tits throughout the whole year. Long-tailed tits are often found at a higher level than great or marsh tits but usually below blue and coal tits. Feeding stations can also vary in kind as well as height. Blue tits, coal tits and treecreepers can be found feeding more often in trees than in the shrub layer which is itself more favoured by great, marsh, willow and long-tailed tits. The various species of *Parus* also have the most specialised feeding habits in summer and the most diverse in winter. Competition for food is high in the nesting season and in the middle of winter, so death from lack of food in winter is likely.

to be density-dependent. The so-called density-dependent factors are those which vary with the density of the birds in an area. The numbers of birds are presumed to be regulated by mortality factors which increase in effectiveness when the population numbers are high and decrease when the numbers are low. Disease, food shortages and the effects of predators are thought to be the three most probable causes of density-dependent deaths. It may be that all three factors interact so that the first two increase the susceptibility to the third which, by limiting the number of diseased and sub-average animals, permits a more effective use of food resources. We shall consider this problem in a later chapter. It is not easy to discover whether food is short in a wood since the richness of a food source may not be too closely or directly related to either its accessibility or its intrinsic food value. One way of discovering whether food supplies are short is by measuring the bird's feeding intensity. Observation of a diurnal rhythm in the weights of many American birds has shown that most rapid increases could be correlated with an increased feeding activity, and also that many small passerines can vary from 8% to as much as 15% of their daily weight depending on air temperature and the amount of feeding activity. After weighing tits in winter at Wytham, 1,500 readings were obtained, and it was found, as one might expect, that the birds weighed least in the early morning and most before going to roost in the late afternoon. The increase in weight fell off about mid-day when feeding activity declined. The average weights of the birds could be inversely correlated with air temperature. Owen suggested that the weight increase in early winter is an adaptation for a possible food shortage later but we do not yet know what the effects of other factors such as dispersal and moult may be.

Most of the birds seen in the winter in the pedunculate oakwoods are in flocks and those of the tits are the best known. The flocks studied at Wytham were probably largely local; these either drifted along at a maximum speed of 200 yards an hour or made distinct synchronised flights when they wanted to change their feeding-grounds. A speed of 390 yards per hour has been recorded, but in the purer oakwood at Badby I found that drifting speeds of 500 yards per hour were not uncommon. In the Wyre Forest a much higher speed – of 1,000 yards an hour – was noted. The winter numbers of tits in Badby Wood have often been higher than those of the breeding season and I suspect that many different individuals pass through in the course of the winter. Extensive ringing in winter by E. R. Parrinder in his Kent garden adjoining woodland has revealed a more or less continuous passage of alien blue tits through the area. It would be valuable to know more of the composition and behaviour of these flocks and to check how much their structure may alter through the winter months. In Badby Wood the largest mixed flock I have ever seen consisted of 114 birds composed of 35 blue tits, 14 long-tailed tits, 4 marsh tits, 2 coal tits, an exceptionally high number of great tits – 56 – as well as 2 treecreepers and a goldcrest. The highest numbers of species other than great tits in a single flock, although not necessarily the same one, were 39 blue, 8 marsh, 4 coal, 2 willow and 40 long-tailed tits. Numbers of long-tailed tits declined to 15 in November 1947, fell to 9 in 1948, rose to 18 in 1949 and were up to 35 by 1950. Many of the flocks ranged in size from about ten to forty birds and these were rather larger than the flocks in the sessile woods where parties were usually from about five to twenty.

It is a very interesting exercise to trace the movement of one of these foraging tit flocks through a winter oakwood. The flock will probably be first discovered through the soft contact calls and harsher scolds of the birds in the trees. It moves slowly on with a track that meanders through the wood and which may include loops where it crosses its earlier path. Even though the constituent species in the flock may be feeding in different zones and employing different techniques the whole group progresses with a loosely knit cohesion. This helps to maintain a roughly continuous dispersal of individuals over the feeding area, for each preserves around itself a sphere of space and if this is violated the occupant will retreat or attack. The value of flocking among birds has been argued for a long time, but it seems fairly clear that one of its most important survival values must lie in the fact that a flock of feeding birds is more likely to become aware of danger and predators than a single individual on its own. Also the single bird in a group is able to spend more time searching for food because it has been relieved of much of its sentry duty. Flocking may have a wider significance by satisfying some psychic need for comfort and reassurance through companionship in a somewhat hostile environment. As winter comes to an end the birds begin to slip back to their breeding territories.

Another device used by birds to avoid the worst hazards of hard weather is the storing of food in early autumn. Tits are known to do this, and great tits and blue tits even look for and rob the stores of other birds. I have watched marsh tits storing berries, and a list of some of the records for food storage among birds records that blue, coal and marsh tits may hide slugs while coal tits also store aphids. Nuthatches will conceal acorns and hazel nuts while jays take a good number of acorns from the oakwoods in autumn and bury them in the ground. Rooks will also visit oaks, pull off the acorns and carry them sometimes a mile or more from the parent tree and bury them in holes in fields. Rooks and jays can be useful agents in spreading oaks since, although a fair proportion of the hidden acorns is recovered, some will be left and so are able to generate in a protected environment, since acorns will not survive prolonged frost or too much drying while lying on the surface. It seems that the jay has a very retentive memory and retrieves its stores remarkably well. The presence of seedlings in such unlikely places as cracks in yew-trees and crevices in walls and the sight of an oakwood growing steadily uphill show how tree fruits can be overlooked. Jays have been seen burying acorns in a Czechoslovak pine-forest with the result that half of that forest now has an underlayer of oak with quite a dense canopy. As many as 300,000 acorns are believed to have been taken from one wood in Germany by jays. Acorns are also eaten, but not stored, by wood pigeons while woodpeckers and nuthatches will split both these and hazel nuts with their strong beaks.

In the autumn and winter months some of the thrushes begin to feed on various fruits, and the song thrush, which often deserts the oakwoods in winter, makes a seasonal change in its diet. Earthworms are regularly taken from January to June, caterpillars in May and June, snails throughout most of the year, while fruits of yew, hawthorn and elder and some other shrubs are taken in late summer and autumn. The song thrush was also seen to maintain winter territories in woodland only in one exceptional year "when fruit was very abundant". It appeared to be a specialist feeder on yew berries, the blackbird on haws, the mistle thrush on both yew and holly berries, while the winter visitors – the redwing and fieldfare – had strong preferences for haws. Although these examples came from a limited but widely-scattered number of localities, they supported the general theory that there were ecological differences in autumn between the closely-allied species in the thrush family.

So far we have been looking at the winter bird-life of the pedunculate oakwoods. What differences are there in the sessile woods? From my observations in the sessile oakwoods of northern England I have found that most of the birds desert the woods after the close of the breeding season. The chaffinches leave and do not start coming back until March or later still in the far north. A visit I made in late April one year to a wood in Sunart in north-west Scotland revealed only three chaffinches. In the sessile woods at Bonawe there were only two in the last week of April 1967 and one in Coille Mheadonach in Glen Creran. The yellowhammer also leaves the sessile woods for the winter. Numbers of song thrushes and robins may depart too, but the picture can alter from year to year and the population can be in direct proportion to the severity of the winter itself. The bird community of the summer sessile woods

contains a higher proportion of summer visitors than the lowland pedunculate woods and the desertion of the former in the late summer seems
more dramatic and complete. Later this loss may be in part balanced by
the small flocks of tits and goldcrests which wander through the trees. The
commonest species is the coal tit but there are also long-tailed, great and
blue tits. An investigation of fifteen sessile oakwoods in winter revealed
that the blue tit shows an increase in its percentage frequency from the
summer while the great tit shows a decline and the long-tailed tit,
although high in its relative abundance, is low in frequency. Fieldfares and
redwings are regular visitors and in Scotland I have found some of the
latter staying on until late April and early May. Crows, wrens and treecreepers seem to maintain their numbers fairly well but the buzzard is less
often seen in winter. Wood pigeons may come into some of the sessile
woods to feed on acorns, but I have visited many woods in winter and
found them devoid of wood pigeons altogether.

The sessile oakwoods of Cumberland seem to be completely empty of
birds in the winter and three untimed visits in September by Dr Yapp
produced only two crows! These woods are high and exposed and I have
drawn a similar blank in many of the sessile woods of Highland Britain.
Twelve sessile woods in lower situations in England and Wales produced an
average of 40 contacts per hour compared with a figure of 62 for the 36
woods I visited in summer. So the sessile woods, like the pedunculate,
contain a smaller number of birds per unit area in the winter than they
do in the summer although the numbers of some species may actually be
higher. In summer the woodland resources of insect food must be able to
support many broods of young birds in addition to the adult population.
The spring growth of vegetation is the factor that with an increase in the
insect biomass enables woodland to support the larger number of birds in
the summer.

Birds in both kinds of oakwood need to search most carefully and
assiduously for what insect and other invertebrate food remains in the
winter months. At Bookham Common a drop in the leaf litter population
during the first two months of the year was found and this probably
affects the number of ground-feeding birds in a wood. I have watched a
male blackbird in February searching for invertebrate food and employing
in one and a quarter minutes 52 sideways strokes of its bill; in this time it
picked up only four small items which it swallowed. Yet the blackbird has
more time for other activities than, say, the blue tit which is constantly
searching for tiny items such as insect eggs. Tits and treecreepers explore
the oaks with immense skill and their acrobatic habits enable them to pry
into cracks and crevices on the underside of boughs as well as the smaller

twigs. Later in the winter when food is usually getting scarcer some of the tits begin to explore the ground more closely. The woodpeckers with their specially adapted bills and tails are able to place themselves on the trees in such positions that they can dig out many of the wood-boring organisms. Wrens and robins can sometimes supplement their winter insect diet with seeds. The departed summer migrants are very largely insect-eaters and some like the nightjar and the three leaf warblers exclusively so. A few individual chiffchaffs and blackcaps are able to over-winter usually in the south-west and in Ireland where winter conditions are often less severe. It may be that of the insect-eating species fewer may survive from a large autumn population than from a moderate-sized one since a large population will devour more of the available insects before the spring. In Chapter 13 we shall look more closely at some of these influences on woodland bird populations since we need to know more about the effect of such factors as these when bird numbers are also subject to other increasing pressures.

CHAPTER 7

THE BIRDS OF OTHER BROAD-LEAVED
WOODS

FROM post-glacial times onwards the dominant trees of the British woodlands have been oak, alder, birch, ash, beech and Scots pine. Mixed
woods also occur, but they are not really typical. Our woods, as we have
seen in Chapter 1, are dominated by individual species of tree although
we can expect to find other species there as well – in fact, consociations
and societies. Dominance occurs because one tree has been successful in
its struggle to survive and prosper in competition with other tree species
in an environment largely influenced by climate and soil. In this chapter
we shall consider the remaining kinds of broad-leaved woodland and the
bird-life associated with each. Sometimes geographical factors may
influence the bird community of a particular woodland type so that the
birds of a Surrey birchwood may be different from those of a birchwood
in northern Scotland. We shall look rather closely at some of these differences. At the end of the chapter there is also a short discussion of the
occasional mixed broad-leaved woods that can be found in the British
Isles.

ALDERWOODS

In very damp valleys and water-logged country, along streams and lakesides and on not too acid marshes and fens the oak is replaced in the
British Isles by the alder. This tree has a dark fissured bark, characteristic
roundish, toothed leaves, and pendulous male and ovoid female catkins
which turn into small false cones. It favours a soil rich in mineral salts and
usually with a mull humus. The alder is widespread in Europe, western
Asia and North Africa; it can grow to as much as 100 ft. tall, but in
Britain it rarely exceeds 25. Once, it was probably a common tree, but
drainage over the years has destroyed much of its habitat, and its flush
soils of the uplands were coveted by the Norsemen who cleared much of
the alder jungles for the fertile soils underneath. Alder was also one of the
best timbers for making charcoal. Today it is well but thinly spread
throughout the British Isles ranging north to Sutherland and west to the
Atlantic coast of Ireland. Alder is perhaps most noticeable in west Wales

and Scotland. Trees often climb quite high up the hills and may be an important constituent of the hillside oakwoods. I have walked through numbers of these woods in the Highlands, generally on a southwards-facing slope and a brown earth; here the oaks were mixed with ash, birch, wych elm and alder. Alder and ash also grow together in the Llyfnant Valley in Wales. Alder can sometimes become the dominant tree and I have found practically pure alderwoods near Dunkeld, near Kinloch Lodge in Sutherland, near Drumnadrochit and at Carnoch near Glencoe. In many other places I have also found pure alder groves and belts along the banks of streams and lochs.

I have been able to visit six almost pure alderwoods in Scotland. The wood at Carnoch provided nearly an hour of hazardous exploration when, one May, I tried to make a line transect across a fairly steep slope that was running continuously with water and quaked ominously under my feet in many places. There were a few small ashes, hollies and six-foot high beeches, an occasional hawthorn and a field layer of bramble, ivy, primrose, violet and wood sorrel. Wrens and chaffinches came equal first in numbers followed by willow warblers, robins, song thrushes, great tits, redstarts and blue tits while a pair of buzzards circled overhead. Another alderwood near Loch Ness contained ash and willow, blackthorn and elder and a most luxuriant herbaceous layer of wood anemones, celandines and marsh marigolds. Here wrens and chaffinches were again the com-monest species followed by robins, willow warblers, blackbirds, starlings and bullfinches in that order. An alderwood in Sutherland with occasional birch and willow produced in order of numbers the following list: 11 chaffinches, 7 robins, 4 each of wrens, willow warblers, goldcrests and wood pigeons, 3 blackbirds and treecreepers, 2 each of starlings, meadow pipits, blue tits and mistle thrushes, a buzzard and, surprisingly, a circling pair of greenshanks. Table 18 lists the results from six alderwoods in Scotland in which I spent two hours in May 1967; there were also single records of yellowhammer, redwing, coal tit and hooded crow.

From Table 18 it is clear that the chaffinch is the commonest species and, with wren, robin and willow warbler, is one of the four dominant birds of the Scottish alderwoods. These species also appear among the top six for Scottish sessile oak and ashwoods. Pied flycatchers sometimes appear in alders in the eastern Highlands.

In central, southern and eastern England the alder is confined to stream-sides, lake margins, occasional damp hollows like those in the New Forest and to the fenland "carrs". This word comes from the Middle English and was derived from the Old Norse, and is used today to describe the alderwoods of the Broads. The succession develops from a

PLATE 7. Acorns and leaves of the two common oaks. *Above*, the pedunculate oak; *below*, the sessile oak.

PLATE 8. Oakwood interiors. *Above*, pedunculate oak with good field layer, Suffolk; *below*, sessile oakwood, Keskadale Oaks, Cumberland, with grassy field layer.

TABLE 18. *The Relative Abundance and Frequency of Bird Species in 6 Scottish Alderwoods 1967*

199 contacts of 23 species in 120 minutes

Species	Contacts	Relative Abundance	Number of Woods Where Found
Chaffinch	37	18	5
Wren	26	13	5
Robin	22	11	4
Willow Warbler	18	9	4
Starling	14	7	5
Blackbird	12	6	4
Blue Tit	9	5	4
Great Tit	6	3	3
Treecreeper	6	3	2
Bullfinch	6	3	2
Wood Pigeon	6	3	2
Meadow Pipit	6	3	2
Song Thrush	6	3	2
Goldcrest	4	2	1
Buzzard	3	1	2
Redstart	3	1	1
Long-tailed Tit	3	1	1
Mistle Thrush	2	1	1
Greenfinch	2	1	1

base provided by the tussock or fen sedge which grows in big clumps above the water and so provides nurseries for the first sallow and alder seedlings. The tussocks grow in size and the weight of the developing trees causes the fen peat to sink. With an unstable foundation the trees no longer grow erect and the roots of some of the larger ones, now in deeper water, begin to die. This swamp carr can be recognised by the fallen and dying trees, by trees with inclining boles growing from a layer of shrubs, and all this is "underlain by an excessively soft and quaking floor of alternating tussocks and black foetid pools" (Ellis 1965). Later, fallen brushwood and compacted mud may make the floor rather more stable. Alder and sallow are the dominant trees, but downy birch, ash, sycamore and an occasional, perhaps bird-sown, pedunculate oak may also occur. The shrubby plants that grow in these carrs include wild raspberry, red and black currants, dewberry, bramble, honeysuckle, wild privet, both buckthorns and guelder rose, while the field layer consists of marsh marigold, nettle, yellow flag, purple loosestrife, meadowsweet and hop. The presence of so many lime-loving plants is due to the fen water draining off the chalk.

The broad-buckler fern is common and in some places the royal fern grows as well. Lichens and mosses also flourish in these unique "jungles."

The bird-life of these alder carrs is varied and interesting since the extraordinary mixture of trees, dead timber, thickets of shrubs and rich field layer is favourable to a wide range of woodland species. The great, blue, marsh, coal and long-tailed tits are common residents and I have also found the willow tit in small numbers. Wrens, robins, blackbirds, song thrushes, chaffinches, reed buntings and pheasants are regular while smaller numbers of redpolls, bullfinches, treecreepers and tree sparrows also breed. Of the summer visitors chiffchaffs, willow warblers, blackcaps, cuckoos and turtle doves are common and widespread. With the presence of so much mature and old timber all three species of woodpecker can be found, but the lesser spotted is the scarcest. Of the predatory birds I have found the tawny owl and the jay to be common while a few pairs of long-eared owls and carrion crows nest in the more remote and undisturbed carrs. The golden oriole is reported on passage in many springs. There is one carr which I have often visited and here the alder is mixed with occasional ash, sycamore and oak. The carr is rich in the bushes of guelder rose. In August it is often alive with goldfinches attracted by its thistles, and with the coming of autumn the berries of the guelder rose bring in flocks of redwings, fieldfares, mistle thrushes, wood-pigeons, and in some winters small parties of waxwings. Siskins and redpolls come to the alders for food while magpies, bramblings and members of the thrush family seek out the carrs for roosting. These carrs in winter are very mysterious and attractive. On a particular boat-trip which I made late one January afternoon I heard the delicate chiming calls of teal, the soft inward piping of bullfinches in the sallows and the harsh scold of a willow tit. In the crown of a tall alder siskins were hanging upside down from the tiny cones and a water rail called in the distance from the reeds. A lesser spotted woodpecker sat motionless in a dead tree. I also heard fieldfares high overhead, a coypu far away and the calls of the first tawny owls as the day quickly came to an end.

BIRCHWOODS

Birch and Scots pine are so often associated with each other in similar conditions of climate and soil that much of the material in this section of the chapter ought to be considered with that in Chapter 8 which deals with our native pinewoods. Indeed, birch and pine represent a climatic climax to the north of the broad-leaved summer forests. In direct competition, as we have already seen, and on a soil that is favourable to both species the pine will oust the birch which needs full light, but birch is better able to survive in a really adverse environment where the soil is poor and the climate severe. In the British Isles, birch extends northward from the pine-forests almost to the far northern coasts of Scotland. In the primeval forests of Ireland it was once plentiful. It is a pioneer species that very quickly invades and colonises bare and waste land and it flourishes extremely well on ground from which woodland has been recently cleared; it is possible that some of the birchwoods of the uplands may have been established on the sites of former oak or pinewoods. Birch often fills up the gaps in hillside oakwoods and grows as a fringe around relic woodlands.

There are two species of tree birch in the British Isles as well as a Dwarf Birch (*Betula nana*). This low shrub is a relic of the ice age tundra and can be found only in high moorland bogs in Scotland. The two native tree birches are the Silver Birch (*B. pendula*=*B. verrucosa*=*B. alba*) and the Downy, or Hairy Birch (*B. pubescens*). The silver birch is an elegant tree of medium size with drooping or pendulous branches and a silvery, papery bark. The base of the mature tree is often rugged and split. The brown twigs are hairless and often warty in appearance. The very pointed leaves are variously toothed, smooth and generally with their bases at an angle to the stem. The downy birch is a smaller tree, often with a smooth base to the trunk. The young twigs are usually darker, without warts and downy although some northern specimens lack this pubescence. The leaves are duller, less pointed, downy on the veins underneath and generally with their bases more at right angles to the stem. The silver birch likes sandy and gravelly soils especially if calcareous in nature, while the downy birch prefers wetter conditions. As a result the former is more abundant and widespread in the south while the latter makes up much of the Highland woodlands. Intermediate forms do exist and can be very difficult to distinguish. In some parts there are woods where one species is dominant, while others in Lakeland and northern England are mixed. However, there is no real evidence that the woods of different types have different bird ecologies, but there are dissimilarities between birchwoods in various parts of the British Isles. I propose therefore to treat separately the birchwoods of Scotland, of central and northern England and Wales, of southern England and of Ireland. It would seem from my observations that these four divisions represent most fairly the variations in the bird communities.

Birch is the third most important tree in Britain in relation to the land area it covers and, since birchwoods are so regular and widespread in the Highlands, I intend to discuss these first. Both species of birch can be found in Scotland with the silver birch appearing generally in the eastern and central Highlands and the downy birch in the west and north. The Highland birchwoods have been divided into two types according to their vegetation. The first type of wood contains birch, rowan, hard fern, wavy hair grass, great woodrush, wood sorrel, tormentil and several species of moss. The shrub layer is often missing but there may be occasional juniper, hazel and honeysuckle. The ground zone is dominated by *Vaccinium*, woodrush and moss and so is called the *Vaccinium*-rich birchwood. The second type of wood includes most of the plant species already named together with wood anemone, common dog violet, fine bent and sweet vernal grass. Shrubs are very uncommon. Because of the rich field layer this is known as the herb-rich birchwood. In the Highlands birches can grow to an altitudinal limit of 2,000 ft. and here at the upper limit of one particular wood the bird-life is restricted to wrens, meadow pipits and red grouse. The wetter, western birchwoods, composed largely of downy birch, often grow on boulder-strewn rocky slopes which, like the trees, are clothed in a velvet mat of green or yellow mosses and lichens similar to those in some of the Killarney oakwoods. In contrast to this, a birchwood in Strathspey on a sandy soil is dominated by silver birch with some downy as well and a few aspens and rowans. Here there is a strong shrub layer of juniper and a field layer of *Vaccinium*, *Calluna*, wood anemone, wavy hair grass and chickweed wintergreen. Birches are not long-lived trees and so many of the woods do not have long histories. Some of the woods are unable to regenerate because of the continuous grazing of hardy black-faced sheep, red deer and rabbits. Grasses now tend to become dominant. The trees age and rot beneath their lichen coats. They are attacked by wood-boring insects and fungi and finally they succumb to the autumn and winter gales. These relic woods are often a very depressing sight.

But in spring when the new leaf begins to spread over the red-brown winter trees, the tits, warblers, chaffinches and redstarts begin to return to the Scottish birchwoods which once more echo with song. This is true of many of the damp birchwoods that lie to the west under the shadow of Suilven, Canisp, Quinag and Ben More Coigach. The arrival of the summer migrants brings its special excitement, to a wood, for example, near the Kyle of Tongue on the 27th of April – the day that year on which the first willow warblers came back.

I have visited many birchwoods in Scotland from Craigellachie and the Glen of Muick north to Loch Eriboll and north-west to Lochinver and the Allt Volagir in South Uist. Many of these woods consisted of downy birch, but some, like those in Strathpeffer, were of the silver species. In the birchwoods of north-western Scotland the willow warbler is the dominant bird followed in order by chaffinch, tree pipit, wren and robin. These five species also dominate Dr Yapp's Scottish birchwood list, but I found the wren more frequent than the robin. The coal tit was the commonest tit in all but two woods near Lochinver where in 1967 the great tit was dominant. Blue tits and wood pigeons were less common although I found 18 contacts in five woods of the latter species but no nests. The song thrush occurs in small numbers but the blackbird is rather scarce. My most northerly birchwood record for the blackbird is of two near Loch Loyal and it would seem that since the blackbird breeds in moorland habitats in Shetland and the Isle of Lewis there is something about these Scottish birchwoods that it does not like. In Irish birchwoods the blackbird is more frequent. Smaller numbers of hooded crows, redstarts, hedgesparrows, treecreepers and yellowhammers also appeared while the meadow pipit was about as common as the song thrush. I have also a few records of red-poll, spotted flycatcher, wood warbler, raven, ring ousel, wheatear, pied wagtail, starling and black grouse. The redpoll which is now so common in many areas of mixed coniferous and broad-leaved countryside seems to occur less frequently in these northern birchwoods than it did. I have found redwings in May in several birchwoods and it now nests in most years. On single occasions I have also come across the whinchat and the red grouse. It is interesting to compare these records with those from a Scandinavian birch-forest which was described in Chapter 2. Although the birchwoods as a habitat differ considerably from coniferous woodlands quite a high proportion of species from the birch-forest also appear among the conifers.

There are some differences if the birds of the northern woods are compared to those of eastern Scotland. Here the chaffinch outnumbers the willow warbler. Counts that I made in the birchwoods of Strathspey in 1953, 1957, 1959, 1963 and 1967 showed that this difference continued. The tree pipit was less frequent in the east than in the north-west. Other species were fairly similar in their frequency; however, in the birchwoods of the Glen of Muick and near Loch Ness great spotted woodpeckers, song thrushes, blackbirds and bullfinches were quite common, but their presence may have been influenced in part by young conifer plantations not far away. Mistle thrushes, crested tits, redstarts, wood warblers and cuckoos occur in the woods of Speyside as well as redpolls, woodcock and black grouse. Buzzards sometimes circle and soar over these woods while a sparrowhawk chases some hapless chaffinch or redstart through the trees. There is an unusual record of common gulls nesting in birch trees near Braemar at about fourteen feet above the ground.

These then are the typical birds of the northern and eastern Scottish birchwoods. How do they compare with those in the birchwoods of Wales and of central and northern England? I have made counts in the Lake District and in the Pennines and parts of Wales. In some of the Pennine woods the field layer is not very different from some oakwoods with plenty of *Vaccinium*, wavy hair grass and various mosses. In Wales many of the birchwoods form the upper fringes to the sessile oakwoods. The order of relative abundance begins with the chaffinch and descends through the willow warbler, tree pipit, robin, wren and pied flycatcher. Less frequent species include the crow, blue tit, wood warbler, yellowhammer and spotted flycatcher. The buzzard is absent and the coal tit is missing from the woods of Cumberland but occurs in birches in Wales, Scotland, and southern England. Willow tits can be found in the older birchwoods of Wales, northern England and southern Scotland. The pied flycatcher is regular in the woods of the Lake District, but occurs in less than half the woods I have visited. The wood warbler is rather less common and also is missing from about half the woods. In the Wyre Forest the willow warbler was four times as abundant as the chaffinch.

In the south of England the birch is common in sandy and gravelly heaths. Often it takes a hold after heath fires and forms part of the succession that culminates in oak/birch heath or oakwood. Sometimes these southern birchwoods are survivors of woods from which the original oak has been extracted. In Surrey there is a large area of birch mixed with pine. The oak/birch heath flourishes on the Lower Greensand and Ashdown Sands in the Weald of Kent, on the Bagshot Sands of the Eocene Period and on glacial drift. There are good examples at Wimbledon, Chislehurst and Banstead of birch heathlands based on sand and gravel. These may be pure *Calluna* heath or, if the ground zone is heavily trampled or grazed, grass heath. In other places the heath may be dominated by gorse and bracken with only scattered birches, or it may develop into a closer network of trees that finally becomes birch and oak woodland. In these woods where the trees are not too closely set the tree pipit is quite common and willow and wood warblers nest fairly regularly. A study of a birch common on Englefield Green in Surrey revealed 33 willow warbler territories over some 11½ acres, giving an average territory size of just over one third of an acre. Wimbledon Common has quite extensive birchwoods and here hawfinch, wood warbler and sparrowhawk have nested in recent years. Coal tits are regular and I have listened to as many as four males singing at the same time in a birchwood near Roehampton.

In Ireland birch is often plentiful as scrub on some of the hillsides and along the margins of bogs. I have been able to carry out transects in five isolated and well-developed birchwoods of which four were in Eire and one in Northern Ireland. One of these which I visited in May 1967 was near Lough Neagh and consisted of about ten acres of close-canopy birch with some rowan and sallows, a field layer of ivy, bramble, and young rowans, and a ground zone rich in various ferns and mosses. The common-est bird was the mistle thrush closely followed by blackbird, wren, willow warbler, chaffinch and robin. There were smaller numbers of chiffchaffs, song thrushes, hedgesparrows, blue tits and a single cuckoo. Another close-canopy birchwood near Roosky in Co. Offaly had a few rowans and hollies with bracken below. Here the dominant species was the wren with robin, willow warbler, song thrush, hedgesparrow, blackbird and chaffinch following in that order. Chiffchaffs, goldcrests and cuckoos were also present. When I put the records for the five woods together I find that the willow warbler and the robin come top of the list of relative abundance with chaffinch and wren close behind. These four species also appear in the top five for the woods of northern Scotland and those in northern England and Wales. The blackbird came fifth – a very different position from that in the Scottish birchwoods. Song thrushes, hedgesparrows and mistle thrushes with RAs from 6 to 4 were quite important members of the community. I also had contacts for the bullfinch, blue tit, spotted flycatcher and wood pigeon. There were no records for the coal or great tit, and the tree pipit and pied flycatcher are absent from Ireland.

In Scotland, as autumn falls the birchwoods begin to glow with gold. In Speyside they stand out well against the deep bottle-green pines. At this time of year I have explored the birchwoods of Glen Feshie and Glen Tromie looking for birds, with the distant roars of the red deer stags at the rut in the background. In these autumn woods tits and goldcrests forage together in loose flocks. I have seen the crested tit in the birches of late winter but there is a November record. Only a few chaffinches are left and their places are taken, as the winter wears on and the trees turn to purple-brown, by redpolls and sometimes siskins. The rowan berries in the woods attract the late-departing ring ousels and the redwings and fieldfares that arrive on the Moray Firth and follow the valley of the Spey south-west. Bullfinches also enter some of these northern woods, but on the whole they belong to the tits, wrens and occasional thrushes and crows. In the southern birchwoods of England bullfinches, redpolls and siskins are frequent visitors to the catkins while small flocks of long-tailed tits arrive from their summer breeding areas in the nearby scrub. From November to April blue tits attack the birch catkins, bramblings may come into the woods in October and in Middlesex in December I have seen flocks of house sparrows feeding on catkins in birch woodland (see also Goodwin 1964).

ASHWOODS

Ash is a very common tree in many parts of the British Isles appearing both as a constituent of other kinds of woodland and as a hedgerow tree, as well as forming in some areas quite extensive stretches of almost pure wood and scrub. It grows well on shallow limestone soils and is often the dominant tree in a successional stage towards beechwood which finally suppresses it. Outside the normal range of the beech pre-climax ash can become the climax forest vegetation. In Sussex in the first stages of succession ash is typically dominant, but it is finally excluded by climax beech or yew. On the steep hillsides of the Carboniferous Limestone in Somerset and the Peak District, where the soils are too shallow to allow oak to grow, ashwood can develop to its finest form. Limestone ashwoods occur on the Mendip Hills and in parts of Gloucestershire, by the South Wales coalfields, in Monmouth, Flint and Denbighshire, in Derbyshire, in the West Riding and north Lancashire. Wigtown and Kirkcudbright are the only Scottish counties with any appreciable areas of ash; farther north there are woods at Loch Kishorn and Loch Creran on the Scottish mainland and at Tokavaig on the Isle of Skye. In Ireland much of the limestone is covered by glacial drift, but in places on the hills and plateaux of Counties Sligo, Galway and Clare almost pure ashwoods can still be found. Ash was probably never very widespread in Ireland except in association with oak. Fragments of ashwood also occur on the chalk in Wiltshire and the Isle of Wight, on igneous rock near Dolgelley in Wales and on the Upper Greensand of south-east Devon. Ash is therefore more widely spread in the north and west.

Ash trees can grow to 90 ft. or so, but in many of the limestone ravines in Yorkshire a height of 45 ft. is more usual. On the deeper soils in the limestone regions oak may be well represented in the ashwoods and if the two species should have to compete on equal terms the oak may overshadow the ash and eventually suppress it. At the highest levels of the hillside woods – just over 1,000 ft. – ash is replaced by almost pure downy birch with perhaps a few rowans. There is an upland ashwood between 900 and 1,250 ft. near Cader Idris. On some of the upper scree slopes the woods may be of the oak/ash/birch type that exists at Naddle Forest in Westmorland; here oak tends to appear on the more leached, and ash on the more flushed, soils. The trees most often associated with ash are wych elm and, in the south of Britain, whitebeam and yew. Bird cherry is common in the Peak District while aspen and field maple can also be found. Birch may also occur in the canopy with rowan in the north and occasional small-leaved lime in the west. Because of its structure the ash lets much more light through than the oak so that luxuriant growth is possible in both the shrub and field layers. In the former, hazel is often abundant with also a great deal of hawthorn, elder and sometimes bramble. Some shrub species are confined geographically to the south while some are local south of the Peak District, and of the shrubs that favour limestone soils spindle tree, dogwood and privet are common; honeysuckle and wayfaring tree are more restricted to the south. The field layer is perhaps the richest of any British woodland for some peculiar species can be found there besides the plants common also to oakwoods. The field layer is often divided into two types depending on the amount of water in the soil. On damp soils the commonest plants are ramsons, celandine, yellow deadnettle, globe flower, stone bramble, melancholy thistle, yellow flag, giant bellflower and spotted orchid. Where the soil is drier I have found dog's mercury, bloody cranesbill, ground ivy, moschatel and, more locally, lily-of-the-valley and, in the north, baneberry. On the limestone pavements of northern England ash often takes hold in the fissures or cracks, locally known as grykes, that run down vertically into the rock. An ashwood can resemble several types of woodland ranging from the open luxuriant oakwood-type through the sessile form and so to the hillwoods of the deep ravines rich in mosses and liverworts.

I have been to five ashwoods in Scotland of which the best known are the Nature Conservancy's wood at Rassal and the ash/hazel wood at Glasdrum. The Rassal wood I visited in June 1966 and May 1967. Some authorities regard the pure ashwood as a clear vegetation type – the *Brachypodium*-rich ashwood – with six regular plants in the field layer; these are *Brachypodium* (Slender False Brome), common bent, cock's foot grass, yellow pimpernel, meadowsweet and violet. The Rassal ashwood covers about 33 acres on the Durness limestone and extends over several broad flat gulleys on a hillside. In the middle is an enclosed area to encourage regeneration in a wood which is nearly a hundred years old. There is some hazel and hawthorn but the shrub layer is sparse. I found lady's mantle, primrose, celandine, wood sorrel and some early purple orchids but the growth inside the enclosure was very much more luxuriant. The wood at Glasdrum contains some birch, alder and wild cherry with a considerable amount of hazel, hawthorn and elder with bracken, yellow flags, primrose, celandines and violets in the field layer.

In Ireland I have only seen two ashwoods of any size. The first was on the southern shore of Lower Lough Erne and contained some birch, alder, holly, hazel and sallow with a rich and varied field layer. The other Irish wood was at Kilbeggan on the Big Esker and here ash was dominant, but there was also some mature birch and beech. The shrub layer consisted largely of hazel, hawthorn, and blackthorn with a herbaceous layer of primrose, wood sorrel, bluebell, bugle, sanicle, arum, lady's mantle and common spotted and twayblade orchids.

About 7% of England's high forest is made up of ashwoods, but in Scotland they occupy only 1%. I have carried out counts in 10 English ashwoods, five Scottish and two Irish. In England the woods are chiefly northern ones and here I have found the commonest bird to be the willow warbler followed closely by the chaffinch. The other important species are wood pigeon, redstart, wren, tree pipit, great tit, blackbird, robin and blue tit, with blackcap common in some northern woods. There are also small numbers of marsh tit, song thrush, starling and crow. Dr. Yapp found the yellowhammer fairly regularly in some of the woods. This community would seem to be intermediate between those of the pedunculate and sessile oakwoods. The ash has a thin invertebrate fauna – only 22 species of mites and insects – so that the tree compares poorly with the pedunculate oak. In Scotland the chaffinch was the commonest bird, but it came only third in the Irish woods. The RA of the Scottish birds was as follows: chaffinch 23, wren 14, robin 9, great tit, wood pigeon and willow warbler 7, tree pipit 5 and blue tit 4. Other species in the Scottish woods scoring over 1 included meadow pipit, blackbird, hedgesparrow, crow, coal tit, woodcock, song thrush, buzzard, cuckoo, redstart and treecreeper. There were also some isolated records of bullfinch, greenfinch, mistle thrush, pied wagtail and pheasant. In Ireland I spent nearly an hour in the two woods I have described. The sample is small and I was unable to find any more woods of sufficient size or structure to suit my purpose. In both these woods the blackbird was by far the commonest species with an RA of 27 followed by the willow warbler with 18 and the chaffinch and robin with 13. There were twelve chiffchaffs in the wood by Lough Erne, but none at Kilbeggan. Song thrushes, wrens, great tits and wood pigeons could be found in both woods, but although blue and coal tits, whitethroats and cuckoos were present in Northern Ireland they were missing from Kilbeggan. Although ash occurs widely as a roadside tree in Ireland, pure or fairly pure ashwoods are not common.

The English and Scottish ashwoods are very largely evacuated in the winter, particularly by chaffinches, robins and some of the thrushes. Coal tits are probably the commonest tits in the winter ashwoods, but I have records of great, blue, marsh and long-tailed tits in the autumn and the month of January. Redwings will sometimes come into these woods to roost during the winter months.

BEECHWOODS

The beech was present in England in the Sub-Boreal Period and in the past probably extended farther north and west than it does today. There are beechwoods in Wales and Wiltshire, but the range has probably contracted leaving them as scattered remnants of the old native woods. As a native forest tree the beech is now limited to the chalk of south-eastern England and the inferior oolite of the Cotswolds where on the shallower soils the beech is the climax woodland. The largest areas are in the Chilterns in Buckinghamshire and south Oxfordshire. The Chiltern beechwoods are perhaps the survivors of a system of coppice management dating from the Middle Ages. Beech seems to be a rather poor developer in the Chilterns and replanting is often done with seed from other districts. Elsewhere it occurs only as isolated trees and small woods and groves. The beech can ripen seed and propagate itself in the south-west of England, Scotland and Ireland, but here the woods are certainly planted. The native tree was a late immigrant from the Continent where there are many magnificent woods in the Alps and Croatian Mountains; in the Carpathians beech grows to altitudes of 4,000 ft. and in the Jura to 5,000 ft.

Beech will grow on acid but dislikes water-logged soils and the heavier clays. Here oakwood normally becomes dominant although beech will grow with oak on some of the plateau soils. Where these soils are brown earths they can support either oak/hazel woods like those of the North Downs and Hampshire uplands or beechwoods such as occur in the Chilterns or the western South Downs. On the shallow soils like the chalk rendzinas oak cannot grow and beech becomes dominant. On easily-podsolised soils beech will be at a final disadvantage as it tends to produce a ground zone with slow-decaying leaf litter and an absence in its acid soil of earthworms, and this is very unfavourable to generation and the growth of seedlings. On the chalk of south-eastern England the most typical of the native beechwoods clothe steep scarps and valley sides forming "hangers" like the one at Selborne written of so lovingly by Gilbert White: "The covert of this eminence is altogether beech, the most lovely of all forest trees, whether we consider its smooth rind or bark, its glossy foliage, or graceful pendulous boughs." A number of the beech-woods in Britain are stands planted to adorn many of the eighteenth-century country houses. Conifers were often used as nursery trees to protect the young beeches – a custom widely used in Ireland today where beech is often planted with larch. In this way beech has been persuaded to grow in quite exposed situations – in clumps on the Sussex Downs, in the northern Pennines and the Derbyshire Peak. Beech occurs widely in Scotland from Fife north to Aberdeenshire and north of the Border forms 9% of the high forest; here it has been established in policy woods and shelter belts. Figure 12 (page 68) gives the distribution of beech in Britain. Beech was probably introduced to Ireland in the seventeenth century; it is now quite a common tree in groves and hedgerows. Well-developed beech nearly a hundred feet in height can be seen at Powerscourt, Dunloe, Birr, Tollymore and Mount Stewart and I have also been to fair-sized woods at Cairnwood near Belfast and in the Vale of Clara south of Dublin.

The native beechwoods of south-east England can be divided into three main types. The first is the beechwood on chalk and other limestone soils so characteristic of the scarps and valleysides of Kent, Surrey, Sussex and Hampshire and growing on slopes varying from 18 to 35 degrees. Oak may get a foothold on the easier slopes, but on the steeper ones the soils tend to be washed away; these are of the rendzina type and may lie under a carpet of leaf litter a foot deep. Beech dominates the tree layer which may rise to sixty feet or more, but occasional ashes and whitebeams appear and, in the Chilterns, wild cherry. There is often a lower, subsidiary tree layer of yew and holly which, being evergreens, are able to take advantage of the light in the wood before the beech leaves open to form a mosaic which effectively cuts off most of the light. Yew can form pure woods on parts of the North and South Downs. The shrub layer is usually poor or absent as the light available is so small, but in the more open-canopy conditions field maple, elder, spindle tree, hazel and sometimes box may occur. The field layer is often poor as well since the ramifying rootlets of the beech take up a lot of water and there is little light. The rootlets are associated with fungal *hyphae* called *mycorrhiza* which are important in the tree's nutritional system. Saprophytes that live on dead organic matter, like the yellow bird's nest, are common in dense beechwoods. In a more open beechwood some of the oakwood plants like the dog's mercury, bugle, herb robert, wood anemone, wild strawberry, sanicle and ivy can flourish while there are also more characteristic plants of chalk beechwood such as woodruff, hairy violet, the bird's nest orchid and several helleborines, spurge laurel and Solomon's seal. The depth of leaf litter in many woods prevents the development of mosses which are thus far less common than in many oakwoods.

The second type of beechwood is to be found on loam on the chalk plateaux of the South Downs in Sussex and south-eastern Hampshire, in the Chilterns in Oxfordshire and Buckinghamshire and in the east and north-east of Scotland. The loam may be heavy or light and range from alkaline to acid. It can support the finest development of beech with trees growing to heights of a hundred feet or more. On these loams oak is locally frequent, ash not uncommon while sycamore is very regular in many of the South Down woods and hornbeam can be found in the Chilterns. The shrub layer is thin with occasional yew and holly but bramble is often abundant and I have been in some Chiltern woods where bramble forms huge and impenetrable thickets. The ground zone vegetation is poorer but not essentially different from that of oakwoods on the same soils and wood sorrel is often dominant with occasional bluebells, dog's mercury, tufted hair grass and hairy brome. On the sandier kinds of loam foxglove is often very common and, as the soils become more acid, fine bent, wood soft grass and wavy hair grass may cover much of the ground zone in the more open parts of the woodland. In Scotland the beechwoods on loam tend to have no shrub layer but I have found elder and seedling ash in one wood in Strathmore. In north Aberdeenshire the woods grow well on a rich loam and along the Firths of Cromarty and Beauly the regeneration is good. Here there are no shrubs but usually a wide range of herbaceous plants. There are notable similarities between the Scottish woods and those of the chalk plateaux.

The third type of beechwood occurs on the sands and podsols and contains smaller and often very contorted trees. Associated trees, apart from a few oaks, are rare and holly is the only regular shrub. Small woods of this kind can be seen on the Lower Greensand, on the Bagshot Sands and in the Hampshire Basin. Near Burnham Beeches the trees may be mixed with oak and birch and sometimes rowan, alder buckthorn, honeysuckle and bracken. In Epping Forest the beeches grow on glacial deposits laid over Bagshot Sands. Most of the Scottish beechwoods of this type have been planted as shelter belts a hundred years ago largely on the glacial drift deposits. The field layer is often entirely absent but where it is present the typical plants are *Vaccinium*, *Calluna*, bracken and wavy hair grass. On podsolised soils regeneration is sometimes uncertain.

In all these different types of beechwood the most important factors for the bird community are absence of light, a thin shrub layer and a field layer influenced by the nature of the canopy above and the leaf litter under the trees. The beech can support from 180 to 200 different species of invertebrate – more than eight times the number for the ash, and this may offset to some extent the adverse factors. In fact, the bird community is a slighter one than that of oakwoods. In European Russia beechwoods have the poorest bird population of all the broad-leaved trees. I have made transects in 16 English beechwoods, chiefly in the Cotswolds, the

Chilterns, in Hampshire and the London area as well as in 6 Scottish and 4 Irish woods. The results of those counts are shown in Table 19, with some figures from Yapp (1962).

TABLE 19. *The Relative Abundance of Bird Species in Beechwoods*

English Woods (Simms) 16 woods. 320 mins. 629 contacts. 29 species.		English Woods (Yapp) 8 woods. 255 mins. 236 contacts.		Scottish Woods (Simms) 6 woods. 101 mins. 230 contacts. 30 species.		Irish Woods (Simms) 4 woods. 75 mins. 136 contacts. 20 species.	
Chaffinch	17	Chaffinch	17	Chaffinch	17	Chaffinch	16
Blackbird	11	Blackbird	10	Blackbird	12	Blackbird	11
Great Tit	8	Great Tit	10	Blue Tit	9	Wood Pigeon	11
Wood Pigeon	7	Wren	7	Wood Pigeon	8	Robin	8
Wren	7	Willow Warbler	6	Wren	8	Song Thrush	7
Robin	6	Wood Pigeon	6	Starling	8	Starling	7
Blue Tit	5	Robin	5	Robin	7	Wren	6
Willow Warbler	5	Blue Tit	4	Song Thrush	5	Jackdaw	6
Blackcap	3	Chiffchaff	3	Hedgesparrow	3	Mistle Thrush	6
Hedgesparrow	3	Blackcap	3	Great Tit	3	Great Tit	4
Chiffchaff	2	Jay	2	Jackdaw	3	Willow Warbler	2
Wood Warbler	2	Redstart	2	Greenfinch	2	Hedgesparrow	2
Redstart	2	Nuthatch	2	Mistle Thrush	2	Long-tailed Tit	2
Nuthatch	2	Song Thrush	1	Great Spotted Woodpecker	2	Coal Tit	2
Marsh Tit	2			Pheasant	2	Redstart	2
Jay	2			Chiffchaff	2	Blue Tit	2
Starling	2			Stock Dove	2	Chiffchaff	2
Greenfinch	2			Wood Warbler	2		
Song Thrush	2						

In all three regions the chaffinch is the commonest bird with the blackbird in second place. In the beech/oakwoods of northern Germany the chaffinch is also the commonest bird. The great tit is third in the English woods but I found it rather less common in Scotland and Ireland. The dominant species of the Irish beechwoods are very much the same as those in the sessile woods of Ireland. The wood warbler I found in seven of the English and two of the Scottish woods. It has bred in Ireland, but I have only a single record for a beechwood in Co. Wicklow and it is very rare. In some of the Hampshire and North Downs woods the wood warbler is not uncommon; in June 1964 I listened to six males singing in a Hampshire beechwood with no undergrowth and a poor ground zone. The wood warblers were singing from the lower branches and there were redstarts in the canopy. I was able to make a sound recording of these birds after a sudden shower of rain. In an over-mature wood the rotten timber provides nesting sites for woodpeckers and stock doves.

When winter comes the summer migrants and some of the robins leave the woods. Chaffinches and winter visitors come in to feed on the beech-mast. Beeches do not normally produce their mast, or seed, every year; their seeding is often irregular and at intervals of more than twelve months. There are sometimes two reasonable crops in alternate years. Research has shown that a warm spring and summer will produce such growth in the trees that plenty of flowering buds are laid down in the autumn. As a result there is a good flowering in the following spring and a rich seed crop ensues in the October and November of that year. In the summer of a good crop year the seeds take up most of the plant foods so that few flowering buds can be formed. This means that one good crop cannot follow another although inferior ones may do so. Chaffinches, and bramblings from the Continent, are typically mast feeders and they often share the crop with other bird species. On the North Downs, the Chilterns and the Cotswolds I have seen tits, nuthatches, jays, magpies, stock doves, wood pigeons, and great spotted woodpeckers eating beech-mast with the finches. On a few occasions I have seen hawfinches eating beech-mast. Great, blue, coal and marsh tits all feeding on mast between September and early March have been recorded. Coal tits, marsh tits and nuthatches have the rather delightful habit of hiding beech nuts for future use, but the great tit has been seen stealing supplies hidden by coal tits, and blue tits searching for the food stores of coal and marsh tits. All seems fair in the jungle of the beechwood!

The tit population of the winter beechwoods may vary with the crop, but the seed in a good year is a valuable way of helping local tit populations to survive until spring. Research has shown that there are larger numbers of breeding great tits after a winter rich in beech-mast than there were before. This may be due to the high survival of young from the summer before as well as both adults and young during the winter. There is a tendency, according to another report, for great tits to move in those years when the crop has been a poor one. There is no attempt to establish a direct connection between the beech-mast years and the breeding of the great tit, but only to show that the crop is a useful indicator of the general level of food abundance so that eruptive movements in birds can be linked with the rhythm of certain trees. Several tree species in Sweden seem to share the same rhythm as that of the beech. Bramblings tend to move more in the winter than the chaffinch in their quest for supplies of beech-mast; this explains why parties suddenly appear to exploit a food source and then move on. Sometimes quite large flocks can appear, but in Britain we do not see parties of 11 million bramblings like the flock which fed on the mast near Porrentruy in Switzerland in the winter of 1946–7 or the 72 million which roosted in 1950–1 near Thun. Although the brambling and chaffinch are rather similar in structure and feeding habits there are some differences. The brambling's bill is some 10% deeper and so presumably stronger and sharper than that of the chaffinch. Bramblings have a stronger preference for beech-mast and, unlike the chaffinch, will feed directly from the trees by hovering or reaching out from the twigs to grasp a seed.

Birds may use beechwoods for winter roosting. Wood pigeons are often common but I have never come across as large a flock as that described by W. H. Hudson in *Nature in Downland* which "could not have numbered less than two to three thousand birds". If there is some cover redwings may come in to roost and a roost in quite tall beech-trees has been reported. Finches, too, may find beech cover attractive for their roosts.

OTHER BROAD-LEAVED TREES

So far in this chapter we have been considering the most important of the broad-leaved species of tree that, in addition to being constituent species of woodland, are able to become dominant over areas of such size as to warrant their separate examination. There are some other species which deserve mention. The first of these is the sycamore which was first intro-duced some four centuries ago and now appears quite regularly in mixed woodlands. With a greyish-brown, smooth bark, coarsely-toothed five-lobed leaves and winged fruits the sycamore is a familiar tree and capable in good conditions of growing to a height of 90 ft. or more. It prefers deep, loamy soils and is widespread in northern England, Scotland and much of Ireland. Sycamores sometimes form small woods which appear as shelter belts in exposed coastal regions and in many parts of the north they can be found in groups around isolated farmsteads. The trees appear able to resist smoke and grow well in many towns and industrial areas. Pure sycamore woods tend to have little cover since their large leathery leaves lie in a slow-decaying mass on the woodland floor. I have many times passed through such a wood in a valley near Cruden Bay on the Aberdeen-shire coast; some of the trees are 45 ft. in height and the wood is 95% pure with only a few horse chestnuts and wych elms. The shrub layer is absent, but raspberry, celandines, ground ivy, *Pulmonaria* and various grasses form the field layer. In one corner of this wood there are usually well over a hundred rooks' nests. Chaffinches and blackbirds are the commonest birds so that the wood can be compared to Irish sessile oak and English,

PLATE 9. A mixed open-canopy broad-leaved wood. Epping Forest.

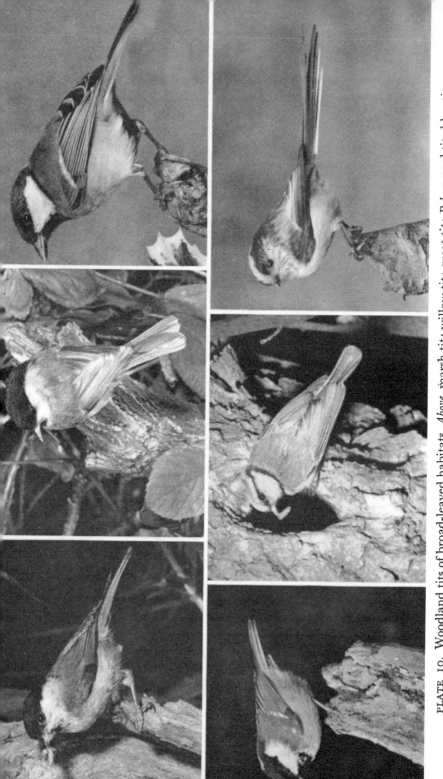

PLATE 10. Woodland tits of broad-leaved habitats. *Above*, marsh tit; willow tit; great tit; *Below*, coal tit; blue tit; long-tailed tit.

Scottish and Irish beechwoods. Hedgesparrows are present in small numbers and I have also found wrens, greenfinches, crows, pied wagtails, great tits and song thrushes. A sycamore grove that I visited in Sutherland had similar species but it held robins that had been missing from the more southerly wood. A sycamore/ashwood near Maas in Donegal had a large rookery and similar species of bird, but here I added two chiffchaffs. The sycamore woods on the South Downs appear rather similar in their avifauna. The sycamore plantations at Kergord near Weisdale in Shetland cover some 9 acres and the trees have grown to 45 ft. or so. Among the dominant sycamores are some larch and spruce with a few ashes, elders, rowans and whitebeams. Here rooks and wood pigeons have bred regularly with more exceptionally long-eared owls, blackcaps and song thrushes. In winter long-eared owls, yellowhammers, bramblings and goldcrests are frequent visitors. Great, blue and long-tailed tits will often feed in sycamores on their aphid resources, but the trees' total of herbivorous invertebrates is low when compared to those of the oaks. Marsh tits, treecreepers and goldcrests have been seen feeding in these trees, and blue tits come regularly in September, October, March and April to a sycamore near my home in north-west London. In August I also have visiting coal tits since the species does not breed in my area. Great tits are very scarce in the sycamores in north London. A pair of carrion crows at home also shows an annual preference for a sycamore to nest in, although there are equally tall and apparently suitable oaks, elms and poplars nearby.

Sweet chestnut, which avoids calcareous soils and casts a shade, produces woods rather like those of beech, but it is best known as a coppice crop. Horse chestnut sometimes appears in groves and may occasionally form nearly pure small woods. Box grows well on the North Downs, willows and aspens may appear in small groves and turkey oaks are spreading locally in Surrey and Oxfordshire. Hornbeams appear in the south-eastern oakwoods and in winter they often attract hawfinches.

MIXED BROAD-LEAVED WOODLANDS

Some woodland consociations are made up of tree communities dominated by several species which may be equally represented in the canopy, but on the whole these mixed woodlands are not common. Typical examples are those of ash, birch, wych elm and sallow which appear on hillsides with occasional bird-sown rowans. Such woods are often a stage in colonisation. Some mixed woods may have a few conifers and these can influence the numbers of coal tits and goldcrests to be found there. The firecrests breeding in the New Forest since 1961 are usually found in mature mixed woodland where conifers, especially spruce, are dominant, but in some of the breeding localities conifers are almost totally missing. Mixed woods can offer a range of habitat to those species of bird that are adaptable in their diet and feeding habits. We have already seen that the oak and beech are rich suppliers of invertebrate food while the ash and sycamore are poor. Sycamores also may attract tits, but great tits prefer caterpillars and aphids from oaks when there is a choice open to them. A mixed wood can provide a varied and rich diet.

I have been able to make counts in 14 mature mixed broad-leaved woods in the British Isles and the co-dominants were oak, beech, sycamore, ash, birch and wych elm. The most important bird species were chaffinch, blackbird, robin and wren. The willow warbler, great and blue tits, song and mistle thrushes rank high in the list although in Ireland the chiffchaff outnumbered the willow warbler. The total number of species was slightly higher than that for pure stands and included a greater variety of finches. In Scotland I had a good number of April and May records for redwings. Forty minutes that I spent on a transect of Tollymore Forest Park in Northern Ireland with fine mature specimens of beech and oak revealed 16 blackbirds, 12 chaffinches, 10 robins, 9 wrens, 4 mistle thrushes, great tits and goldcrests, 3 hedgesparrows, wood pigeons, long-tailed and blue tits, 2 chiffchaffs, coal tits and bullfinches and a single jay.

At this stage it is not possible to offer any firm conclusions about these woodlands whose composition can vary so much. What can be done is to compare the number of contacts per hour in the pure woods, both coniferous and broad-leaved, with those for mixed broad-leaved woods. If the average number of my contacts per hour for pure coniferous forest is given the value 1, then the number of contacts in pure broad-leaved woods of the five main species is represented by the figure 2 and the mixed broad-leaved woods by figure 3. Figures of 3 and 5 have been put forward for single species woods and mixed woodlands respectively in the lowland deciduous forests of Slovakia, and proportions of 1, 2 and 2.5 for coniferous, broad-leaved and mixed woods. The highest densities of birds in Europe and the United States – over a thousand per 100 acres – are generally in the mixed woodlands of the flood plains; good examples are the poplar/willow/ashwoods of the River Danube and the mixed broad-leaved woods in parts of eastern America. More comparative material is urgently needed so that firmer deductions can be made about the relative densities of birds in these different types of woodland.

Much of the broad-leaved woodland in Northern Ireland is of mixed species and there are few woods of pure oak or ash. This mixed woodland often appears as a belt, perhaps forty yards wide, along the edge of larger conifer plantations. Although I was not able to make counts I walked along one such strip in Narrow Water Forest near Newry in Co. Down. It was full of chiffchaffs, willow warblers, blackbirds, wrens, chaffinches, robins and goldfinches, and the shaded floor of this belt of trees was a mass of bluebells. There is a very fine mixed wood at Baronscourt which I was able to visit through the kindness of His Grace the Duke of Abercorn. This is composed of oaks, beeches and alders with some elder, holly, ash saplings and rhododendrons and a field layer of bramble, bluebells and ramsons. I walked for twenty-five minutes through this mixed wood and in that time recorded 30 chaffinches, 29 wood pigeons, 16 blackbirds, 14 chiffchaffs, 13 robins, wrens and pheasants, 9 willow warblers, 8 mistle thrushes, 5 song thrushes, 4 hedgesparrows and blue tits, 3 great tits, 2 greenfinches, stock doves and starlings and single goldcrest, treecreeper, goldfinch and wood warbler. There are similar woods at Ardnamona and Beltra and here I found the same dominant species, but I also added bullfinch, which was common in both places, spotted flycatcher, cuckoo and sparrowhawk. One of the features of Irish forestry is the development of young plantations of broad-leaved trees mostly in mixture with conifers but as those I visited at Port Glenone in Co. Antrim and Seskinore in Co. Tyrone were under twenty feet high I shall postpone a discussion about them until Chapter 10. Suffice it to say that the number of species present was lower than in a mature wood.

Many woods are made up of both broad-leaved and coniferous trees. Some are large like Parkhurst Forest in the Isle of Wight while others are little more than groves often near great houses and the result of private planting. Many have been taken over to form the nucleus of new State forests. Since their coniferous element is important I shall leave these mixed coniferous and broad-leaved woodlands until the end of the next chapter.

CHAPTER 8

THE BIRDS OF CONIFEROUS
WOODLAND

MOST people today recognise coniferous woodland by the serried ranks of introduced exotic trees that climb the contour lines and cover the hills with a carpet of dark green woodland; but coniferous forest is also a climatic climax type which occurs with birchwoods to the north of the broad-leaved summer forests. In Scandinavia the northern coniferous woods are dominated by spruce, but this is replaced farther north by birch and pine and then, at the polar limits, by birch alone. In the British Isles there are only three native species of conifer – the Scots pine, the yew and the juniper, which appears as a shrub and will be discussed in Chapter 10. Scots pine and birch have very similar requirements and are often found on the same soils but there are some differences in their bird-life. In the British Isles the Scots pine can occur in three forms: first, as the old native pine-forest still surviving in parts of the Scottish Highlands; second, as the naturalised woods of the heaths of southern England, and, third, as part of the extensive conifer plantations of the State forests and private plantings in the last hundred years. It is useful to consider these separately and in order, but before doing this we should take a closer look at the tree itself.

The Scots pine, which was originally called "fir", is a native of Europe from Russia west to the Iberian Peninsula and our native tree is a short-leaved endemic form. It has also been planted and flourishes from self-sown seed in many places. The Scots pine bears cones about two inches long on curved stalks while each scale on the cone has a central projection or knob which is without a point. The young tree tends to be pyramidal or cone-shaped with relatively short blue-green needles; these, except in the smallest seedlings, are set in pairs. As the tree matures, its lower branches die and the crown becomes flat or dome-shaped and where the trees grow in close formation the round-topped shape will be lost. The Scots pine develops a typical orange-red colour as the outer bark falls off and reveals the reddish shade underneath. Trunks of old mature pines often bear deep and irregular fissures and some of these trees grow to heights of from 60 to 100 ft.

Small patches of indigenous pine-forest still exist in the north and their survival from Boreal times is almost entirely due to their remoteness and the consequent difficulties of extracting their timber. The most important of these woods, often broken and rather scattered, occur in Rothiemurchus, Glenmore and Abernethy Forests in Inverness-shire, at Ballochbuie and in the Forest of Mar along Deeside, on the southern shore of Loch Rannoch in Perthshire, in Glen Affric, Glen Torridon and Glen Shieldaig, at Coille na Glas Leitir and in a few other isolated areas such as Loch Hourn and Glen Carron. I have been fortunate enough to visit all these pinewoods as well as smaller patches of woodland in the Highlands. There has been heavy felling in these areas and some of the woods are now so open that they really constitute not woodland but a heathland dominated by *Calluna* and *Vaccinium* with some trees. New plantations of alien conifers such as those in Glen Carron have replaced much of the old pine-forest. The Forestry Commission has fenced many of the pinewoods in Glen Affric, Glen Loy and elsewhere, and in the first area the Commission has set up a pine reserve in which planting will continue over a period of seventy years. Regeneration has often been absent or slight due to the effects of grazing and controlled moorland burning. The ground zone is often so deeply choked with *Calluna* and plant debris that seedlings have no chance to develop. In the western woods at Loch Maree and Glen Shieldaig as well as in the eastern woods some regeneration is taking place and the Nature Conservancy has fenced part of the woodland at Coille na Glas Leitir to help in its recovery. Many of these pinewoods are of the open type and some may reach quite far up the hillsides as they do in parts of the Cairngorms. There is well-grown pinewood in close canopy near Loch an Eilein where the trees grow from 70–90 ft. in height and the field layer consists almost entirely of *Calluna*, two species of *Vaccinium* and two mosses. Close canopy of this kind also occurs in Glenmore where the trees are less than twenty feet apart; some of the pines like those of the Black Wood of Rannoch are well over 200 years old. In many parts the trees grow more densely along the sides of burns.

These native pinewoods do not contain a wide range of plant species. Of the associated trees birch and rowan are frequent while alders and more rarely aspens appear along the burnsides. Holly can sometimes be found in some of the western woods. In the eastern forests juniper is common growing sometimes to heights of twenty feet or just forming a low shrub layer. The field layer is characteristically heathy with *Calluna* and *Erica* in the more open, less shaded places and the two *Vaccinia* (blaeberry and cowberry) growing under the trees. In this layer the typical plants are creeping lady's tresses, twayblade, wood anemone, various species of wintergreen and an Arctic relic – *Trientalis* or chickweed wintergreen, while more rarely it is possible to find the coralroot orchid and twinflower in the eastern Highlands. In many instances the pinewoods have a grassy ground zone which is similar to that of oak and birchwoods and the three tree species are known to have been intermixed in parts of the Highlands. In June the northern pinewoods are fresh with blaeberry and cowberry and the resinous scent of wood while the songs of chaffinches, willow warblers and wrens echo under the bottle-green canopies of the trees.

In Ireland the Scots pine is an indigenous species, but the native race appears to have become extinct and is now replaced by trees of foreign origin. Pines spread widely in Ireland in the warm period around 2000 B.C., but a subsequent rise in the rainfall led to the growth of blanket bog and the death of the trees. There is some evidence that the native pines survived in Ireland until the sixteenth century.

In the forests of Speyside I found the dominant birds in descending order of abundance were: chaffinch, willow warbler, wren, coal tit and gold-crest. Dr. Yapp's list for Rothiemurchus and Glenmore, based on counts over nine and a half hours, gave the same order for the first two species, but the third and fourth places went to tree pipit and coal tit. In my list the tree pipit came sixth followed by redstart, crested tit, robin and meadow pipit. A count of singing males made in early June in 130 acres of the old forest revealed 52 willow warblers, 16 chaffinches, 9 robins, 7 redstarts and 7 coal tits (Perry 1948), but chaffinch song was beginning to fade at this time and the results of this survey therefore differ from mine. The wren seems to have increased, as it has done elsewhere, over the last decade. My most recent counts also show that the crested tit which often suffers badly in severe weather was more common than perhaps is generally believed. In the wood at Coille na Glas Leitir in the west the main species in order of abundance are willow warbler, chaffinch, wren, robin and tree pipit; another survey gives willow warbler followed by chaffinch with robin and tree pipit equal third. Here, too, the wren has increased in recent years. The crested tit does not occur in this western pinewood. There are similarities between the dominant birds of these indigenous pinewoods and those of the Scottish birch and sessile oakwoods but the overall density of birds in the former is fairly low compared to that in the broad-leaved woods. Certain species in the pine-forest are unique to this habitat while others can be found in other environments without Scots pine. Before discussing the more adaptable birds it might be valuable to look first at the species peculiar to the ancient pinewoods.

After the osprey, the bird that probably draws more ornithologists to the valley of the River Spey is the attractive and lively crested tit. This species is a true lover of coniferous woodland and is based in Strathspey, but in recent years it has spread to plantations well away from the old forest. More than twenty years ago there were reports of crested tits only seven miles from Portsoy on the Moray Firth. Now it has spread to coastal and upland plantations in Moray, Nairn and Banff almost to the Aberdeenshire border, as well as northwards in Ross and it has also been reported in east Sutherland. A count that I made lasting ninety minutes in June 1963 in the forest of Rothiemurchus between Loch Morlich and Glen Einich covered over four miles and produced a total of ten crested tits; a similar count in late April 1967 on the same route revealed eleven birds. Six contacts per hour seems to be a good average figure. D. Nethersole-Thompson estimated a pre-war population of about 120–125 pairs in the 208 square miles east of the Rivers Feshie and Spey. In the old forest in a good season there might be some 11 to 15 pairs per 1,000 acres and the whole Scottish population may be in the region of 300 to 400 pairs. The crested tit spends a good deal of time searching the pine trunks for insects and their larvae. Its altitudinal range stretches from near sea-level to about 1,600 ft. or so. Crested tits seem more common in Rothiemurchus and Glenmore than they are through the Ryvoan Pass in Abernethy where my contacts are about 4 per hour. The bird prefers the older part of the forest and most of the nests are built in pines although alder and birch are sometimes used as well. It can be very confiding, and my first ever sound recording of this species was made by following a male near Loch Morlich with a hand microphone from tree to tree. The very restricted range raises several interesting points. The crested tit is a very unadaptable bird and on the Continent is almost exclusively confined to well-developed coniferous forest. I have watched crested tits in the pine-forests of Switzerland and in Spain, where they share their habitat with the great spotted cuckoo. These birds may appear occasionally in mountain beechwoods, but then only near the limit of the coniferous zone, and I have recorded them in birch in the Scottish Highlands. This failure to embrace broad-leaved woods does not lend much support to the theory that the crested tit once depended on the presence of oak in the native pinewoods. Why also is this species of tit missing from the pinewoods of northern and western Scotland? Campbell (1958) has written about the natural history of the crested tit whose survival would seem to depend on the way in which its forest habitat can be preserved.

Another special bird of the pines is the crossbill. I have often watched these birds in Speyside, not least in July when the thirsty family parties come to drink at the gutters and water-butts of isolated houses in the forest. Sometimes they appear in Aviemore itself. The numbers vary from year to year and their fluctuations seem to be related to the Scots pine seed crop. Although crossbills will feed on larch and spruce they are very dependent on the Scots pine whose seeding seems to take up a cyclic form rather like that of the beech. The pine cycle seems to run more on a three or four year basis and the crossbills travel around in search of the enhanced supplies of food. It is certainly rare for large numbers to nest in the same area in two consecutive years. The crossbill is also a bird of artificial plantations and has a wide distribution in eastern Scotland. It has been reported from Coille na Glas Leitir, too, where I have collected cones that have been worked in the typical crossbill way, but I have never seen any birds. Crossbills have a very distinctive flight call, but they often feed high in the trees and may be missed. I wonder how many crossbills would have gone unreported had they not called as they flew over! There is no more delightful sight than that of a party of crossbills hanging upside down like diminutive parrots and extracting the seeds with their twisted asymmetrical bills and horny tongues. Sometimes parties of Continental birds come over after the failure of the pine crop following on a successful breeding season. These foreigners pass through the pinewoods but do not seem to affect the local birds; the immigrants are smaller billed and more catholic in their diet.

The third species which is generally associated with coniferous woods is the siskin. It nests in Scots pines, spruces and larches often at a considerable height above the ground and frequently out towards the tip of a branch. Siskins breed regularly in the east from Perthshire northwards and in some parts of the western Highlands as well. Since the siskin is very much an arboreal bird delighting in the high canopy it may also be overlooked unless its extravagant flight song draws attention to its presence. The varied chatters and liquid notes blend into a lively and charming song. Siskins are spread thinly through Speyside reaching to heights of about 1,500 ft. on the hills. They sing less after the middle of June and in July I have often come across small family parties feeding on seeds by the roadsides as well as in birch groves and hedges. It is then that the plumage of the male can really be studied for it is one of the delights of the old pine forests.

The capercaillie is not rigidly confined to woods of pine but does seem to need coniferous woodland of some kind. This handsome game-bird came eighth in my list of relative abundance for the Speyside forests. I found it rather more common in Abernethy than in Glenmore with a contact every twenty minutes or so. There is a communal display ground of this bird in Abernethy where twenty males collect to strut up and down and disport themselves rather like blackcock. The typical habitat of the capercaillie has been described as "hillsides with woods of mature Scots pine". The woods should not be too dense and plenty of *Calluna* and *Vaccinium* is desirable in the field layer. Capercaillies can be found in the eastern Highlands from the Upper Forth to the Moray Firth and they are commonest in the larger river valleys. The diet varies with the season, but in summer birds will feed on the male flowers of Scots pine, larch shoots, berries, fruit, seeds and corn while invertebrates may also be taken. They are large birds but can be easily overlooked on the ground or even when sitting in trees until they are flushed out by one's passage through the wood; they then launch themselves with much crashing and wing-beating to rocket off and weave their way between the trees with alternate glides and bursts of wing-flapping. In Speyside they go up to 1,600 ft. on the hillslopes. The original stock of British birds became extinct about 1770, but birds were imported from Sweden by Lord Breadalbane and released near Aberfeldy in 1837. They established themselves there and aided by further releases have spread to other areas. Of the other game-birds black grouse can be seen in small numbers and I have also recorded pheasants in the Inverness-shire pinewoods.

A bird of the freshwater lochs and rivers which uses the old pine-forest for breeding is the osprey. Once ospreys bred widely in the Highlands of Scotland, but their extermination was almost complete by the end of the last century. Many of the ospreys still breeding in Scandinavia pass through the British Isles in spring and autumn and can sometimes be seen fishing in undisturbed lakes while on their migration. I have described in another volume how I watched three ospreys at Minsmere on the Suffolk coast in May 1952; then in May 1963 I saw another fishing the same pool, and this time I had with me a BBC cameraman, Geoffrey Mulligan, who was able to film three dives, of which the last was successful. In the early or mid-1950s the osprey came back to the Highlands to breed – the exact date is still uncertain. In 1963 cameraman Charles Lagus and I made a film of the second pair of ospreys nesting that year in Scotland and in one sequence in which the male bird brought a fish it was possible to see that he carried a ring on his left leg – presumably Scandinavian in origin. In 1967 three pairs of ospreys nested and two raised broods of young. The osprey builds now in tall Scots pines, but past eyries were constructed on ruined castles and towers like those at Loch an Eilein or Loch Assynt or on rocky stacks in the middle of lochs. In Sweden most of the nests are in pines.

The osprey has returned, but the other raptors of the old pine-forest were not so fortunate. The goshawk was present as a breeding species in the nineteenth century but finally succumbed to persecution. The kite did not last much longer – one was seen in 1902 near a mature Scots pine plantation by Ballinluig. There is an interesting photograph of a kite's nest in a pine in Seton Gordon's *The Charm of the Hills*. When pine-forest covered much of the Highlands the golden eagle used pines for breeding much more widely than it does now; today most of the nests are built on rocky ledges and buttresses. I have seen several tree eyries, but none quite as large as the pine tree nest which was believed to be four feet across and seventeen feet in depth. Eagles were thought to have been using this eyrie for at least sixty years. Recently the breeding success of eagles has fallen sharply (see the Systematic List). The hobby used to frequent the Black Wood of Rannoch until about 1900. Today the commonest birds of prey in the pinewoods are almost certainly the owls. The long-eared owl I have seen in Abernethy and it occurs elsewhere in Speyside. The tawny owl is quite common and in 1957 I heard four calling at once in Rothiemurchus. Buzzards can sometimes be seen soaring on broad pinions over the forests where they take rabbits, hares and young capercaillies. The buzzard had an RA of 1 in Speyside but it did not qualify for the list in the western pinewoods. The sparrowhawk has decreased a great deal in recent years, but the kestrel just holds its own. What a contrast to the umbrella pine-woods of south-western Spain where I found that perhaps one bird in three was a raptor of some kind!

The goldcrest was sixth in my list for Speyside and I found it less common in the western pine forests. It often nests in the juniper bushes under the pines, but feeds and sings in the canopies of the trees. The goldcrest was, in fact, the only bird I found in May at over 1,800 ft. in the low pines growing between Creag Mhigeachaidh and Geal-chàrn above the River Feshie. The redstart – another canopy bird – came seventh in my Inverness-shire list, but it was scarcer in the west. Among the warblers the whitethroat is said to occur in the ancient pinewoods, but so far it has eluded me.

Among the tits the coal tit outnumbers the crested, and I have found that a contact rate for the former of about 10 an hour is usual. I have records of the blue tit in Speyside as well as in Coille na Glas Leitir where there were also great and long-tailed tits which tend to be winter visitors in the eastern woods. Treecreepers are very thinly scattered through all the woods and great spotted woodpeckers may breed on the lower ground in Strathspey. Crows had an RA of 2 and there are some records of jackdaws in the Spey woods. The jay is not present, but it seems to be increasing in the neighbourhood of Rannoch. The mistle thrush I have heard singing in some of the most remote parts of the Rothiemurchus Forest, but the rare blackbird and song thrush come to the clearings only. The robin is not so scarce in the eastern and western woods, but, like the hedgesparrow, which nests in the juniper, is much less frequent than in the broad-leaved ones. Whinchats breed in the more open parts of the forest and ring ousels and wheatears sometimes enter the fringes. Bullfinches are regular in small numbers and redpolls nest in both western and eastern pinewoods. Yellowhammers are found to be rather scarce. The cuckoo is often quite common and I have heard it in Glen Feshie in some years among the pines as insistently as anywhere in Britain. The nightjar is sadly reduced in numbers and very rare. Woodcock nest in many places and in June I have seen birds "roding" at dusk between the great pines or over the canopies, calling as they go, while the roe deer graze unconcernedly beneath. Wood pigeons are common but not as abundant as they are in many coniferous plantations. In the east the spotted flycatcher is a regular inhabitant of the old forest, unlike the pied flycatcher which, although it has bred occasionally in Speyside in recent years, has shown no real liking for the pines of the Caledonian Forest. In northern Europe at higher latitudes than those of Scotland the pied flycatcher breeds in many mixed and coniferous forests "preferably with tall pine trees". Many meadow pipits can be heard in their ecstatic song flights in the forest clearings while grey wagtails flip their tails on the stones and banks of many woodland burns. The black-headed gull now forages regularly through the woods and its harsh scream is typically heard in many parts of the forest area.

The summer forests have their bird-songs but the overall density of birds is low and one can walk for quite long periods without hearing any bird other than a chaffinch. Yet there are often surprises for the walker in these pine-forests – a solitary redwing in song in May, an osprey beating low over the canopies of the pines, a great northern diver passing high overhead, a goosander pair flying along the river or a goldeneye displaying on one of the lochs. In June some years ago I walked round the shore of Loch Morlich under a low, forbidding sky with gusts of rain and high wind. Six blackcock rose quietly from a belt of pines, followed almost at once by three clumsy capercaillies. Crested tits and goldcrests called from the canopies and, despite the gale, willow warblers, meadow pipits, chaffinches and redstarts all managed to sing brief snatches of song. I heard a greenshank giving its deep anxiety calls and when I returned to the old boathouse I found two chaffinches sitting on my camp bed. The following day the wind had gone and the still water of the loch reflected the mountains above. The air was full of bird-song and I could hear the trout rising to the fly.

In late summer and autumn the old pine-forests become increasingly deserted – chaffinches, song thrushes, siskins, wood pigeons and other species leave for the winter months. Through the Pass of Ryvoan in Glenmore come streams of October migrants – grey lag geese, redwings, fieldfares, skylarks and meadow pipits all moving south from the Moray Firth. On 10th October, 1953, I found hundreds of redwings and scores of fieldfares in the Forest of Glenmore. At this time of the year I have watched parties of crossbills, up to thirty strong, feeding on the cones and small parties of crested tits, coal tits and goldcrests foraging in the canopies and near a little burn several woodcock, dippers and a single kingfisher. Some of the capercaillies and black grouse tend to leave the forest in late summer, but they return again in the autumn. The capercaillie in winter in north-east Scotland feeds largely on Scots pine and shifts about mid-November from forests with little or no pine to those with a fair amount. It is possible to find crows, kestrels, wrens, bullfinches and a few robins in mid-winter, but the wrens seem to become scarcer in January and February. The winter pine-forest is thus regularly and widely inhabited by only eight species of bird. It is possible to walk through the pinewoods for a long time in winter before finding a small band of tits and goldcrests, a treecreeper and a great spotted woodpecker or two. Peregrines sometimes sweep through the forest and I have seen golden eagles soaring high above the trees or ravens tumbling and croaking wildly over the canopies of the pines.

On the sands and gravels of southern England pines are often the dominant trees. Here they were widely planted in the eighteenth and nineteenth centuries and have spread and colonised the adjoining heathlands; there are good examples in Surrey near Oxshott, Esher and Leith Hill. Birch often appears with the pine and sometimes there are small beech, oak and sweet chestnut in the shrub layer. Purple moor grass and *Erica* are common. There is considerable shade with only 17% full illumination in many of these woods. On the heaths where the trees are well spaced and contain an element of birch the willow warbler is abundant; among the pines coal tit, goldcrest and treecreeper appear regularly. The wood warbler is an uncommon breeding species. Crossbills are often visitors in the winter after irruptions; there were up to 25 in the area of Oxshott and Esher in March and April 1959. Flocks of up to sixty, apparently all adults, were reported in late spring near Oxshott in 1963. Many of these latter birds remained for much of the year and a nest, built at Wisley, may well have been of the large-billed species – the parrot crossbill.

Yew is the other native British coniferous tree and it appears as a constituent member of some of our woods, as scrub and sometimes as the dominant tree of woodlands in the south of England, the Wye Valley and in southern Ireland. The yew is widespread and rather local in dry scrub and in oakwoods such as those of the Welsh Marches, in ashwoods on the Permian limestone and in western England, and in beechwoods on the South Downs. It seldom forms pure woods, but when it does it grows especially on slopes running south-west and north-east around the heads of chalk valleys, often with a beechwood to protect the yew and allow it to grow properly. Juniper and hawthorn scrub may also act as nurses to young yew trees and the former is very effective in this role. In a mature wood trees grow to as much as forty feet in height with ridged and fluted columnar trunks. With their flat spreading branches yews cast such a dense shade all the year round that the suppression of all other plants is often complete; occasionally whitebeam, holly and hawthorn may penetrate the yew-wood canopy. Shrub and field layers are usually missing and mosses are rather scarce. Yew can grow in many kinds of soil but does best on limestone and chalk. Some yews may have survived because grazing animals have destroyed the edible and competing trees and shrubs. Yews are also very long-lived trees.

Some of the finest yew-woods in England, and, in J. E. Lousley's opinion, "perhaps in the whole of Europe", can be found at Butser Hill, Box Hill and on the hills east of the Medway. Perhaps yew, like the beech, is a climax vegetation over small areas, particularly on slopes too steep for beech. Lists of relative abundance for the two woods at Kingley Vale and Butser Hill for late May have been published. The former wood consists of dense patches of yew running as a strip along a grassy hillside. Butser Hill has two patches of nearly pure yew in close canopy with a few ashes, hollies and hawthorns and no vegetation below. Jay, willow warbler, chiffchaff, hedgesparrow and turtle dove were found at Kingley Vale, but not at Butser Hill; this may be attributed to the scrubby nature of the woodland. Butser Hill, on the other hand, provided a few records of linnet, green woodpecker and tawny owl. The wood pigeon was the commonest bird followed by chaffinch, blackbird, robin, goldcrest, wren, magpie, bullfinch and great tit. There were also single records of yellow-hammer in each wood. The song thrush was missing while warblers and tits were almost entirely absent. Goldcrests which came fifth in the list are often associated with yews when they appear in broad-leaved woodland or as isolated trees in hedgerows, gardens and churchyards. Yew also forms nearly pure woodland at Box Hill on the North Downs and here in summer I have found many wood pigeons and a few blackbirds, goldcrests and wrens. The only Irish yew-wood that I have visited is in the limestone area around the Lakes of Killarney. On the Muckross Demesne yew grows in limestone pavement made up of blocks lying obliquely on their sides. The canopy is often closed but I found holly, rowan, hazel and strawberry-tree growing in a few places; the rocks were covered in moss and hart's-tongue grew in the crevices. My visit took place in late May and a sixteen minute count in the wood revealed 5 wood pigeons (the commonest birds also in the yew-woods on the North Downs and at Kingley Vale), 3 robins, 2 chaffinches, 2 goldcrests and single blue tit and chiffchaff.

In Chapter 3 we have already seen how reafforestation is going on at an ever-increasing rate in the British Isles. Today both the Forestry Commission and private landowners are chiefly planting conifers often on moorland where, in time, the wheatears, skylarks and meadow pipits are replaced by warblers and finches and thrushes. The succession in conifer plantations and the consequent changes in the bird-life will be the subject of Chapter 10, since we are dealing here with trees of 26 ft. or more in height. The Forestry Commission has used conifers for several reasons and the trees most regularly planted in the Commission's forests are the Norway and Sitka spruces, the Scots and Corsican pines, the lodgepole pine, the European and Japanese larches and the Douglas fir. The distribution in the British Isles of these species of tree has been given in Chapter 3. The past policy of the Commission has been to plant these conifers in homogeneous blocks for eventual clear felling. Commercially useful crops can be obtained in this way in a comparatively short time; the plantations are often divided into compartments, the trees have been planted in lines and have developed long straight stems, few branches and close canopies which result in the greatest amount of useful wood. These plantations effectively suppress all the vegetation below and also prevent regeneration of the trees. Under the dense shade of the trees carpets of needles form which produce an acid ground and later perhaps a mor humus. A natural wood contains trees of different ages and types. The plantations, however, are even-aged monocultures with trees too sound to have natural holes, and the absence of shrub and field layers limits the numbers of birds to be found in them. Only in the clearings where trees have fallen or been felled and along the rides are there any appreciable concentrations of birds. The addition of nestboxes can increase the population of some species.

Conifers have different soil requirements and the pines are often planted on sandy, heathery ridges resembling those of their native habitat, while spruces favour the flushed soils at the lower levels. Scots pine plantations tend to be in the warmer, drier areas of the east and south including north-east Scotland, Northumberland, East Anglia and parts of the English Midlands. Not a great deal has been planted in Ireland in comparison with other coniferous trees. It is in the mature Scots pine plantations of north-east Scotland that there is the closest resemblance to the fauna of the old Caledonian Forest. From the figures in Table 20 it can be seen that the four commonest species are chaffinch, coal tit, goldcrest and wren in that order; this can be compared, by the way, to the results obtained for East Anglian mature Scots pine plantations in which the most abundant species were chaffinch, coal tit, wren and goldcrest in descending order. In the closed Scottish plantations there are also siskins, redpolls, crossbills and great spotted woodpeckers. I have also recorded capercaillie, occasional black grouse, long-eared owl and, much more rarely, sparrowhawk, and crested tit. Mistle thrushes and hedgesparrows also occur, and in the more open Scottish woods I have found blackbirds, tree pipits, redstarts, spotted flycatchers and even nightjars. If there is some shrub layer a few warblers such as chiffchaffs, willow warblers and whitethroats may come in as well. The woodcock can be found in the wetter parts of these plantations. Nevertheless, plantations do differ from native forests and I have had only two-thirds the number of contacts per hour in the plantations compared to the numbers in the best part of the old native forest. My figures for one Irish wood are interesting in that they show the blackbird second in the list – a position it occupies in the lists for Irish sessile oak, and British and Irish beech. The chiffchaff was present in the Irish list, the crossbills were my only record for Ireland and the wood pigeon was absent. Crossbills were present in Co. Wicklow during the breeding season in 1963 and 1964, but birds have not been proved to nest in Ireland in recent years. A close-canopy plantation in Glen Poer in Co. Waterford included a little holly, beech, rowan and birch with a field layer of bracken, bramble, ivy and bluebells; it was full of the songs of goldcrests, blackbirds, chaffinches, coal tits, robins and wrens.

The Forestry Commission plantations of Thetford Chase in the Breckland of East Anglia extend over 50,000 acres and consist largely of Scots and Corsican pine. The Corsican pine has been extensively planted in the English lowlands, in eastern Scotland and in parts of Wales. It has characteristic grey-green twisted needles, one-sided or oblique cones and a greyish, never red bark. The most extensive plantings are at Thetford and in the Culbin Forest on the Moray Firth. It is difficult to establish in Ireland, but there are stands in Co. Wexford, mixed with lodgepole pine, as well as pure stands in the Vale of Clara and in Co. Wicklow. A count in a Corsican pine plantation near the Comeragh Mountains made in May showed the commonest birds to be robins, mistle thrushes, treecreepers and chaffinches; there were smaller numbers of song thrushes, blackbirds and jays.

In Thetford Chase, about 50 species of bird were recorded during a five-year study. In the mature pine plantations nine species bred regularly – pheasant, wood pigeon, coal tit, willow tit, long-tailed tit, treecreeper, wren, goldcrest and chaffinch. If nestboxes were supplied, the great and blue tits came as well. In the breeding season the coal tit was the commonest species; in Britain they are more numerous in conifers than in broad-leaved woods. In winter there are eleven species to be found regularly in the Breckland pine plantations – pheasant, wood pigeon, great tit, blue tit, coal tit, willow tit and long-tailed tit, treecreeper, wren, goldfinch and chaffinch; of these pheasant, wood pigeon and chaffinch use the plantations for roosting. In late summer and autumn, but more rarely in the winter, crows, jays, magpies, mistle and song thrushes, blackbirds, robins and green woodpeckers may also appear while chaffinches, goldfinches and bramblings come into the plantations in March and April to eat the pine seeds. Barn owls have used pine plantations in Northumberland for roosting, and ravens the mature plantations near the Dovey estuary for the same purpose.

In the plantations, compared with the numbers of tits in broad-leaved forests, great tits were only one-fiftieth as numerous, blue tits one-third and long-tailed tits two-thirds. Conversely, willow tits were twice as numerous in the pines and coal tits ten times. Although the goldcrests were about equally well distributed in plantations of both species of pine it was clear that blue, coal and willow tits much preferred the Scots pine while the long-tailed tit showed a slight preference. A suggestion of interest to foresters has been made that a greater variety of trees in the plantations would provide additional food in winter for those birds best able to control or at least stabilise insect populations. Tits in winter take an appreciable proportion of the invertebrate population and one can calculate that each bird examines 1,100 trees every day and needs 5 mg. or the equivalent of 24 average-sized insects every minute of the day to keep itself alive! Coal and willow tits store food in autumn, but this forms only a small part of their diet. In mid-winter coal tits have to feed for about 90% of a nine-hour day. On the principle that the smaller the species the longer the time required each day for feeding, goldcrests must feed for nearly 100% of the time.

I have spent many hours in the Breckland pine plantations and during the early part of 1953 made recordings of the crossbill. I found that the songs of tits, goldcrests and chaffinches enlivened my long waits for a chance to make a recording of the very rare full song of the crossbill. Crows were common and woodcock went "roding" through the pines sometimes in the middle of the morning. Blackbirds, robins and woodlarks helped to make this spot, although not as rich as a broad-leaved wood,

PLATE 11. Alderwoods. *Above*, grazed wood in Inverness-shire; *below*, alder carr in April with sallows.

PLATE 12. *Above*, open birchwood in Strathspey, Inverness-shire; *below*, willow warbler an abundant bird of the birchwoods usually breeding on the ground.

W.B.

TABLE 20. *The Relative Abundance of Bird Species in 35 Mature Conifer and Mixed Plantations*

Scots Pine		Norway Spruce	Sitka Spruce	Mixed Pine/Spruce/Larch	Mixed Coniferous/Deciduous	
12 Plantations N. & E. Scotland	*1 Plantation Ireland*	*6 Plantations Scotland*	*4 Plantations Scotland*	*4 Plantations Scotland*	*3 Plantations Ireland*	*5 Plantations Ireland*
Chaffinch 28	Goldcrest 11	Wood Pigeon 38	Wood Pigeon 47	Chaffinch 21	Chaffinch 21	Wood Pigeon 16
Coal Tit 17	Blackbird 7	Chaffinch 18	Chaffinch 21	Wren 21	Mistle Thrush 19	Chaffinch 12
Goldcrest 8	Chaffinch 6	Goldcrest 15	Wren 7	Robin 7	Willow Warbler 17	Blackbird 11
Wren 6	Coal Tit 6	Wren 6	Goldcrest 6	Goldcrest 6	Blackbird 14	Robin 10
Siskin 5	Wren 5	Crow 5	Greenfinch 5	Willow Warbler 4	Bullfinch 5	Wren 8
Wood Pigeon 5	Robin 5	Coal Tit 4	Blackbird 4	Coal Tit 3	Goldcrest 4	Goldcrest 8
Crossbill 5	Chiffchaff 4	Blackbird 3	Heron 3	Wood Pigeon 2	Coal Tit 4	Chiffchaff 8
Pheasant 4	Hedgesparrow 3	Greenfinch 1	Pheasant 2	Hedgesparrow 2	Wren 4	Willow Warbler 7
Robin 3	Treecreeper 3	Great Tit 1	Coal Tit 1	Song Thrush 2	Hedgesparrow 3	Coal Tit 3
Redpoll 3	Song Thrush 1	Hedgesparrow 1	Robin 1	Crow 2	Song Thrush 3	Song Thrush 3
Great Spotted Woodpecker 2			Crow 1	Redpoll 1	Robin 1	Blue Tit 2
			Linnet 1	Blackbird 1	Chiffchaff 1	Spotted Flycatcher 2

M

certainly delightful since it is along the edge of the pinewoods that many of these song-birds can be found.

During the summer there are certain differences in the size and kind of invertebrate food given to nestlings of great, blue and coal tits just as there are differences in an oakwood. In the Corsican pine plantations of Breckland the coal tits, like the great and blue tits, lay their clutches on average some 5 days later than in Scots pine even when in adjacent plots. The insect population of the Corsican pine appears to be lower than that of the Scots pine. It is also of interest to note that the birds do not take caterpillars at random, for the geometrid larvae brought to nestlings in May 1955 and 1956 were respectively 14% and 24% longer and 43% and 62% heavier than larvae present in the pine needles at the time. In 1956 the coal tits over a period of six weeks took some 4,800 *Evetria* larvae from each plot of just under $2\frac{1}{2}$ acres, or roughly a hectare. This was thought to be one-fifth of the available population of larvae, but was an exceptional figure and the proportion was sometimes as low as 3%.

The lodgepole pine from western North America has been widely planted on the poorer soils and windswept lands of the British Isles – in Wales, north-west England, west Scotland and throughout much of Ireland. The needles are mid-green in colour and overlap a great deal while the bark is a brownish-black which tends to break up into small squarish sections. The cone is shaped like an egg and each scale is armed with a diagnostic sharp prickle. The bird faunas of these plantations seem fairly similar to those of Corsican pines, but the bird population is often rather small. A visit I made to the plantation on Allt Mhor in the Cairngorms revealed only one wood pigeon. On the Hampshire and Dorset borders, in Devon and at Mullaghmore there are also plantings of the maritime pine from the Mediterranean. It has a deeply-grooved, reddish bark and big pointed cones. It has been used to reclaim large areas of the Landes in France where its resin is gathered for commercial use. In the Landes, eight transects were made, revealing that the commonest species were chaffinch, Bonelli's warbler, swallow, long-tailed tit, blackbird and greenfinch. In the British Isles the trees cover a much smaller area than those at Arcachon and Biscarosse.

The spruces are well known, largely because one of them – the Norway spruce – is the familiar Christmas tree. The Norway spruce grows well on most woodland soils. It has a grey-brown bark with a slight reddish tinge and soft needles of a mid-green colour. The other common spruce is the Sitka from British Columbia which flourishes on peaty soils with a high rainfall and in the most exposed situations. It does not compete well with heather. The Sitka spruce can be recognised by its bluish-green foliage and hard, sharp-pointed needles; in 1963 this species accounted for one-third of all the conifer planting. It is apparent from Table 20 that the wood pigeon dominates the spruce plantations in Scotland with chaffinch, goldcrest, and wren solidly in the next three places. In woods of both tree species the wood pigeon and chaffinch make up more than half of all the bird contacts. In the spruce forests of Slovakia, the most dominant species were seen to be coal tit, chaffinch and song thrush. Also in these central European spruce-forests were serin, nutcracker and turtle dove and, in the late summer, nuthatches as well. In the Norway spruce plantations of Kielder Forest in the Borders – strange and moss-covered, with a green gloomy glow over the dead branches piled up beneath the trees – I found the goldcrest to be the commonest bird. At Craigvinean and in the Forest of Deer, north of the Border, the wood pigeon was the most abundant species. In Durris Forest in both belts of spruce the chaffinch was the commonest bird. The Sitka spruce at Kielder was dominated by coal tits and goldcrests in about equal abundance, but on the whole the coal tits showed a preference for Norway spruce. The blackbird, greenfinch and crow all occurred regularly in both kinds of plantation and there were also heron, pheasant, robin, great, blue and long-tailed tits, treecreeper, mistle thrush, song thrush, linnet and yellowhammer. Siskins have been seen over the Sitka spruce plantations on central Dartmoor and some have bred. Magpies are not uncommon in Aberdeenshire and jays are spreading north from Angus and Kincardine. Herons nest in Sitka spruce in the Forest of Deer and up to 56 cormorants have been recorded roosting in mature Sitka spruce in Dumfriesshire. Starlings also roost in spruce plantations during the winter and their weight can do a great deal of damage to the trees. I have seen one roost in Norfolk where the guano was eighteen inches deep, and recently great injury has been caused to Port Laoise Forest in Ireland.

Larches are unlike other conifers in that they are deciduous and, as each spring returns, they don a fresh green foliage that darkens as the summer wears on. The European larch from central Europe has twigs of a pale buff colour and needles of a beautiful green, but to the forester it has been a rather disappointing tree. The Japanese larch, which is more adaptable and faster-growing, has red-brown twigs and needles that start the summer bluish-green in colour and then turn to orange in the autumn. The hybrid larch was the result of a cross between the female flowers of a Japanese larch and the male flowers of the European species. This took place at Dunkeld in Perthshire at the beginning of the present century and the hybrid grows faster and in less favourable environments than either of its parents. I have been to many larch plantations in Inverness-shire in the summer and here the chaffinch is the most abundant bird. There are also coal tits, goldcrests, wrens, robins, siskins, redpolls and crossbills. All three of the common thrushes appear with willow warblers and spotted flycatchers. In the mature plantations of the hybrid larch at Dunkeld I found the capercaillie to be very common and the wood pigeon abundant. I have one record of a reed bunting in a larchwood near Scourie in Sutherland. In Ireland larches are sometimes grown in pure stands or mixed with Scots pine and beech; chaffinches and mistle thrushes are common in these Irish woods.

I have also shown in Table 20 the results of my counts in 7 plantations of mixed pine, spruce and larch in Scotland and Ireland. The wood pigeon is missing from the Irish list and demoted in the Scottish from its position in pure spruce plantations. The willow warbler appears well up on both lists and in Ireland the mistle thrush is the second most abundant species. The bullfinch with an RA of 8 ranks high in the Irish list and this artificial habitat seems to be favoured by this species. The mixed plantations of Scotland have a bird community similar to that of the Scots pine. There are plantations of other coniferous trees as well, but on a smaller scale. Douglas fir has been planted widely on fairly good ground and there are good stands in several places – the New Forest and the Forest of Dean, for example. In 1953 Douglas fir plantations made up 2% of all our high forest. Chaffinches, goldcrests and coal tits were the commonest species in the big fir plantations. The Western Hemlock (*Tsuga*) occurs on a small but increasing scale and there are well grown stands in Bedgebury Forest in Kent and at Killarney, Castlecaldwell and Rostrevor in Ireland. I made a transect count lasting a quarter of an hour in a large western hemlock plantation at Castlecaldwell; this was close-canopied with no field layer, but bramble, bluebell, violet and wood sorrel grew along the rides. Here there were 17 goldcrests, 3 chaffinches, 2 chiffchaffs and a single mistle thrush, song thrush and blackbird. The third species of tree is the western Red Cedar (*Thuja*) which has well-developed trees in Friston Forest in Sussex and there are Irish plantations at Ballykilcavan, Stradbally, Lackendarragh and Avondale. I have not been able to assess fully the bird-life of the red cedar plantations, but it does not seem very different from that of the western hemlock.

One of the features of Ireland is the presence of mixed coniferous and broad-leaved woods, often with the former dominant. The young plantations of pine, spruce and larch mixed with ash, birch, beech, rowan and sycamore will be discussed in Chapter 10. There are mature woods, however, for example at Pomeroy, of larch, pine and spruce mixed with beech, birch and oak; here *Vaccinium* grows under the pine and wood sorrel under the beech. At Castlecaldwell spruce grows with oak, beech and ash with a shrub layer of beech saplings and holly and a field layer of ivy, bramble, bluebell and ramsons. Another wood in the same forest is made up of Scots pine and oak with only bramble growing under the trees. At Dunfanaghy in Co. Donegal I found spruce, sycamore and ash as co-dominants in a wood. There were mature sessile oaks growing with spruce at Pontoon in Co. Mayo and here the shrub layer was composed of beech and birch. In the Vale of Aherlow Norway spruce and Scots pine growing to 60 ft. or more were mixed with beech rising to 25 ft. and oak to about 15 ft. in height. In the last column in Table 20 I have shown the relative abundance for five of these mixed woods. Other species not qualifying for the list included redpoll, hedgesparrow, jackdaw, crow, great and long-tailed tits, blackcap, garden warbler, sedge warbler, treecreeper, siskin, bullfinch, starling, cuckoo, heron and pheasant. In the table the robin, chiffchaff and wood pigeon are seen to be more frequent than in solely coniferous plantations, but the willow warbler is rather less common and the mistle thrush considerably so. Although the sample was not a large one, I located ten more species in the mixed plantations and I had $2\frac{1}{2}$ times more contacts per hour there than in the purely coniferous stands.

An English example of a mixed forest where the coniferous plantings are more extensive than the broad-leaved woods is Parkhurst Forest which covers some 1,100 acres of the Isle of Wight. Of the total area about 350 acres consist of oak over a hundred years old and there are 50 acres of sweet chestnut coppice and other managed hardwoods, over 200 acres of mature Scots and Corsican pine and over 400 acres of post-war conifer planting. I spent nearly three hours in the Forest on 19th March, 1967. The first half-hour was largely occupied with crossing the south-facing oakwood, the second an area of more coniferous woodland and the third half-hour the pinewood. In that second, or mid-section, of the Forest, I had 20% more contacts in the half-hour than in the first and nearly twice as many as in the pinewood. Goldcrests and coal tits occurred in all types of woodland, but were more common in the conifers. The mistle thrush appeared only where there was a small area of beech. The great spotted and the green woodpeckers appeared in the proportion 3 : 2. The jay was more frequent in the coniferous woodland. At that time of the year the wren was the most abundant bird, being more than twice as common as the chaffinch, six times as common as the robin and eight times as frequent as the blackbird which was very shy here. The commonest tit was the coal tit followed by blue, great, long-tailed and marsh tits. Treecreepers were regular, wood pigeons rather scarce and there was a party of siskins as well.

In Britain our native mixed woods would primarily have been those of Scots pine, oak, alder and birch, but these would not have had the character of the transitional belt in Canada where pines and broad-leaved trees grow to the south of the pure stands of pines, spruces and firs which define the northern limit of the trees. In the British Isles the most remote mixed woods I have visited are those in the grounds of Stornoway Castle in the Isle of Lewis. Here I have observed rook, raven, hooded crow, starling, wood pigeon, collared dove, blackbird, song thrush, robin, wren, blue tit, treecreeper, whitethroat, chiffchaff, willow warbler, goldcrest, grey wagtail and tree sparrow. The rooks used to fly out over the sea from Stornoway. The Hebridean wrens whose songs I recorded for the first time used to sing from extremely high perches and their especially fine deliveries were characteristic of these woods.

CHAPTER 9

WOODLAND BIRD-SONG

A T an earlier point in this book I described the always varied and beautiful choruses of bird-song encountered during my walks through the woods. One of my special interests has been that of bird language and through my sound recording work I have been able to pursue this study in a way that has been granted to very few ornithologists. Some of this work I have described elsewhere, and several fascinating works on the subject have appeared in recent years. It is not my intention to go over the same ground, but a book on woodland birds should include something about bird-song. Further, I would like to say something about recent research and to refer to certain personal observations that may be of interest.

The terms song and singing are now generally used to include all the different and complex sounds uttered by most of the smaller birds. It is often not possible to separate song, as we understand its meaning, from call-notes and it may be that some "songs" are really only a run of call-notes. Among many species of bird there is a quite highly-developed sound language, but this depends not, as it may do in the human species, on conceptual processes, but much more on an innate ability to make the sounds and react to them through inborn mechanisms. We do know, however, that some birds can increase their inherited complement of sounds by means of trial and error learning.

To regard bird sounds as language is convenient, of course, but there are certain difficulties where calls and song are close in form or function. The physiologist tells us that song is controlled by the sex hormones and is invaluable in the setting up and defence of a territory. Singing replaces actual battle between birds and is also useful in advertisement and in establishing and maintaining the bond between the members of a pair. A song, of course, can have various results. Its effect may be to attract, intimidate, stimulate or even to be disregarded according to "whether the receptor is of the same or opposite sex or a bird in or not in the appropriate condition" (Armstrong 1963). Call-notes tend to be used in more everyday situations and without a sexual basis; they occur within the framework of such activities as finding food, keeping in touch and giving warning of possible danger and in the presence of a ground or aerial predator. Bird-calls may have the function of territorial warnings, of aggression, of distress, of general and more specialised alarms and may accompany feeding, flocking, flying and even be expressive of pleasure. The blackbird is reckoned to have seven call-notes besides song and subsong, and other estimates for separate calls include twelve for the nuthatch, fourteen for the whitethroat, thirteen for the wren and twenty-one for the chaffinch. The call-notes of birds do seem to have a genetic origin and the responses to them are also innate. It seems that fifteen is the approximate limit for the number of pieces of information that can be conveyed by calls.

So much for calls, but what is bird-song? It cannot really be defined, but it tends for us to be a pleasing experience. Its functions may range from a proclamation of territorial rights to aggression, courtship and simple displacement activity. The affinity between songs and calls is often close in the case of birds with simple songs which make use of alarm or flight calls, such as the meadow pipit and skylark. In some species song, like the calls, is largely innate, while species like the chaffinch, which learns much of its song, may also use call-notes in the stages towards the development of its full song.

We have already seen that territorial song can be a substitute for actual fighting and it must therefore be far-carrying, unmistakable and maintained over quite long periods to be effective. For these reasons it is often distinctive and noticeable. Nearly all woodland birds have fairly clear, loud songs. There is evidence that some species, including the great tit, may employ certain calls with almost the same function as that of territorial song. The loudness and far-carrying quality of territorial song are very apparent to any visitor to a lowland forest during the May dawn chorus.

The second characteristic of territorial song is its specific distinctness and there are many birds in which the song is a certain guide to both the species and the genus, suggesting that the song is innate. A song with good specific characters has generally a recognisable length of song-burst and pattern of notes, whereas the generic character depends more on the quality of the notes. If one has a good ear without "blank" patches one can usually separate species from species and this is true of even as big a sub-family as the warblers. At a first hearing there may be some likeness between the songs of the garden warbler and the blackcap, but there are usually good characteristics which enable them to be distinguished from each other. The birds themselves are obviously better at it than we are. There are sometimes aberrant birds, including a Staffordshire garden warbler that sang an extraordinary rattling phrase, but it never collected a mate. The chiffchaff and willow warbler so close to each other in plumage, but so different in song must have diverged a long time ago from a common ancestor. It is now clear that there can be variation within the recognisable limits of some specific songs which serves to distinguish one local community of birds from another. Where a species like the blue tit of mainland Europe has to live alongside several other members of the same genus, the songs tend to remain fairly stereotyped and constant, but the island blue tit on Tenerife is the only tit species there and its voice is complex and its calls bewildering. The chaffinch inherits part of its song, but in the wild young birds acquire parts of their songs from adults they hear in their first summer, while the detailed polishing up takes place in the young birds' first breeding season. In this way local "dialects" can be developed and carried on, especially if the young birds have a tendency to return to the areas in which they were bred. Chaffinches quite often have more than one song and males in full flow may switch from one version to another. One recording I made reveals a chaffinch singing in competition with a yellowhammer and using a song ending with the phrase "ter-seeoo". Suddenly it changes to a higher-pitched song with an ending "tissireeOO". Both song types had obviously been learned from neighbours. Singing can arouse members of the same species to perform, and I have many times heard a great tit begin to sing after a quiet period and this has quickly set off others within earshot. It has been suggested that among pied flycatchers birds sing more in areas where they are thinly scattered than in more densely-populated regions where alarm calls are used in preference to song. Yet when the blackbird population at Dollis Hill was at its greatest density, after the cold weather of 1962–3 had broken down the territorial patterns, the blackbird songs were of unparalleled brilliance. Conversely when there was only one pair of stock doves in my local park song was very rare and spasmodic.

The third characteristic of territorial song is persistence, and this is valuable in telling the neighbourhood that a male is in residence, on guard and ready to defend his patch, or to accept a mate, or both. Unmated birds tend to sing more regularly and for longer periods than mated males. A song thrush in Middlesex without a mate used to sing for 80% of his day compared with only 30% for his nearest mated neighbour.

In brief, territorial song serves to identify the singer as to kind, sex, uniqueness and position as well as helping to reveal its motivation and the nature and location of its environment. In many species there is also a softer courtship song which often lacks the more rigid form of the louder type of song. The male of such species as garden warbler and blackcap uses a song to attract the female to a previously prepared nest-foundation, while the male great tit employs a song to entice his mate into a nest cavity. Song can thus draw and indeed hold the members of a pair together. Some songs are uttered during the building of nests by birds like the wren. A few territorial birds which do not have loud, well-developed territorial songs like the carrion crow, jackdaw and jay resort to warbled songs during incubation. Wrens will sing a whispered song when brooding, feeding young, leading the young from the nest and even going to roost. In view of this it is difficult to define song in any easy terms and it will depend upon the analysis of many more types of song from different species.

Birds may also be heard singing a soft inward type of song which is generally called subsong. This is usually quieter with longer bursts of notes and a lower fundamental frequency. It is common in the late winter among some young birds and among birds with a low but rising sex hormone rate. It is frequent in thrushes and blackbirds and it has been described as the "raw material" out of which the full song develops. Dr. Thorpe has published sound spectrograms from recordings I made in Britain of the subsongs of blackbird, mistle thrush, redwing, crossbill, Scottish crossbill and hedgesparrow. Some woodland birds such as haw-finch and bullfinch have quiet songs which have less of a territorial significance and are useful in establishing and keeping the pair-bond. Their songs are much more like the subsong of the chaffinch. The developmental basis of bird-songs has yet to be worked out for many species, but valuable work has already been done on the chaffinch and on the blackbird. And to what extent do birds just sing for pleasure? Some birds, including the starling and hedgesparrow, sing for much of the year. Most, however, lose their vigour or cease to sing during the post-breeding moult. There may also be a resumption of song in the autumn and this occurs often among robins, which hold autumn territories, as well as song thrushes, great, blue and marsh tits; black grouse often display at their "leks" but in a belligerent rather than amorous way. Migrating birds such as chiffchaffs and willow warblers almost invariably sing when they pass through the area of Dollis Hill in the autumn. There are also instances of females singing, but these I shall discuss under the individual species described later in the chapter.

Mimicry is a fascinating aspect of bird-song and so far has not been very fully explored. It is believed that some thirty species of British bird are mimics, but some of these are only occasional while others include imitations only in their subsongs. On the other hand, the starling and the jay are good mimics. It seems that among the best mimics the songs have lost some of their territorial significance, but the inclusion of imitations may help to underline the particular character of an individual's song. I have recognised many individual starlings by the excellence of their imitations and it would seem not unlikely that other birds could do this. It would be interesting to know from the detailed study of natural mimicry in, for example, the jay, what advantages may accrue to the species through its use.

The extent to which birds may sing depends not only on their internal states and their psychological preparedness but also to some extent on environmental factors. I have often noticed that blackbirds start singing earlier at Dollis Hill than in the rural areas north of London and many of my earliest records of blackbird song have come from Inner London and other towns. Here it is possible that the higher temperatures due to the buildings as well as noise and light may all stimulate earlier activities including song. Certainly the temperature in London is higher than in the surrounding areas. It is not uncommon to hear blackbirds singing in London and the suburbs in December if the weather is warm. It is often the sudden rise in temperature that produces the most dramatic effects rather than the actual temperature reached.

I have already mentioned the pleasure that the dawn chorus of early summer can give to the bird-watcher. One of the delights is to list the order in which species first begin to sing and to calculate by how much each species anticipates the dawn. The order in which different species sing remains pretty constant over the years. Among the woodland birds blackbird, song thrush, carrion crow and wood pigeon come at the top of the list followed in approximate order by robin, redstart, pheasant, garden warbler, blackcap, mistle thrush, willow warbler, wren, great tit, chiffchaff, great spotted and green woodpeckers, blue tit, nuthatch, chaffinch, whitethroat, treecreeper. Insect- and invertebrate-eating birds tend to rise early while the grain-eaters, apart from the wood pigeons, tend to stir much later. The times at which birds rise are related to their feeding behaviour and the amount of light; the early-rising redstart and robin have larger eyes than the late-rising house sparrow. A dusk chorus count I made in Badby Wood early one June showed that the order of cessation of *song* for the last twelve species to sing was as follows: chiffchaff, wren, chaffinch, blackcap, garden warbler, blackbird, willow warbler, wood pigeon, cuckoo, song thrush, robin. Of course, some species like blackbird and redstart were heard to *call* after their final songs.

In 1951 I directed an operation in which BBC Mobile Recording engineers recorded the dawn chorus at various points throughout the British Isles on the same June morning. In early June, if the morning is a clear one, the light of dawn strikes Britain first at Caithness and moves south-south-west across the country, reaching the Midlands, Cheshire and Northern Ireland at about the same time. Then it sweeps on to southern

Ireland, Wales and south-west England. The passage of the dawn from the extreme north of Scotland to Land's End takes about an hour and ten minutes. In the same way the earliest bird-songs move across the British Isles, but in advance of the dawn light. On the morning of the experiment the time taken to pass from the Cairngorms to Dorset, which represented the two recording points farthest apart, was forty-three minutes – a somewhat faster speed than that of the bird-songs which preceded it. A full account of this recording experiment has been given elsewhere. Figure 17 shows the relationship between the song of the blackbird and the spread of dawn on that June morning.

So far I have reviewed the background to the songs of birds very broadly so that I can now describe in more detail individual performances that can be heard in the woodlands of the British Isles. We shall find that many of the singers that use the concealment of the foliage in the woods also have continuous or well-maintained songs. These birds can advertise themselves well without being conspicuous to predators. Chaffinches, wrens and hedgesparrows can often be seen singing from exposed perches, and so their songs are discontinuous which enables them to listen and look out for predators. In the case of the chaffinch, the bird can also listen to other performers and enrich its own deliveries. Blackbirds and jays that frequent cover also have loud, far-carrying alarm notes, and bullfinches, which like dense shrub growth and overgrown hedges, can be heard continuously calling to each other so that contact is maintained. Some birds sing while foraging like the chiffchaff and the goldcrest, while others like the song thrush rarely do.

Before we take a closer look at the true song-birds of the woodlands there are several non-passerine forest birds which have displays and song substitutes rather than true songs. In April and May in Scotland the cock capercaillie produces a conspicuous and remarkable courtship display. This can be delivered from the ground, a boulder or a tree. The capercaillie's "song" is made up of three parts: the first consists of a series of "Tuk-up, tuk-up" notes which increase in speed, the second is a thumping pop and the third resembles an inspired breath. The whole performance lasts about five seconds. During this display the tail is fanned and held upright, the head elevated and the wings often flapped very noisily. It occurs quite regularly at dawn and sometimes continues until late in the morning. So noisy and conspicuous a display is possible because the capercaillie is a match for most predators. The blackcock on its "lek" or display ground in a clearing in the conifer forest has an elaborate display, too, accompanied by a dove-like cooing "roo-koo", a plaintive note and an explosive, hissing "Ker-showw" (with the last syllable sounding as in

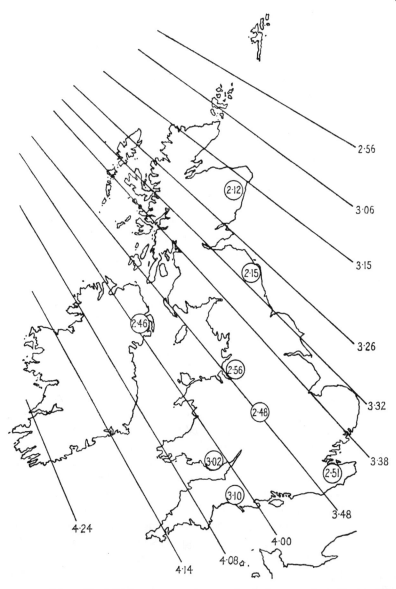

FIG. 17. First blackbird songs and spread of dawn, 5 June 1951. The diagonal lines represent the dawn and times are given G.M.T. The figures in the circles are the times, also G.M.T., of the first blackbird songs in eight localities.

"cow"). After the displays mating takes place. A familiar component of many woodland choruses is the crowing spring display of the pheasant – a double "Korrk-kok" – often but not invariably followed by a short whirr of wing-flapping which does not carry as far as the vocal call. Thunder and explosions will often set pheasants crowing and I can remember many occasions during the last war when air raids and distant naval gunfire brought on a fine chorus.

Only one member of the group of wading birds qualifies for inclusion in this chapter – the woodcock. This bird starts its slow, owl-like display flight, known as "roding", in the dusk and at dawn. The bird beats its way over the tree canopy or even between the trunks calling "Quarrnk – quarrnk" and following this amphibian-like call with a high-pitched "Tit-ick". This is one of the few forest birds with a display flight that might render it vulnerable to predators. I have seen woodcock "roding" in the late morning in Breckland in bright sunlight. The birds are reported to begin their flights five minutes later each evening in spite of the weather. In the British Isles "roding" usually takes place between early March and July; there are a few isolated records of it in autumn and winter.

Of the three species of woodland pigeon, the best known song is that of the wood pigeon. It is territorial in function and rhythmic in character, consisting of a phrase of generally five notes – "Coo-coo, coo-roo-coo" – repeated several times. The third and last notes may be double or the last only, and the sequence might end with a single, abrupt "Coo". Nearly 8,000 songs were examined by Huxley and Brown (1953) and as a result the description of the typical song was corrected from that of *The Handbook of British Birds* to the one I have just given. The bowing display of a male to an unmated female consists of a special "Co-roo-co-co-co-coo" suggestive of a dove-cote pigeon. The nest call is a groaning "Ooh-ooh" of which the first note is low and strained and the second louder and more vehement. Territorial song is regular from February to September, less frequent in January and more exceptional from October to the end of the year. In a special display the wood pigeon claps its wings following a rising flight and this serves to advertise its territory. This display in woodland and around the isolated trees in London squares was confined to the defended territory. The stock dove has a musical "Ooo-er-oo" for a song with usually a duration of some 8 seconds for its 18 to 20 song phrases. It is not a loud song, but it fits the woodland scene well and is persistent enough to be distinguished from the other songs. The rhythm is that of the phrase "to hurry up". The turtle dove has the poorest song of the three but "the blowing hawthorns of May, the drowsy days of June at once rise to the mind when that odd, placid noise is heard" (Robertson 1954). The song is a purring, caressing "Roorr-rr-ror-rr-rrr". Phrases consist of from two to five notes while each song may have from three to twelve phrases. The display note is a speeded-up version of the ordinary song. One recording I have listened to reveals very clearly an echo-note consisting of a quiet background "Aarnk" immediately before the first syllable or between the first and second of each trisyllabic phrase. It can be heard in a recording included in the first British sound-guide. The song period of the turtle dove lasts from May to July.

Perhaps the best known of British bird-calls is that of the cuckoo with its often two-syllabled note. I have recorded a bird in Kent with a descending trisyllabic call. There may be variations in pitch and rhythm, but the call remains distinctive. Males may often "cuckoo" in flight. The call of the female is a shrill, bubbling "Whit-it-it-it-it". There is some evidence that the same bird can both bubble and cuckoo. Both sexes also have a hoarse "Kwow-wow-wow".

In parkland barn owls can often be heard hissing and snoring and little owls plaintively fluting, but the two woodland owls are the tawny and the long-eared. The former lives in dense woodland and is consequently noisy, with a number of far-carrying calls. The song is a two- or three-syllabled "Hoo-hoo" followed by a long quavering "Hooooooo". This hooting is regular from mid-January to May and June with a fair resumption in October and the winter months indicating that territories are being held. The birds regulate their activities according to the length of the dark hours; the mean time after sunset in August and September for the first call was 9 minutes compared with 35 to 46 minutes after sunset in December and January. Tawny owls often hoot by day; when being mobbed by small birds they may use a very strangulated kind of hoot. The typical call is a shrill "Ke-wick" although the tawny owl is capable of a wide range of calls and hoots. The long-eared owl of the conifer woods has a long drawn out cooing moan with notes spaced at a few second intervals and carrying quite well in still conditions. Its song period is from January to April and it is especially vocal in February.

The nightjar finds concealment for singing in the darkness of the night and sits crouched low along the length of a branch. The song is a vibrant churring, rising and falling – "Kirrrrrrrrrrr-oo-kirrrrrrrrrr-oo-kirrrrrrrrrr". By slowing down a recording of the nightjar I discovered that there might be as many as 1,900 notes used per minute and the song can be maintained for five minutes or more. The flight call is "Croo-eek" and the alarm a fast "Crick-crick-crick". The male also claps his wings over his back to call the female. The song period lasts from May to late July, but I have heard song in early August on several occasions.

A mechanical drumming is the characteristic song of the great spotted woodpecker which is essentially an arboreal and not a ground-feeding bird. The male deals with its bill a series of blows from ten to twenty or so in number on a suitable sounding-board in a tree. A drum of 11 beats lasts half a second while one of 19 is just under three-quarters of a second in length. Drumming can take place in every month of the year but it is at its peak in spring and early summer and falls off after pairing. The call is a sharp "quet" which may be rapidly repeated in courtship and territorial activity. There is also a hissing kind of subsong. The lesser spotted woodpecker has a somewhat faster, higher pitched and longer drum. The call is a high "Pee-pee-pee" with some affinities to the call of the wryneck. The green woodpecker has a shrill laughing call of some five to fourteen notes often but not always of the same pitch – "Kew-kew-kew". The notes come in groups and I have timed nine notes at 1.4 seconds and thirteen at 2 seconds. This gaily-coloured woodpecker does not drum very often and is more of a ground feeder; it seems to have diverged from the other species in both plumage and habit. The wryneck has a harsh, ringing series of two-syllabled calls – "Keyu-keyu-keyu", up to twenty-six in number and lasting then about five seconds. Calling takes place between April and mid-June. The wryneck when disturbed at the nest can also hiss like a snake.

So far I have been considering only the non-passerine denizens of the woods. It is, of course, the passerine birds that make up the greater part of the woodland bird community. Here we begin with one of the loveliest of all songs – that of the woodlark. It is a sweet, sustained warbling composed of phrases of from eight to twelve notes with changes rung on some three or four phrases, sometimes more. One hundred and eight distinct motifs in eight minutes of continuous song from one woodlark have been recognised and only five or six of these were repeated. The notes are produced in a leisurely cadence with many diminuendos of wistful beauty. The song can be sustained for long periods, even up to ninety minutes. It may be delivered from a tree, from the ground or in a song-flight of wide spirals ending in a slow veer earthwards and a final drop. The song has great charm and especially in the dark. Birds may begin to sing in February and continue until June with a fall in the summer and a resumption in the autumn. The call note is a characteristic musical and cheerful "Tillooeet".

The six members of the crow family which can be found in wooded areas are all generally recognised by harsh croaking, cawing, chattering and explosive notes. The raven has deep croaks and clucks, the carrion and hooded crows harsh and sometimes querulous caws, the rook soft caws,

PLATE 13. Ground-nesting birds of woodland. *Above*, nightjar yawning; a bird of the tree-heath ecotone; *below*, woodcock settling on nest — a bird of open, damp woods.

PLATE 14. Ashwoods. *Above*, interior of mature wood, Ravensdale, with rich shrub and field layer; *below*, interior of most northerly ashwood in Britain, Rassal National Nature Reserve, Wester Ross.

the jackdaw chatters and "chaks", the magpie rattles and the jay raucous screams and mewings. Yet the raven and the crows have a rare kind of warbled song often associated with incubation; the rook with its more than thirty calls may also attempt a rudimentary starling-like kind of singing (*The Handbook*). The song of the jackdaw is quiet and bubbling but I have only heard it twice, both times in the Midlands, and I did not find any evidence of mimicry. The magpie has a subsong which has been compared to the warblings of blackcap and garden warbler, and many of its calls have been analysed. The jay has a crooning, gurgling "song" and here both sexes may be imitative showing a distinct preference for tawny owls, magpies, crows and herons.

The tiny acrobatic tits are often very widely distributed in some parts of the British Isles and their voices are an important part of the woodland bird songs of both winter and summer. The largest common tit is the great tit and its typical "Teecher-teecher-teecher" song, like the sound of a man pumping up a bicycle tyre, is one of the promises in January of a spring that may still be far away. A classic study of the very varied vocabulary of the great tit revealed at least forty distinguishable utterances from a single individual who constantly extended his vocabulary "by adoption from his neighbours and by personal improvisation" (Gompertz 1961). Great tits may sometimes acquire the notes of other tit species and I was once completely deceived by a great tit's rendering of a nuthatch's call. On the other hand the song of the blue tit, unlike the double or treble note of the great tit, consists of a high-pitched "Tsee-tsee-tsee-tsee-ch-ch-churr" with a burred ending. From many records I find that the average length is just under one second and there are from ten to thirty-two songs each minute. The great tit's song period is from December or January to June with a revival in September and October but birds at Dollis Hill tend to sing earlier and later than birds in the country. The blue tit sings mainly from February to early June and spasmodically in all the other months. The coal tit has a song which is sometimes superficially like that of the great tit but it is typically the repetition of a double note – "IF-he, IF-he", "Tcher-wee, tcher-wee" and so on but the notes are less strident, thinner and faster than those of the great tit. The song is often given from high up in a conifer while the bird is foraging for food. It is this song which announces the presence of passing birds at Dollis Hill in March, April and August. Coal tits sing from January to June with a resumption from August to September and occasionally in the remaining months as well.

The marsh tit and the willow tit are often confused but their voices are valuable in separating them, both for the two bird species and ornithologists. The marsh tit has a distinctive loud "pitch-ou" note which the willow tit does not possess and a loud, ringing finch-like song of medium pitch. There are some seven to ten notes in the song and I have heard up to sixteen songs in a minute. Song generally starts in mid-January and goes on into May with a peak in February and March. The willow tit has a rarer song than that of the marsh and this consists of a series of loud and melancholy notes from three to six in number. It is much slower than the song of the marsh tit and recalls the piping of the wood warbler or the nightingale. The song when it occurs generally does so between January and late May. The long-tailed tit also has a rare musical and rippling song made up of its call-notes, and this I have only heard in April.

The crested tit comes last because of its rather restricted distribution. Its most familiar call is a low trilled "Ch-ch-ch-ch-churr" which is used both as a contact and an alarm note. There is also an exceedingly rare liquid utterance which I have still not been fortunate enough to hear.

The nuthatch and the treecreeper are both birds which live by searching the trunks and branches of trees for food and it is convenient to discuss them together. The nuthatch has a wide vocabulary, and twelve call-notes and three types of song have been listed. The most familiar songs are the rapidly repeated "Tui-tui-tui-tui" at a rate of two notes per second, a long trilling "Pee-pee-pee-pee" at a speed of eight to the second and a repeated "Kwit-kwit" in groups of from two to five with varying pitch and interval. Care needs to be taken not to confuse this species with wryneck, lesser spotted woodpecker, kestrel, hobby and great tit which have calls of a similar type. The nuthatch can be heard particularly from January to late May, and more occasionally in September and December. The treecreeper's territorial song is composed of from three to five thin, high-pitched single notes followed by a sibilant flourish – "Tsee-tsee-tsee-tsee-tsissi-tsee-pee". It lasts about two seconds and eight songs a minute is a good average. It might be confused with the song of the goldcrest, but this tends to start with double notes. The songs are often given as the bird searches the tree for food and occasionally even in flight; they are most common from March to May. There is a hesitant subsong but I have not yet been able to hear it clearly or to record it.

A monograph in this present series by Armstrong has dealt most comprehensively with the behaviour of the wren, and Chapter 5 of that work provides a detailed discussion of its vocabulary. The territorial song is loud and dramatic and is made up of high-pitched phrases about five seconds in length with a trill near the end of each phrase. It was found that only 6 songs out of 4,500 were of more than fifteen seconds duration. Singing sometimes takes place at night and the female has been known to sing a whispered song quite commonly and a full song very exceptionally. At Dollis Hill wrens sing in every month of the year, but most strongly from February to July.

We come now to the group consisting of five species of thrush – mistle thrush, song thrush, blackbird, redwing and fieldfare. The mistle thrush has a loud, wild song with no great variety and a repetition of short phrases – "Tee-aw," "Tee-aw," "Tee-taw-tee-awtee" and so on. There are usually from four to seven notes in each phrase which lasts from one to three seconds. Songs may flow out at a rate of from fourteen to twenty-one per minute. Each phrase is clear right to the end and, although it bears some resemblance to those of the blackbird, lacks the rather scratchy, indeterminate ending. Imitations are sometimes included in the song. The bird often sings in windy weather when it lives up to its popular name of Stormcock. The subsong is rather like an imperfectly formed full song. When sound spectographs were made of recordings of a mistle thrush singing both territorial song and subsong in Kent in March, 1954, it was clear that the subsong included harsh, impure notes with a wide range of pitch and many rambling phrases. This subsong is just audible at eighteen feet and I have heard it from December to March; the full song lasts from December to early June and the mistle thrush is an early nester. The territorial song of the song thrush, compared to that of the mistle thrush, is higher in pitch with short phrases of greater variety and with more vivacity and clearer enunciation. It is the many clear repetitions that make the song so distinctive, but the component phrases can be combined in different ways. One song thrush was heard giving only two repeats in eighty-five phrases. The song can be heard in most months, but the bird is often silent in August and September; such persistent song is characteristic of isomorphic species such as the wren, robin and song thrush. Imitations of the call-notes and song phrases of other species do occur and I have noted the following: song of blackbird, nightingale and great tit as well as calls of blackbird, chaffinch, jay, lapwing, mallard, curlew, stone curlew and redshank; other observers have noted mimicry of the blackbird and of whitethroat, snipe, redshank, oystercatcher and curlew. Song is occasionally heard at night. The bird often chooses high and conspicuous song posts but a bird in 1967 sang full song on a boulder on a bare moor in Sutherland; in Ireland in the same year song thrushes often sang in deep cover quite close to the ground. The subsong is a low robin-like warbling, rather sweet and often with a curious twittering quality.

The finest song of all the British thrushes belongs to the blackbird with its beautiful pure fluty notes and effortless delivery. Its only weak point is an occasional scratchy and rather poor ending. It is utterly in keeping with a summer woodland glade. From more than five hundred timings I have found that phrases last from two to an exceptional eight and a half seconds with from nine to fifteen phrases a minute. The output of song depends on the stage in the breeding cycle, the weather and situation. The birds at Dollis Hill come into song earlier than those at Oxford and in the country. I have heard birds in London singing even from mid-December to January; of course London enjoys the highest summer isotherm of anywhere in the British Isles. The typical song begins in January or February, increases during incubation and decreases at the time of the hatch, remaining then at a low but constant level; it may also be heard on warm days in the autumn. Young males may produce subdued songs in the autumn and song from a female blackbird has been reported. The subsong is a quiet continuous singing, sweet and character-istic, sometimes halting, sometimes flowing and often imitative, and not audible for more than a few feet. It is often given on the ground or in fairly dense cover. I have records of subsong from September to March, but it has been heard in August. Blackbirds sometimes imitate other species and I recorded a male in the grounds of Crowland Abbey in May, 1963, giving many repeated single phrases and notes like those of a song thrush. An outstanding observation is that of two to five or six blackbirds in Essex mimicking human whistles. There are a few records of birds sing-ing at night.

The redwing is better known for its call, but in Staffordshire in December, 1951, I heard a bird give a typical territorial song at dusk – a wheezy, conversational and warbler-like song in phrases of three seconds or so followed by pauses of several seconds. The notes were fast and fairly elaborate. It has been recorded in November and, of course, with regular breeding taking place in Scotland the song is worth listening for. I have rendered it phonetically "Tchurri-tchurri-tchurri-tchurri-titeetit-it-it-it". The first notes are clear and fluty and the ending is reminiscent of some of the blackbird's curiously weak terminal flourishes. Subsong, on the other hand, with its bubbling and gay twittering notes occurs in March and April in many places and these may be interwoven with the richer, warbled notes given at intervals from ten to thirty seconds; this pre-departure subsong is of a different character from that of the winter roosts. The fieldfare is best known in Britain for its harsh, chacking flight calls, but I have heard in spring on Holy Island a feeble, warbled subsong which is a quiet version of the rather poor song often given in flight above the breeding ground.

It is convenient to group the next three singers – redstart, nightingale and robin – together. The redstart is not a common bird and it is always delightful to hear its song whether it be high among the pedunculate oaks of a Midland wood, the sessile oaks of Co. Wicklow, the pollarded hornbeams of Epping Forest or the Scots pines of the old Caledonian Forest. The song is a mechanical but pleasant run of warbled notes with a weak ending – "a promise never performed" (Hudson 1909). The song lasts from one to two and a half seconds and there are usually from six to nine songs a minute, generally from a high song post. A good performer is well worth listening to. The redstart is in full song from mid-April to mid-June. On three occasions a hen was heard singing softly a version like the typical song of the cock. The redstart is also strongly imitative and John Buxton noted mimicry of willow warbler, chiffchaff, lesser whitethroat, robin, treecreeper, serin, chaffinch, white wagtail, great tit, nightingale, song thrush, nuthatch and wryneck. The nightingale has a familiar and remarkable song with outstanding qualities – "the beautiful, pure rounded tone; the mellow deep notes and the clear high notes; the crescendos and diminuendos; the clear musical intervals; the speed and virtuosity of the first notes with the' slowness and pathos of the sustained notes, and the highly artistic alternation of the two" (North and Simms 1958). In English woodlands the song is usually given from dense cover whereas in the south of France nightingales often sing from rooftops and telegraph poles. The song period is short – from mid-April to mid-June – and most of the birds will be heard singing south of a line from the Humber to the Mersey. The song is associated with the hours of darkness, but daylight songs are regular although sometimes submerged by the diurnal woodland chorus. It was found that one singer was quiet for only one and a quarter hours in the twenty-four. According to *The Handbook* "genuine imitations occasionally occur", but I have not yet separated any myself. Despite its close relationship to the nightingale the robin has a song with a sweet-sharp quality containing warbled phrases of long, clear notes and various runs and trills. There is also an autumn song beginning in late August which is thinner and more melancholy than the spring song; autumn territories are taken up and defended as well. The song period is a long one and July is the only month in which song is infrequent. The female defends a territory for part of the year and sings as well. The robin has an innate capacity to learn its parent's song. Song may take place at night and in 1967 I listened to a robin singing near Stanmore at 2.25 a.m. under a sodium street light. Robins may also sing without any artificial light. The subsong is a low, sweet introspective warbling with many high notes and is often used in display.

There are seven species of warbler which can be regarded as regular woodland birds and these add greatly to the attraction of the woodlands.

We have already seen that garden warbler and blackcap often overlap, but the blackcap's song – a pure rich warble with clean, musical intervals – is slower, less even and less uniform than the corresponding utterance of the garden warbler. The low, warbling subsong of the blackcap is somewhat like the full song of the garden warbler, but I find it coarser and more wavy in pattern. In full voice the latter bird has a softer, more sustained outpouring which does not carry so far and is more clarinet-like; it may sometimes include imitations. The blackcap is more mimetic. Males of both species have nest-invitation songs to guide a potential mate to the rudimentary nest already constructed. The garden warbler sings from cover while the blackcap often takes up song posts in tall trees where it gives voice as it feeds. The former species sings from late April to early July and the latter from early April to early July. When a single pair of blackcaps nested at Dollis Hill song was very erratic, but from 1955–6 when a pair of willow warblers was present there were some imitations of the other species. The following species were listed as having been mimicked by the blackcap: nightingale, garden warbler, starling, linnet, treecreeper, great and long-tailed tits, sedge warbler, whitethroat, mistle thrush, song thrush, blackbird and redstart, and also nuthatch. The song of a female blackcap has been described as "a rich warble" in short phrases of two or three seconds each.

Both species of whitethroat may appear in or close to woodland although their preference is for more open, dry and bushy places. The common species has a very lively short warble of fast notes, but with a few longer ones inserted, in short phrases. The variations in pitch may span an octave. The songs last from one to four seconds, occasionally to nine or even fifteen. A rapid opening phrase "Che-che worra che-wi" is typical. The song may be given from a perch or in a song flight and a rate of six to twelve songs a minute is a good average. The subsong is a quiet inward warbling with an occasional rattle like the full song of the lesser whitethroat. The lesser's often starts with a warble followed by a much louder series of rattling notes – "Chicker-chicker-chicker", in bursts of from ten to twelve and lasting from $1\frac{1}{2}$ to 2 seconds. It is given in thick cover, usually tall hedges and sometimes along a woodland edge; there is no vertical song flight. Very occasionally a common whitethroat may have a rattle identical to that of the lesser added to its full song.

The closely related Phylloscopid warblers – willow warbler, chiffchaff and wood warbler – often cause confusion by their plumages, but their songs are fortunately very distinctive. The abundant willow warbler has a short, silvery, liquid cadence constantly repeated every few seconds. An average of 150 timings showed some nine to the minute. The chiffchaff produces a series of staccato musical chirping notes not really like "chiff-chaff, chiffchaff", but an alternating series of loud and quiet notes "Chip-chip-cheah-chitty" often followed and sometimes preceded by subdued dry "Tchrr-tchurrs". Of 19,144 chiffchaff songs timed in 1948 and 1949 nearly half were from $1\frac{1}{2}$ to 5 seconds in duration. The wood warbler has two songs – the first is a high series of identical notes gathering speed into a shivering trill, e.g., "Tip-tip-tip . . ." sung from nine to fifteen in number and hastening into a trill of from 15 to 25 "Tips". A good example is 12 slow "Tips" lasting $1\frac{1}{2}$ seconds followed by a trill of 25 "Tips" given in just 1 second. The second type of wood warbler song is a cadence of clear, plaintive, falling whistles from four to seventeen or so in number. This second type can be given on its own or introduced into bursts of the trilling, shivering song. The song period lasts from early May to late July and starts a month later than for the other two species. It is sometimes possible for an abnormal song of the chiffchaff to resemble the cadence of the willow warbler, and vice versa. A willow warbler song which sounded like that of an abnormal linnet has been heard. Song has also been recorded from the hen willow warbler. Both chiffchaff and willow warbler sing quieter songs as they drift on migration through Dollis Hill in August and September. In September 1951 I located sixty chiffchaffs in some currant bushes near my home and of these ten were in song. Overwintering chiffchaffs can sometimes be heard in song in January and February.

The icterine warbler I once heard singing for three days in Badby Wood in May 1947 had a long sustained run of clear and melodious notes with harsher rattles like those of the lesser whitethroat and chatters like those of the starling. It included two characteristic notes "Bik-bik-bik" and "Biberoy". It is an extremely imitative bird. This European warbler is worth watching out for and looks like a heavy wood warbler with lemon-yellow underparts and bluish-grey legs. Bonelli's warbler breeds in France and its song is a loose trill on the same even-pitched note, suggestive of a cirl bunting. A typical phrase contains eleven notes lasting just over half a second.

Both goldcrest and firecrest are now breeding in Britain. The former has a very high, thin double note, repeated from five to seven times and followed by a little flourish at the end – "Cedar-cedar-cedar-cedar-cedar-stichi-see-pee". The song lasts from three to four seconds and is delivered from five to seven times a minute. Its carrying power is very limited, but it penetrates quite easily the roar of cable winches, tractors and power saws in a Scottish Sitka spruce plantation. The song can be heard in most months of the year, but it is less frequent from late summer to early autumn. There is also a low, sweet rambling subsong rather like the notes of a robin. The song of the firecrest has some resemblance to that of its more common relative, but it is stronger, lower and is made up of a repeated single note, gaining in volume and with a terminal flourish which is discarded later in the breeding season. A firecrest in Hampshire has been known to sing a version of the goldcrest's song.

The two species of flycatcher are distinct both in plumage and in voice. The commoner spotted flycatcher with its streaked mousy feathering has a poor hurried run of thin, scratchy notes – "Sip-sip-tsee-tsitti-tsee-tsee" with a pause between each note. I have twice heard a delicate warble at close range which is presumably similar to that described in *The Handbook*. The much rarer black and white pied flycatcher has a more complex and pleasing song. It is generally in two parts; firstly there is a repetition of two up and down notes – "Syet, syet, syet" or "Per-fu, per-fu, per-fu" – and secondly a flourish of varied liquid notes, perhaps a cadence or an upward arpeggio. There is something of the redstart's quality and it is often given from quite high up. Pied flycatchers were heard singing in the tree-tops when the weather was cold but nearer the nesting holes when the temperature rose. The song may be persistent before pairing and a singing male may reduce his songs from 3,620 to 1,000 per day on the arrival of a mate. The song period lasts from late April into June.

One of the commonest and yet perhaps the most disregarded of woodland songs is that of the hedgesparrow. It is a high brisk warble made up of short linked phrases lasting from three to five seconds and given at a rate of from seven to eight songs a minute. I have in my notes a record of one bird in Middlesex producing up to twelve a minute. There are many rapid and irregular jumps in pitch and there seems to be some affinity with the warblers. It is a song that I have often heard given at night. There is also a softer version used in display. The subsong is a low warbling lasting up to eighteen seconds or longer and audible at about thirty feet. It sounds a bit like a garden warbler in low voice, but bears quite a strong resemblance to the hedgesparrow's full delivery. Song occurs in every month of the year, but it is least frequent in August.

The only woodland representative of the pipits – the tree pipit – has a very fine song. It is composed of a single phrase repeated with deliberation – "Tsip-tsip-tsip-tsep-tsep-tsep" – and the song is rounded off by a shrill musical finish, rising and falling – "Seeeaa, seeeaa". It can be delivered from a perch, when it is less good in performance, or in flight, with the bird beginning to sing near or at the peak of a sharp climb, and giving out the major part of the song as it "parachutes" down to a perch. A full song in the special display flight may last for ten seconds or more. I have seen the bird sing a shortened version on the ground. The tree pipit is not a great mimic, but imitation of a great tit has been noted. In Britain birds sing from April to June.

The very scarce red-backed shrike is a bird of ecotones, but I have seen a male singing from a hawthorn on the edge of a wood so that it just qualifies for inclusion. The song is a low, musical, often continuous but jerky warbling, mixed with call notes "Chak-chak" and sharp "Chee-wiks", "Jick-jicks", "Cheweeoos" and so on. A typical full phrase may last ten seconds or more and the whole ramble of a slow soliloquy may go on for many minutes on end. I once filmed a bird in Suffolk singing for more than five minutes. The red-backed shrike is noted for its mimicry and I have heard imitations of blackbird, and mistle thrush alarm, lesser spotted woodpecker and songs of great tit and chaffinch, while another report adds reed and sedge warbler, robin, song thrush, linnet, greenfinch, blue tit and house sparrow. The red-backed shrike's song I have heard in May and June, but it is not certain that all male birds sing.

The starling is a species that almost requires a book to itself. The male sings a remarkable and disappointing song – a shapeless medley of rambling, inconsequential sounds. "Warbling, whistling, chattering, wheezing, gurgling, chuckling, clicking, bubbling and even popping sounds flow out in an unending stream" (Nicholson 1951). The very successful starling does not need a territorial song and so he relies on a subdued utterance comparable to the sub-song of many territorial singers. As a mimic he is unsurpassed and I have noted many instances of imitations all over Europe of warblers like the melodious and the great reed, of game-birds such as the red grouse and capercaillie, and of waders like the green sandpiper, spotted redshank and little ringed plover. I shall quote here from something I wrote about this species and its behaviour at Dollis Hill. "In the case of the starling, song is regular in every month of the year but most frequent from mid-July to early June. Indirect evidence of Continental immigration came from one which gave perfect imitations of the fluting song of the golden oriole in my garden in February 1952; starlings in the area have also produced imitations of buzzard and little owl which they must have heard elsewhere. In addition, I have records of starlings mimicking the song and low alarm of a black-bird, the song of a song thrush and the calls of chaffinch, carrion crow, greenfinch, mallard, tawny owl and domestic hen. Other imitations have included the miaows of cats, the squeals of brakes and, on one occasion, a duet with a crying baby which was so good that it was almost impossible to separate the two performers."

Of the forest species of finch there are eleven which ought to be considered here since at one time or another I have heard all of these birds in a woodland habitat. The first of these is the elusive hawfinch, more often identified by its loud, explosive call – "Ptik" – than by its song. This is a short, quiet, uncertain, two-part performance and is composed, according to a description by Mountfort in a monograph in the New Naturalist series, of "an introduction of two or three short, evenly spaced, unmusical notes, followed by one or more longer and slightly more liquid notes, with quiet grating noises and clicking notes irregularly interjected". There is some affinity with the songs of bullfinch and chaffinch. A phonetic rendering of a bird I heard in Suffolk can be written "Deek-deek...tur-wee-wee" and this matches quite closely the renderings given on page 63 of Mountfort's monograph. The song is often given from a tree-top, is at its best from dawn onwards and again in the late afternoon; it can be heard from February to early June. There appears to be little territorial significance in the male's singing and the female has an infrequent feeble song as well.

The greenfinch's song is based very much on its calls and is introduced by a high-pitched, canary-like twitter admirably described in *The Handbook* as "chichichichichit-teu-teu-teu-teu". There is often an inclusion of a deliberate rising and nasal call "Za-wee". The song may be delivered from a tall tree, but the singer will also fly and circle around in the air in a curious bat-like display flight with the wings curved forwards and the tail fanned. The general effect of the greenfinch's effortless song is pleasing and ideally suited to the leisure of a summer's day. Greenfinches may also sing at night. The female, too, has a song at the nest, described as more tuneful and sweet than that of the cock and consisting of a long-drawn-out warble with a twitter at the end. A deep halting song from a hen greenfinch during courtship has been observed. The song period for the male is from late February to August. Sometimes the song of the goldfinch is confused with that of the last species, but the delivery is gay and liquid, full of sweet and melodious phrases without any harsh or nasal notes. There are often little bursts of short notes "Vitti-vit" and many jumps in pitch and tiny trills. It is not so far-carrying or vigorous as the song of the greenfinch and is often maintained for quite long periods. There is sometimes a song flight with slowly beating wings rather like that of the greenfinch. Song begins in March and continues into July with a revival in the autumn.

The siskin has a song suggestive of that of the goldfinch with pleasant warbled phrases full of liquid charm. It tends to flow more sweetly and more persistently, but at the end of a phrase there is often a prolonged bleating note – "Baaa-er" with a scolding quality; this is quite distinctive and most regular at the start of the breeding season. There is also a song flight in which both members of the pair rise up above the trees while the male pours out his song. From December 1961 to March 1962 a male siskin was a daily visitor to my bird-table at Dollis Hill and here in early March he began to develop his song. The first phrases separated by quite long intervals were "Tser-sooeet" and "Tser-sooeet-weet". As the days went by the phrases grew in strength, were strung more rapidly together and were delivered from a prunus tree near the bird-table. Before he left, his song went on for minutes on end. In Scotland and Ireland the song is at its height from spring to the end of May.

The linnet is a bird of scrub and heath and its quick bursts of notes, pleasant twittering and sprightly strains, may be given from the top of a gorse bush on a heath or equally from the top shoot of a conifer in a plantation. The linnet's song is fuller and more rounded than that of the goldfinch and can be heard in every month of the year and in almost every circumstance – near or far from the nest, from a perch or on the wing, in or out of the breeding season.

The tiny redpoll is a bird of birch, alderwoods and conifer plantations; his song is a brief, high-pitched rippling trill made up of from twenty-five to thirty even notes given in only 0.4 to 0.6 seconds at a rate of up to eighteen songs a minute. This trill "Krrreee" is often followed by the metallic twittering notes 'Che-che-che-che': the whole performance is very different from the musical efforts of greenfinch, goldfinch and siskin. I have sometimes noticed a softening of the flight call when it has been incorporated in the song. The redpoll also has a characteristic song flight in which the little bird flies in loops and circles with hesitant wing-beats and occasional glides. The trilling song begins in March and can be heard up to August and occasionally September. In April 1968 I saw a bird singing over Hampstead in north London.

Since the serin bred in England in 1967 it is worth keeping a lookout for its song. I made several recordings of singing serins in Spain in 1956. The song is a jingle of rapid and rushed sibilant chitters with a few canary-like trills. Songs may last from one to five seconds with short intervals between each.

One species of finch without a full song is the bullfinch. It has instead a subsong of poor quality made up of low piping warbles with creaky double notes – "Gyur-gyur" – suggestive of an unoiled door swinging back and forth. Both sexes may sing, but the female is a poorer learner than the male. The subsong is not of great value in pair formation or the defence of territory, but it is not infrequent in species with strongly sustained pair-bonds. The bullfinch can be a good mimic.

I have given an account of the development of the song of the common crossbill elsewhere, but basically there are four stages from the threshold of song to full song. The first stage is a series of chipping calls – "Jip-jip-jip" – run together in a slow, emphatic trill of from five to ten "jips" with each trill lasting about one second. There may be as many as twenty trills to the minute. At the second stage a "Ter-chee" note is added to the "Jip-jip" series and this indicates that the bird is at a song post. In stage three the song advances to double notes – "Jeeaaa" – with some four to ten of them at the same rate as in the first two stages. The fourth and final stage is the full song and this I was once able to record on tape in Suffolk in March. The song includes the "Ter-chee" phrases of stage two and this is followed by a warbled song like that of a redstart and some chipping notes. Complete and sustained songs are rare, and the late Commander Alec Robertson in a twenty-one-year study of the Breckland crossbills heard it only twice. After a number of years of disappointment I was able in 1959 to make a recording of the full song of the Scottish crossbill in Inverness-shire; I had already recorded the calls and subsong. The song of the northern bird included a number of phrases such as "Tip-tip-tip", "Tsee-tsee-tsee", as well as a warbled "Tseeker-tseeker". The subsong of the common crossbill occurs in both sexes and is mellow and trilling sounding like "the song of distant linnets" (Robertson 1954). The subsong of the Scottish race consists of creaking notes "Crrook-crrok", "Yeek-yeek", "Ip-ip-yureek-yureek", and "Grrr-grr" and so on, run together in an inconsequential way. After making a range of recordings of both common and Scottish crossbill I am certain that there is a difference in the flight calls, the former's ringing "Jip-jip-jip" being replaced in the Scottish bird by a deeper, coarser, more rounded "Tyoop-tyoop". According to *The Handbook* song in the common crossbill has been heard at night.

The chaffinch's song is essentially in three parts – introduction "Chip-chip-chip-chip", trill "Cherry-erry-erry", and terminal flourish "Chip-cheweeoo". The duration of song is usually from 1½ to 3 seconds with a rate of from five to twelve songs per minute. Songs vary a great deal and their number is almost infinite; a single individual may have more than one version. Birds may differ geographically in their songs, but there is hardly a variation confined to one region, although songs in any given area may differ according to the way in which local birds favour or disregard given variations. After all, full chaffinch song is "an integration of inborn and learned song patterns, the former contributing the basis for the latter" (Thorpe 1958). Differences in songs may be instrumental in starting as well as maintaining evolutionary divergences in species but in the chaffinch they are not consistent enough nor are the birds sufficiently isolated for the species to break up into a number of subspecies. However, in the Thames Valley there is a song variant sufficient to identify the place of origin.

Young chaffinches start with a subsong of chirps and rattles and then when the first autumn comes they produce sustained bursts of chirping notes that vary in pitch. This simple subsong can be uttered by the female too. The subsong of the ensuing spring includes rattles and borrowed notes which finally emerge as the full song. When the young male takes up a spring territory he is stimulated and aided by the singing of neighbouring males. Indeed as the song develops the young bird's utterance comes more and more to resemble that of its neighbours. This copying can be very clearly recognised in the terminal flourish which shows great differences over the chaffinch's range. It is then that birds may learn two or more versions of song from other chaffinches. There is a strong tendency for chaffinches to imitate other species in their subsongs, but they leave them out of their territorial songs. Adult chaffinches have twelve calls – a flight call "Tsup", a social call "Spink" rather like the call of a great tit, an injury and an escape call used by both sexes throughout the year; there are also an aggressive call, two escape calls, two courtship calls, subsong and song confined to the male in the breeding season as well as a female courtship call. Full chaffinch song may begin in January or early February in the suburbs, but tends to start a little later in many rural areas; it often revives in September and October.

A good example of how unreliable song is as a generic character is the strange song of the brambling, made up of four or five sweet notes often with an extra phrase – a rasping "Tsweee", – which has been regarded as part of the subsong and not typical of the full song. The full song is characteristic of the start of the breeding season. I have seen a male in Breckland in mid-April with almost full breeding plumage utter a quiet inward song. Since bramblings bred in 1920 and may have done so in other years as well, it is worth listening out for this soft "Zit . . zit . . tswirrit . . . zee-wee-it" song and also the louder rasping call as well.

Only three species of buntings can be regarded in any way as woodland birds – the yellowhammer, cirl bunting and reed bunting. The first appears in often quite dense woodland and I have heard one singing deep in a New Forest glade. The familiar traditional rendering of the yellow-hammer's song is "A little bit of bread and NO CHEESE", but I have recorded songs such as "A little bit of bread", "A little bit of bread and NO", and "A little bit of bread and CHEESE". The pitch and timbre may also change and there may be three or four variants in one individual, and even six. There is also a twittering kind of subsong audible in the autumn. Full song begins uncommonly in late January and more regularly in

February and continues through to September. One yellowhammer sang 3,482 songs in one day in August spread over twelve hours and eleven minutes; it was suggested that this was "a form of end of season unmated song due to the absence or passive behaviour of the hens" (Rollin 1958). The song rate is something of the order of six a minute. The cirl bunting has two songs – a rare one, fortunately, which is like the first phrase of a yellowhammer's song and a second, more typical one, which is a sharp, high-pitched and prolonged trill. A bird I tape-recorded in Dorset, and whose sound spectrogram has been reproduced, produced from eighteen to twenty-three notes in a trill lasting about $1\frac{1}{2}$ seconds. There may be from three to six of these trills in a minute. A song more like the trill of a grasshopper and called the "insect" variant has been heard. The female may also sing. The song of the male can be heard in every month of the year but is most constant from February to late autumn. The reed bunting I am including because of its move into drier habitats including conifer plantations. Its song, like that of the other buntings, is short, simple and often repeated; it is composed of two or three notes of medium pitch followed by a short trill – "Zeep, zeep, zerrr" – and I have also notes of the following; "Jink-jink, tillee", "Jink-jink-jink, tississik", and "Jink-jink-jink-tchurr-jink-jink" and so on. The song lasts about $1\frac{1}{2}$ seconds and is "churned out" at a rate of from ten to fifteen songs a minute. The song can be given from the air but it is more familiarly given from a spray of bramble, the top of a bush or a young conifer. A bird was once seen singing from the top of a tall oak in Richmond Park. The song commences about mid-February and goes on until July or even August.

The last species I have included is the tree sparrow, since it now appears in Midland oakwoods as a real forest bird, singing its songs deep in the heart of the woodlands. In Badby Wood in April 1968 I counted six cocks singing within a radius of two hundred yards of me, and the nearest to the edge of the wood was some two hundred and fifty yards from it. The notes resemble those of the house sparrow, but the song is higher and a little more musical – a sustained series of chirping notes without much pace but sometimes a little rhythm, e.g., "Tcherrup, tcher-to-chit, tcherrup, tcher-to-chit, tchit-tchit, tchirr-chirp" and so on. Boyd (1949) listened to "a sustained musical warbling song" from a Swedish tree sparrow, but I have never heard this in Britain. Song can be heard occasionally in all months, except perhaps January and August, but its frequency is highest from March to May.

I have reported in a rather matter of fact way the chief differences in the songs of woodland birds, but many have brought me great pleasure and all have brought variety, interest and often surprise. It now seems clear that birds sing best when relaxed and with some degree of detachment from emotional situations. Some ornithologists believe that there may be some kinds of aesthetic experience that can be shared by birds as well as man. A serious attempt has been made to correlate both biological and aesthetic principles, and we must welcome this approach, although it seems clear that birds have not yet advanced quite as far along the paths of appreciation. The great difficulty is to decide what facets of bird-song are really non-utilitarian. Not only do the songs of birds bring personal delight, but also they are indispensable in bird census work; I have always pitied those bird-watchers who say "I can't tell one from another!" A field-worker without either a knowledge or an appreciation of bird voices is incomplete. There is, of course, no substitute for personal effort and experience. I learned to recognise the song of the willow warbler as a young boy in Kew Gardens after many times fruitlessly chasing a tiny, elusive yellow-green bird that flitted annoyingly about high up in the trees. I have never forgotten the moment I recognised the willow warbler's song, nor, for that matter, how to identify it. I now take regular aural sensitivity tests to see whether I am yet beginning to miss vital components in the songs of birds. Some people have difficulty in hearing certain frequencies or may have blank spots within the normal range. However, today there are many sets of bird recordings available to help the beginner and to intrigue the expert. I have prepared for the BBC's Radio Enterprise series of Wildlife Records a 12 inch long-playing disc of woodland bird songs and choruses. There is still a great deal that is not known about the songs and utterances of even quite common species, but with the increase in the number of reasonable and suitable tape recorders I am sure that some of the answers will be eventually found.

CHAPTER 10

THE BIRDS OF SCRUB AND
DEVELOPING WOODLAND

BEFORE the last war – even before the effects of the blitz so dramatically
revealed themselves in London – I came to know a piece of wasteland in
Kensington; it was the site of a building cleared away in 1936. Within
twelve months wind-dispersed rosebay willow herb carpeted the ground
with lavish colour. Further pioneers like groundsel and bracken arrived
and other plants needing sunlight and space. By 1939 there was elder and
woody nightshade. Twelve years later clumps of buddleia and a fig-tree
were well established while sallow, ash and sycamore trees had grown to
heights over twenty feet. The land was then cleared and redeveloped but
I had been able to watch a natural succession of vegetation moving
towards a climax which through circumstances it was never able to reach.
This early stage of developing trees and shrubs we call scrub, but the term
can also be used to describe the bushy growth that cannot progress
further and tree growth that is limited in height by the effects of climate,
its situation or the activities of man. Most of it is below the 26 foot level
which is used to define the upper limit of scrub. In natural scrub the
saplings of trees may push their way through to grow up and eventually
to suppress the shrubs that first gave them shelter. Even these trees may in
turn have to give way to the final climax species. Besides these seral
communities there are also plantations made by man, often on felled
woodland or on land such as peat-bogs and moorland, which has not
previously or for many years borne a timber crop. The various stages of
development in both seral communities and artificial plantations are
reflected in the bird-life and in this chapter we shall look at the changes
that take place as the succession progresses. We shall look first at woodland
scrub, then turn our attention to hillside scrub and bushes that do not
develop further through grazing, and finally to the man-made plantations.

Woodland scrub, since it gives rise to woodland, has been described by
Sir Arthur Tansley as "dynamic". In this kind of scrub the bushes are
mixed with tree seedlings which have taken root and grown under the
protective shrubs. This scrub is fairly open in its nature and, as it allows
varying amounts of light to enter, it is usually rich in its flora. Many of the
plants are typical of hedgerows, the margins of woods and coppiced

woodland. In fact, dominated as it is by bushes and woody shrubs, scrub is an ecotone halfway between forest and prairie. Before forest can conquer the grassland surrounding it, shrubs are needed as the pioneer invaders. The complete succession to climax oakwood is not as common in Britain as one might expect. However, an area of arable land after bearing a wheat crop was allowed to revert to woodland. After 28 years it had become "a dense thicket of trees and shrubs" (Tansley 1949). After passing through the stage of hawthorn, which develops quickly on arable land, and other spiny shrubs which gave early protection to young oaks, the complex finally became an oak/hazelwood. As the wood matured hazel, sallow, elder, dogwood and blackthorn all appeared. Scrub floras are usually large since they represent a mixture of the plants typical, firstly of arable land, then of semi-shade and finally of mature climax forest. A list of 143 species of plant for scrub at Bricketwood Common in Hertfordshire was made in 1918.

On chalk grassland where grazing is reduced there is a succession from pasture to climax beechwood, and here the scrub plant communities are as varied as any in the British Isles. In the Chilterns dwarf juniper scrub may start a succession on the steeper, more exposed slopes that moves straight to beechwood; on the deeper soils in more sheltered places a hawthorn sere may be followed by ashwood before the beech climax appears at a later stage. Blackthorn, dogwood, privet, wayfaring tree, spindle, elder, field maple, hazel and traveller's joy are very common – this is often favourite cirl bunting country. Later, as the scrub grows, wild cherry, whitebeam, holly, rowan and occasional oaks may appear. In some places yew colonises the downland and can form, as we have already seen, pure societies. Beechwoods on the loams of the plateaux may arise after a succession that moves through hawthorn and blackthorn to ash/oakwood and then to beech. On heathland podsols succession may start with birch and pine and lead on to oakwood and then beech. On limestone rock ash/hazel scrub may be the natural succession from heath to climax oakwood.

English scrubland is very much dominated by hawthorn which thrives on many kinds of soil and so can figure in the successions to both beech and oakwood. The other most important members of the scrub community are blackthorn, sallow, elder, wild rose, wayfaring tree, privet, spindle and ivy. The majority of these plants are largely dispersed by birds so that there is a close relation with berry-eating species. The bird-life of scrub has been very much neglected, but its study throws light on the communities of woodland birds. There are, for example, several species common to both habitats. Fortunately the survey of Bookham Common has been extended to include scrub and the population changes that take place with its development. Melluish (1960) has described the bird community of 61 acres of grassland and scrub not far from the oakwoods of Bookham Common. Over a period there was an appreciable increase in the amount of vegetation, especially of bushes of hawthorn, blackthorn, rose and bramble growing on grassland dominated by tufted hair grass. Counts made of the number of hawthorn bushes showed increases from 93 in 1951 to 415 in 1955 and 609 in 1959. There were also scattered and growing numbers of oaks, birches, willows and ashes. The whole complex was clearly a stage in the succession to oakwood. The land had been originally grazed and it was noted that skylarks and tree pipits commonly bred and at least one pair of whinchats nested every year. Between 1948 and 1960 the number of bird species on the Bookham scrub rose by some 15%. The survey recorded 72 species in all and the most important of these, excluding the vagrants, were as follows:

Resident (16 species)
> Pheasant, moorhen, wood pigeon, magpie, jay, long-tailed tit, wren, mistle thrush, song thrush, blackbird, robin, hedgesparrow, bullfinch, chaffinch, yellowhammer, reed bunting.

Species resident locally but visiting only (18 species)
> Mallard, kestrel, green woodpecker, great spotted woodpecker, carrion crow, jackdaw, great tit, blue tit, marsh tit, willow tit, meadow pipit, pied wagtail, starling, hawfinch, greenfinch, goldfinch, redpoll, house sparrow.

Breeding summer visitors (8 species)
> Turtle dove, cuckoo, nightingale, grasshopper warbler, whitethroat, lesser whitethroat, willow warbler, tree pipit (not after 1957).

There was an increase in wood pigeon, turtle dove, reed bunting and jay, a slight increase in willow and grasshopper warblers, a slight decline in wren, hedgesparrow, yellowhammer, cuckoo and nightingale, a more pronounced drop in the number of robins and chaffinches and a disappearance of the tree pipit. The basic population was one of shrub-nesters and as the vegetation grew it adversely affected the ground-feeding birds. There are no obvious reasons for the decline of the chaffinch but there are other indications of a more general decrease in its numbers. The breeding list is very similar to one I obtained for an extensive area of hawthorn scrub near Preston-on-Stour between 1948 and 1950. About 10% more birds were recorded in winter than in the summer but the number of species was smaller. Great and blue tits were more frequent in the winter, but these, like the marsh and willow tits, are hole-nesting birds and scrub does not provide them with suitable sites. I have occasionally found a hawthorn with a natural hole being exploited by great or blue tits, but this is not common. If elder is present then willow tits can sometimes excavate nesting holes in the soft wood.

From 1959 to 1963 a detailed analysis was made of the various feeding stations used by birds in the Bookham scrub so that direct comparisons could be made with those in oakwoods. An enquiry was carried out into all the feeding sites "not only in space but also in time, of day or year". The upper limit for the scrub was set in fact at 15 ft. When the canopy of a shrub reached a diameter of about 10 ft., bare ground formed underneath. The size of this bare patch was increased by the density of the bush and the amount to which the lower branches came down within twelve inches of the ground. If other shrubs grew near to the south or south-west of the bush this also extended the area of bare ground by reducing the light. Leaf litter accumulated underneath and attracted ground-feeders such as robins, blackbirds, hedgesparrows and occasionally great tits. On the bare ground in the summer the numerically dominant birds were blackbird, chaffinch and robin and in the winter blackbird, wren and hedgesparrow. In the spring the commonest species feeding in the shrubs were great and blue tits, willow warblers and whitethroats while in the summer bullfinches, long-tailed and willow tits became more frequent. At the end of the summer the warblers have gone and thrushes, blackbirds, redwings and fieldfares come into the scrub to feed on the autumn fruits; in some years they are joined by waxwings.

Table 21 illustrates the preference of various species for different kinds of small tree and shrub at Bookham. Of all the feeding records 63% were in hawthorn, 9% in blackthorn, 8% in willow, 7% in oak and 6% in birch. Just over half of the Bookham scrub was composed of hawthorn, one quarter was rose, 15% was bramble and 3% blackthorn. Redpolls preferred the birch catkins and greenfinches the rose hips. Sloes were sought after by fieldfares and blackbirds while blue tits and willow warblers used to resort to the willows. Although oak-trees made up only 1% of the total of scrub three essentially woodland species – great tit, blue tit and goldcrest – had a special liking for them.

Beven's admirable study of a sadly-neglected habitat reached a number of interesting conclusions. The first was that some woodland birds such as great, blue, marsh and willow tits as well as bullfinches and chaffinches have moved into scrubland and successfully adapted their feeding stations to a lower level than those in oakwood. Blackbirds feed on the ground in both habitats, but have moved up to higher levels because of the attraction of the berries. Essentially ground-feeding species like the song thrush and

TABLE 21   The Feeding Preferences in Trees and Shrubs of 18 Species in Scrub at Bookham Common (shown as percentages)

	Fieldfare	Blackbird	Redwing	Wren	Hedgesparrow	Great Tit	Blue Tit	Marsh Tit	Willow Tit	Long-tailed Tit	Greenfinch	Redpoll	Bullfinch	Chaffinch	Whitethroat	Willow Warbler	Goldcrest	Waxwing
No. of Records	(50)	(90)	(186)	(65)	(22)	(95)	(376)	(29)	(29)	(282)	(34)	(41)	(82)	(18)	(60)	(121)	(28)	(25)
Hawthorn	76	75	97	66	86	61	46	55	59	75	32	0	74	78	63	51	53	52
Rose	2	1	2	10	0	4	6	24	13	2	68	0	6	5	13	3	0	12
Blackthorn	20	20	1	10	0	3	9	3	11	10	0	0	12	5	7	9	14	0
Willow	0	2	1	3	0	3	14	0	0	7	0	10	4	5	7	20	4	20
Birch	0	0	0	2	5	0	2	0	0	1	0	90	0	0	0	1	0	0
Oak	0	0	0	0	0	19	18	0	0	6	0	0	1	5	7	7	21	0
Other Species	2	1	1	8	9	9	6	17	17	1	0	0	2	0	3	10	7	16
Total	100	99	102	99	100	99	101	99	100	102	100	100	99	98	100	101	99	100

The figures in brackets denote the number of records being analysed

Reproduced from *The London Naturalist*, No. 43, by kind permission of Dr Geoffrey Beven robin have preserved the same feeding niche. Four species – wren, white-throat, willow warbler and hedgesparrow – may have penetrated the woodlands and their shrub layers from the scrub. The long-tailed tit is perhaps also a scrub bird that on moving into woodland has looked for its food at a higher level. Certain species regularly seen in the scrub, such as greenfinches, goldfinches, redpolls and reed buntings, do not commonly feed in dense oakwoods. When oakwood finally replaces the scrub there will naturally be a reduction in the number of birds. The more important losses would be grasshopper warblers and lesser whitethroats. The nightjar was not present at Bookham, but it breeds in scrub on open downland in Sussex, in hawthorn, blackthorn and bramble in Worcestershire, and in thorn, bracken and bramble in Anglesey. There has been a steady decline in the nightjar's numbers and its distribution in 1957–8 is shown in Fig. 18. The red-backed shrike has also decreased, but it is often associated with scattered trees and bushes, especially those with thorns on which it can impale its prey and so form its larder. The shrikes like areas of hawthorn in grass and big thorny hedges; I have known a pair build in Essex in such a site but this was completely surrounded by houses.

In winter, dense thorn scrub up to about 20 ft. in height is often very attractive to roosting starlings and, when I lived in south Warwickshire, I took part in a number of expeditions to trap starlings for ringing in some of the dense hunt coverts and spinneys near my home. One such roost in blackthorn and hawthorn had to be opened up with an axe. Well over a million starlings used it one winter and after five months of occupation, by sheer weight of numbers, they broke its well-developed young trees right down to within four or five feet of the ground. Three sparrowhawks and a peregrine also roosted in the thorns, often sharing their branches with a dozen starlings or more, but they only took them in flight as they rocketed down into the roost at dusk when conditions were most difficult. Thrushes and blackbirds often use thorn scrub for roosting and I have also seen chaffinches and bramblings retiring to hawthorns on a winter's evening. House sparrows, too, often choose thorns and the number using such a roost near my home in north-west London is as high as 300, but larger roosts of several thousand have been reported in hawthorn scrub on Banstead Downs and at Motspur Park.

Where the lowland woods reach up the hillsides – perhaps at heights of from 1,500 ft. above sea-level or more – the upper limit of wooded growth generally consists of broken and stunted woodland scrub. Much of this is made up of oak, birch and more rarely Scots pine. The bird-life of these fell-woods is not sharply divided from that in the lowland woods and the general conclusion was that "while the lowland sessile oakwoods have fewer birds than the pedunculate woods, the density of these may not be much higher than that in some of the fell-woods" (Yapp 1962). The two commonest species are willow warbler and chaffinch, while tree pipit, robin, wren, and coal tit occur in reasonable numbers and great and blue tits are missing or rather rare. The most constant species in these marginal scrubby woods were also those with a considerable northerly range in Europe, with a propensity for nesting in holes and with an almost exclusively insect diet. Yellowhammers, ring ousels, wheatears, whinchats, and pied wagtails may also penetrate these woods even if they do not nest there. In the Sutherland birch scrub I have also seen ravens, hooded crows, wood pigeons, song thrushes, hedgesparrows and bullfinches, but the first three species do not find the saplings suitable for nesting. Willow warblers and robins are very common and in the stunted birches of the wild country around Loch Loyal and Loch Hope I have seen reed buntings as well. Meadow pipits are more frequent and have been found breeding in the fringe of the birch scrub. Some of the degenerate scrub with rotten trees, many of them fallen and riddled by bark-boring insects, may attract occasional treecreepers and great spotted woodpeckers. A pair of redwings that nested in northern Sutherland frequented "a wild district of moorland and birch scrub" (Lloyd 1947).

In the birch and willow scrub that grows around the southern shores of Lough Neagh in Ireland I have found willow warblers, chiffchaffs, grasshopper warblers, wrens, greenfinches and goldfinches. Near Dunfanaghy in Co. Donegal in 1967 I recorded the following species in an area of birch scrub with some alder: willow warbler, chiffchaff, robin, wren, hedgesparrow, goldcrest, spotted flycatcher, blue tit and greenfinch. Near Lough Eske and Lough Gill I added cuckoo, song thrush, blackbird, wood pigeon and bullfinch. In Co. Cork I investigated some pure willow scrub of less than 2½ ft. in height and found that this supported a breeding population of reed bunting, stonechat and, surprisingly, chiffchaff. Sallow scrub appears along rivers in Britain in many places, but none of it approaches the unique woods in the Danube Delta with their hoopoes, rollers, collared flycatchers, river warblers and doves. Much of the Irish scrub is very mixed, and in Co. Donegal I found ash, alder, hazel and sessile oak growing together, particularly around Mulroy Bay, and there were also admixtures of sallow, birch, holly, hawthorn, rowan and gorse. Scrub is common in some parts of Co. Galway and Co. Mayo and it often flourishes on the islands in the lakes where, protected from grazing, oak, birch, holly, rowan, yew, sallow and juniper may grow well.

We have already seen that much of the scrub in the British Isles is subseral, but in some windswept places where trees cannot grow then

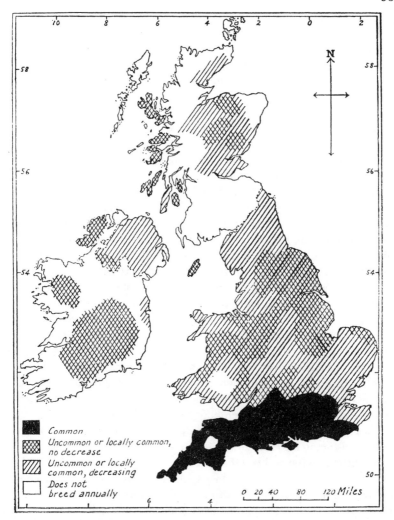

Common

Uncommon or locally common, no decrease

Uncommon or locally common, decreasing

Does not breed annually

0 20 40   80   120 Miles

FIG. 18. The distribution of the nightjar, 1957-58. *Black*: Common; *Cross-hatched*: uncommon or locally common. No decrease. *Single-hatched*: uncommon or locally common, decreasing; *White*: does not breed annually. Reproduced from *Bird Study* by kind permission of Dr John Stafford.

climax scrub may occupy the ground. A particularly good example of this is the hazel scrub growing on the carboniferous limestone that runs south of Galway Bay in Ireland with its heavy rainfall, strong winds and very high humidity. On the Burren the exposed grey limestone lies in flat terraces or forms hills several hundred feet high. Here calcicolous grasses, bracken, hawthorn, spindle tree and ivy grow in the cracks in the limestone, while in May the mountain avens and spring gentian make the Burren an extremely attractive botanical haunt. The woody growth is dominated by one scrub plant – hazel; this grows to heights of from two to three feet where the effects of wind and grazing are at their most severe but in one protected spot the hazel reaches over six feet in height. Much of the flora is typical of woodland with primroses, wood anemones, celandines and early purple orchid but the number of species is not high. In the more sheltered parts there is a tendency for progression towards ashwood. Incidentally, ash scrub is also common on the downs where it often marks the transition from grassland to beechwood. I carried out a number of summer counts in the hazel scrub of the Burren in 1967 and found the wren to be the commonest species followed by whitethroat, robin, chaffinch, skylark and great tit in that order. To see how the bird community would change, if the hazel scrub was allowed through circumstances of weather and land use to develop, I also toured the extensive scrublands between Ennis and Kilfenora where the hazel ranges from 12 to 18 ft. in height. Here four new species appeared – blackbird, willow warbler, chiffchaff and bullfinch. Blackbirds were the commonest species and then in descending order of abundance, chaffinch, chiffchaff, robin, willow warbler, bullfinch, wren and great tit; it was clear that the wren had lost ground while the whitethroat and skylark had disappeared. Near Ennistymon hazel scrub was growing to 20 ft. or more in association with a little hawthorn, blackthorn and ivy, and here I was only able to make counts by following the low paths that cattle had forcibly made through the dense growth. In this more developed hazel scrub the chiffchaff was the dominant species, with blackbird and robin equal second and then willow warbler, song thrush, chaffinch, bullfinch and rook with smaller numbers of hedgesparrows, wrens, great tits, whitethroats, which had reappeared, yellowhammers and wood pigeons.

On the downs, yew scrub may form and this attracts goldcrests but not whitethroats which are often typical members of a scrub fauna. The latter species requires a certain amount of low, dense vegetation which cannot develop under yew scrub. Near High Force in Teesdale there is quite a growth of juniper scrub and here the bushes grow like parasol pines or churchyard yews up to heights of about 16 ft. or so. A twenty-minute transect in late April produced 11 song thrush contacts with 8 for blackbird, 5 for hedgesparrow, robin and meadow pipit, 2 for greenfinch and redpoll and single contacts for chaffinch, whinchat, wood pigeon, snipe and red grouse.

The young oak-forests of the lowlands tend to have a rather weak community of birds since, without nestboxes to aid them, the hole-nesting species are absent and there are also undeveloped field and shrub layers. Oak-trees grow very slowly and so, as yet, no one has been able to carry out a systematic study of this successive growth of an oak-forest although counts have been made in various parts of the Wyre Forest in Worcestershire. In the young woods of oak and birch under 23 years of age there were just under 20 species of bird present in the summer. In more developed oakwoods about 40 ft. high but underplanted with a certain amount of beech there was a decline in the number of nesting wood warblers and tree pipits but a very slight rise in the number of species present. At Seskinore in Northern Ireland, in a wood of young oaks up to 18 ft. in height with no shrub layer and a field layer of bramble, nettle and celandine, I recorded only 14 species. At Port Glenone also in Ulster there was a plantation of ash, birch, beech, rowan and sycamore mixed with pine, larch and spruce rising to about 20 ft. in height. There was a shrub layer of thorn and elder, made possible by a broken canopy, and a rich field layer of bluebells, wood anemones, primroses, ramsons and celandines. This time I found 18 species and this figure for a young wood can be compared to the figures for mature woods – 32–34 for Badby Wood, 35 for a number of oakwoods and 36 for Dallington Forest in East Sussex. After some 200 acres of Dallington were burned a recording was made of the bird-life returning to the devastated area – an indication of the bird communities in the early succession of broad-leaved woods. In the first season after the fire only two species were present – mistle thrush and nightjar. By the fourth season tree pipit, willow warbler and robin were breeding over the whole area with chaffinch, whitethroat and wood pigeon on the fringes of the burnt section only. Fire at Bookham Common, which affected some of the scrub by destroying all the grass and severely charring some of the bushes, brought about a decrease in the number of willow warblers but a rise in the number of whitethroats.

The succession in conifer plantations follows a rather different pattern. The young trees are reared in forest nurseries and most of them are put out for planting when two or three years old. In the meantime, woodlands may be cleared and perhaps drained to receive the young plants, while bare ground is frequently deep-ploughed by giant trench-diggers that turn over enormous furrows which break up the podsol hard-pans, drain the peaty ground, improve the soil and stop competition from other plants on a heather moor. Many of the plantations are on grass moor with mat-grass or purple moor grass. In autumn, when the ridges have dried out the tiny conifers are planted in the sides of the furrows. Nearly five thousand trees are planted to the acre if the distance between each is three feet, while 1,750 are put in to the acre if the distance between each is increased to five feet. The newly planted land is fenced against deer, cattle and sheep and wired against rabbits. The area of the new plantings is usually divided into compartments by open strips of land which may be new access roads, rides and fire-breaks. In the first two or three years some clearing of weeds and climbing plants may take place. The young conifers grow until their side branches extend and begin to overlap those of their neighbours and this eventually shades out the plants growing below. This stage, when the trees are from about 8 to 12 ft. high, is called the thicket stage. Not only does the field layer disappear, but competition among the conifers is high. At a certain point, usually when the trees are about fifteen years old, the foresters trim away the dead side branches from ground level up to a height of about 6 ft. This cleaning process is called brashing; it allows better access to the plantation, as well as ensuring better formed logs without knots and deformities, and it also saves the trouble of doing it later on as well as lessening the fire risk. The trimmed branches are usually left where they fall and this provides a thin, artificial field layer of sticks and debris under the trees. Further competition among the conifers is reduced by periodic thinning which gives the better trees a chance to grow well in the air and space given to them. The survivors grow rapidly and the thinnings have to be repeated until only a small proportion of the original planting survives. The volume of timber actually taken out by the thinning process is about equal to what is left in the final crop.

The bird community slowly changes with the growth of the young conifers. I have found it convenient to divide the succession of trees into four stages:

1. the *establishment* of the trees to a height of about 3 ft. (heathland with shrubs).
2. *early thicket* up to a height of about 7 or 8 ft.
3. *late thicket* up to a height of about 12 ft., often at about 11 years after planting.
4. *pole plantation* (after brashing).

Of course not all species of tree grow at the same rate and there may be variations in the same species over different periods of years. For most comparative purposes this classification is satisfactory.

The first, or establishment, stage is that of heathland when the small conifers do not yet dominate the compartment. Many of the birds of heath, grassland, moor and waste still go on living among the trees. On many of the newly afforested areas of the British Isles the commonest birds at this time are the skylark and the meadow pipit, but there may also be numbers of snipe, lapwing, curlew and, in places, common partridge. In Scotland the red grouse may survive the planting for several years and near Glen Feshie I recorded five in as many minutes among trees up to three feet in height. In England the red-legged partridge may survive in plantations right up to the thicket stage. In Breckland the commonest breeding birds at the heath or establishment stage were skylark, meadow pipit, stonechat and whinchat with occasional yellow wagtail, yellow-hammer and wheatear. There was no record of tree pipits which I have seen in the Midlands of England and in Scotland, and the stonechat has declined in numbers in recent years. In Wales the black grouse favours the hill plantations at all stages from their first establishment since the pine shoots constitute an attractive source of food. The black grouse was scarce in Snowdonia, but since its first slow increase in mid-Wales it has made considerable progress. When moors are afforested voles often seem to flourish and this may attract kestrels, buzzards and occasional hen or Montagu's harriers. Hen harriers find safe breeding places in some of the undisturbed young conifer plantations and many of the score or so of Montagu's harriers breeding in Britain have shown a distinct preference for this new and artificial habitat. I have also watched short-eared owls over newly planted moors in Wales and Scotland and between 30 and 40 pairs have been recorded nesting, after a vole plague, on some 3,500 acres of Forestry Commission land in Stirlingshire. In northern Scotland I have also seen twites in the establishment stage of conifer plantations. In Ireland I found the meadow pipit and skylark fairly regularly while the linnet was common. In spruce plantations in Slovakia the linnet was found to be the most abundant bird, but it totally avoided the pines. Grasshopper warblers were frequent in Co. Down and Co. Fermanagh and there were many stonechats, particularly in Co. Cork. Snipe were characteristic of the damper moors and corncrakes could be found in many establishment stage plantations in western Ireland. Redpolls were occasional but their numbers increased as the trees developed.

In the early thicket stage when the trees are from about 3 to 8 ft. in height the heath birds begin to decrease and the scrub birds to appear. As the trees grow pheasants may replace the partridges. Willow warblers begin to come in about the fourth or fifth years, reaching their peak in the eleventh year or so in the late thicket stage when the last of the heath birds disappears. The Lacks found that the willow warbler formed 50% of the passerine population of the plantations from seven to twelve years of age. The whitethroat reached its peak in the eighth year and the yellow-hammer, after the tenth year, was found much more at the edges of the plantations. Hedgesparrows, blackbirds and song thrushes reached their peak about the tenth year and were present in good numbers until brashing took place. The birds that favour the undergrowth now fail to come any more. I was very impressed by the foresters at Gortin Glen in Northern Ireland who tied bundles of brashings to the pole stage trunks at heights of from 5 to 6 ft. in the plantations. These were used for nesting sites by blackbirds, wrens and other species which thus persisted into the tree stage.

The tree birds begin to appear in the seventh or eighth year after planting. The commonest of these in the Breckland plantations was the chaffinch which even before brashing was nearly as common as the willow warbler; after brashing it was the most abundant species. Goldcrests, bullfinches and coal tits also come in about the same time as the chaffinch. By the twentieth year the tree species are dominant but the wren persists because of the brashing litter and debris.

Table 22 gives the breeding populations found by the Lacks in the conifer plantations of different age in Breckland in early summer. It does not give the heights of the trees and so it is not possible to make direct comparisons with other forests. Nevertheless, Table 22 shows very clearly the way in which the scrub or thicket birds follow the birds of heathland and how eventually the tree birds take over. In Fig. 19 the fortunes of three characteristic species of heath, thicket and woodland can be clearly traced. The Lacks, summing up the changes in bird numbers that took place in Breckland as the land went from heathland to mature plantation, wrote: "Assuming an average density of 50 birds per 100 acres of heathland, this means that there are now about 18,500 fewer heathland birds breeding on the Breckland than were present 30 years ago, when the plantations were started. Likewise, assuming an average density of 180 birds per 100 acres of conifer plantation, there are now about 66,600 more breeding woodland birds on the Breckland than there were 30 years ago" (Lack and Lack 1951).

By the time the conifers are about thirty years old when the trees have grown towards maturity and the compartments have become rather draughty, larger species of bird can be found – crows, occasional ravens, magpies, jays, wood pigeons, great spotted woodpeckers, kestrels, sparrow-hawks, tawny and long-eared owls and, in places, herons, buzzards and

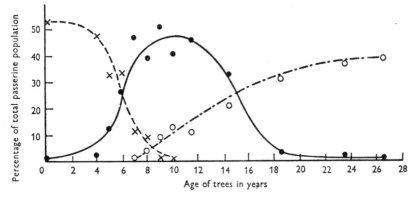

FIG. 19. Changes in the population of skylark, willow warbler and chaffinch as conifer plantations develop in Breckland. Reproduced from an article by Lack and Lack, courtesy of *Journal of Animal Ecology*, 1951.

even the kite. Elsewhere siskins, redpolls, crossbills, turtle doves and various tits may breed.

A number of Forestry Commission plantations in Devon, Wales and the Lake District have been studied and in the early thicket stage the species in descending order of abundance were meadow pipit, skylark, willow warbler, tree pipit, whinchat, linnet, robin, chaffinch and wren. In the late thicket stage of Sitka spruce the willow warbler was the commonest species followed by chaffinch, goldcrest, robin, and wood pigeon, but the order for Norway spruce was slightly different – willow warbler, chaffinch, goldcrest, redpoll, robin and wood pigeon. I found in both English and Scottish plantations that linnet, redpoll, yellowhammer, hedgesparrow and whitethroat were commoner in the thicket stages of Norway than of Sitka spruce. Reed buntings sometimes overlap into the more typical habitats of the yellowhammer, and this may have arisen from a change in the "psychological" requirements of the reed bunting, especially for water. I have found reed buntings in a number of plantations a long way from water. In all 39 thicket species were recorded of which 18 were dominant in at least one type of wood. Thirty bird species were observed in the Slovakian plantations of Norway spruce and Scots pine. I have made counts in a number of Scottish conifer thickets and I found an order of relative abundance of, firstly, chaffinch, and then willow warbler, wood pigeon, coal tit, hedgesparrow, redpoll, robin, blackbird, linnet and song thrush. In Ireland the order I found was rather different – willow warbler, redpoll, wren, chiffchaff, sedge warbler, hedgesparrow and chaffinch:

TABLE 22. *The Breeding Population in Plantations of Different Age in Breckland*

(Percentage of population formed by each species; × means present but less than 0.5%)

	Unplanted Heath	Scrub									Trees		
Age of Plantation (years)		4	5	6	7	8	9	10	11–12	14–15	18–19	23–24	26–27
Heath Birds													
Skylark	52	47	32	33	11	9	1	×	.	.	.	.	.
Meadow Pipit	27	29	31	19	5	9	1	1	.	.	.	.	.
Yellow Wagtail	1	.	1	1	1	.	1	.	.	.	.	.	.
Whinchat													
Stonechat													
Scrub Birds													
Willow Warbler	×	2	12	26	47	39	51	41	46	31	3	2	1
Whitethroat	1	.	3	4	9	11	5	7	6	×	.	.	.
Yellowhammer	1	2	2	3	1	2	3	5	2	.	.	.	.
Hedgesparrow	.	.	.	1	6	6	6	4	9	5	×	.	.
Blackbird	.	.	.	1	3	6	8	8	7	5	1	.	.
Song Thrush	.	.	.	.	1	1	4	7	1	1	.	.	.
Wren	1	.	2	3	7	6	7	12	9	9	12	12	16
Tree Birds													
Chaffinch	.	.	.	.	1	4	9	13	11	21	31	37	39
Goldcrest	.	.	.	.	.	1	2	1	3	6	8	11	8
Coal Tit	.	.	.	.	1	1	1	.	4	11	26	24	25
Great Tit													
Blue Tit	.	.	.	.	.	.	.	.	1	2	5	4
Willow Tit													
Long-tailed Tit	.	.	.	.	.	.	.	.	×	4	.	1
Treecreeper	.	.	.	.	.	.	.	.	×	1	2	1
Jay	.	.	.	.	.	.	.	.	3	6	3	2
Robin	.	.	.	.	.	1	×	.	1	6	5	3	2

Omitted were Wheatear (Common heaths with rabbit burrows but not elsewhere), Grasshopper Warbler (2 in 6th year) and Chiffchaff (Less than 1% in 14–15 year old and occasional at edges of older plantations). The totals are not comparable.

From Lack and Lack (1951), by courtesy of *J. Anim. Ecol.*

these results come from visits to nine thicket stage plantations. Redpolls were very characteristic in the Irish plantations and were in fact the dominant species in early and late stage thickets at Tully and Gortin Glen. At Castle Archdale chiffchaffs and willow warblers were co-dominants. Sedge warblers were dominant at Cairnwood and in one plantation at Castle Archdale, but their percentage frequency was 44. Grasshopper warblers had an RA of 7 in the early thicket stage and there were small numbers of robins, blackbirds, long-tailed tits, reed buntings, meadow pipits, wood pigeons, song thrushes and magpies. There were a few records, too, of mistle thrushes, goldcrests, siskins, whitethroats, great tits and hooded crows. Although I have come across a few blue tits in thicket stages in England, Wales and Scotland, they were missing from all the Irish ones that I visited.

A study of the bird community during the different stages of the succession in a State forest of Corsican pines has been made on the sand-dunes of Newborough Warren in Anglesey. Table 23 gives the numbers of pairs breeding in six quadrats representing different successions in 1964. The early thicket stage shared with the unplanted grassland only about a quarter of the bird species recorded for both the dune and stable grassland areas. With the trees advancing through the late thicket stage the proportion fell to 12%. There was a density of 4.8 pairs per 10 acres of the original grassland – a figure which sank to 1.9 pairs per 10 acres at the establishment stage in the change-over from open land to thicket species; then the density rose again to 4.7 in the early thicket, 10.1 in the late thicket and 12.9 per 10 acres in the early pole stages. This kind of pattern has been recorded before in Georgia. At Newborough Warren the population of 2 adult passerines on 10 acres of duneland rose to about 20 per 10 acres for the 17-year-old Corsican pine plantations.

A rather different succession of birds was found on observation of the changes after a broad-leaved wood was felled and replaced by conifers. By the second year willow warbler, tree pipit, hedgesparrow, whitethroat and wren had advanced into the new plantation while two other species strange to the area – whinchat and grasshopper warbler – also appeared in small numbers. It seems that the early arrival of woodland birds was made possible through the absence of the heathland species which in other areas would have been in direct competition with them.

My experience in winter of the establishment stages shows that the heath birds are often present in somewhat larger numbers. The thicket stages are also visited by redwings and fieldfares and starlings may use them for roosting. Coal tits and goldcrests are generally more common in the winter months and make up a high proportion of the contacts. Finch and bunting species may increase in number and some will also roost in the thickets. Census work is difficult, for the well-developed plantations are almost impenetrable. Table 24 is adapted from one drawn up by Jones (1966) to show the total number of birds recorded in four stages at Newborough Warren in 160 minutes of transect time between November 1962 and February 1963. The high number of crossbills was due to the large immigration into Britain and Ireland during the sampling period. Since the winter of 1962–3 was especially severe the same counts were repeated in the much milder winter of 1963–4. The commonest species on the open dunes were skylark, partridge and meadow pipit and in the trees goldcrest, wren and reed bunting. Numbers fluctuate over the course of a winter and the total will be very much affected by the severity of the weather. During the bad winter of 1962–3 the number of birds recorded at Newborough fell by 76% of the November population but in the succeeding mild winter that followed the decrease was only 44%. The population drop could be attributed to the death of some of the residents and the departure of birds who were present in the area at the onset of winter. Absolute numbers for the plantations in Anglesey could not be obtained because of the difficulty of carrying out censuses, but it appeared that it was the size of the population at the end of the preceding winter which influenced the size of the subsequent breeding community. There was a gradual rise in the winter population of birds in the Breckland pine plantations, and some broad comparisons with the winter numbers of different regions in plantations from 17 to 36 years old were made. The results are shown in Table 25 where relative abundance figures are laid out for ten species. The counts were made in varying weather so that actual numbers cannot be compared. What was clear was that the gold-crest and the coal tit were common everywhere, while blue tits were regular in Norway spruce and often Scots pine but they were rather scarce in Corsican pine, Douglas fir, Scots pine in Fife and mixed pine in Dorset.

It would seem that birds are rather more demanding in their habitat needs in summer than in winter. The height of the vegetation rather than its nature plays an important part in birds' choice of breeding site. Many of the species that occur in the conifer plantations are those that we have already met in the broad-leaved scrub – thrushes, robin, chaffinch, hedgesparrow, wren, bullfinch, tits, yellowhammer, reed bunting, white-throat and willow warbler. It is only crossbills, siskins, redpolls, goldcrests, coal tits and some game-birds that have exclusive or very strong attach-ments to conifers. When the trees reach maturity it is only those bird species that can survive the closed canopy that will persist. There are similarities between the birds of broad-leaved and coniferous woodland, and 31 species of summer birds in 18 broad-leaved woods and 27 in 9 woods predominantly of pine and 4 mixed woods were noted. The differences in the faunas are particularly important among animals near the bottom of the food chain like the plant-eating invertebrates, fairly so among the insect predators but much less so among the passerine birds. The higher the consumer level the fewer and larger are the animals, but the wider also is their habitat range. Adaptable herbivores like the wood pigeon can be regularly found in both broad-leaved and coniferous woodland. With a few notable exceptions the birds of the new coniferous plantations have come in from the surrounding broad-leaved woodlands and will presumably return to them when conditions become adverse again. Woodland succession means instability and this will fluctuate during the stages of development. It is obvious that the vegetation on an acre of heathland will be less than that on an acre of scrub or an acre of climax woodland. The total amount in a climax wood varies only slightly from decade to decade and there is an ecological stability that was missing in the earlier stages of succession. In broad-leaved woods the later stages of succession are richer in animal species and habitats than the early ones and the climax forest may be the richest of all. The abundance of a species alters as the woodland succession provides habitats that are marginal for it, when a species is uncommon, until favourable habitats are formed when numbers are high. Birds may also spread from the optimal environments when the population is at a high level into the less-preferred marginal ones which thus assist in the control of populations.

WOODLAND FRAGMENTS, FARMS AND FOREST EDGE

So far it has been easier to consider the habitats in which woodland birds occur as simple consociations or associations. But there are also fragments of woodland and areas of overlap called ecotones which can be found between two adjacent but different kinds of environment. Examples of these ecotones are woodland and arable, woodland and grassland (or parkland), woodland and heath, woodland and water and the forest edge itself. Early Britain, even when well wooded, had a distinctly varied countryside made up of forest, hills, marshes, fens, heaths and small areas of grassland. These varied features would all provide instances of overlap which would be of significance to birds. The blending of two communities would often occur in a habitat which tended to be intermediate between those habitats on either side. It is difficult to know how widely these ecotones occurred in the past because a complex pattern has been further modified and altered in historic times by biotic factors, especially those of man and his domestic animals. Some authorities believe that the ecotone with its isolation has been of greater importance in the evolution of species than an area of unbroken, unchanging habitat. If any species of animal can satisfy its needs entirely in one environment there is then no selective advantage in widening its range of habitat and there are no pressures for trying new diets or experimenting with breeding sites. The present day distribution of many species includes both semi-natural and artificial ecotones as well as pure woodland, and this suggests some adaptability in the species concerned. We shall look more closely at those birds that have been able to make the transition to urban and suburban environments in the next chapter. The areas of overlap may contain all the apparently vital characters of the original habitat – food supply, breeding site, song posts or display grounds – and yet a species may find itself unable to move into the new area. There can still be a psychological preference for the ancestral type of habitat. However, in this chapter we shall consider the bird-life of the small woodlands, of the areas of overlap and of the clearly defined forest edges which are themselves a special kind of ecotone.

In tropical Africa I was interested to see how often the forest came to a sudden end where the savannah began. This is a different situation from

TABLE 23. *Numbers of Pairs of Different Species Breeding at Newborough Warren, Anglesey, in 1964*

Species	Mobile Dunes	Grass-land	Establish-ment	Early Thicket	Late Thicket	Early Pole
Open Country Birds						
Shelduck	1					
Curlew	1	1	1			
Skylark	1	6	3			
Partridge		1				
Thicket (Scrub) Birds						
Reed Bunting	1	1		4	2	1
Yellowhammer				1	2	
Redpoll				2	4	1
Willow Warbler				2	4	4
Early Pole Stage Birds						
Goldcrest				1	2	3
Pheasant					1	1
Robin					2	2
Chaffinch					1	4
Wood Pigeon					2	5
Coal Tit						1
Wren						4
Chiffchaff						1
Ubiquitous						
Mallard		1		1	1	2
Total Pairs	4	10	4	11	21	29
Passerine Pairs	2	7	3	10	17	21

From Jones (1966) by courtesy of *British Birds*

that in northern Canada where the forests become more and more open at their most northerly limits and the trees more stunted and straggly in their appearance. In the same way the birch forests of Scandinavia become less thick and tall as they reach the wastes of the Arctic tundra. In most of the mountain ranges of Europe conifers extend up the hills to the zone of alpine vegetation, but in Iceland, Norway, Sweden, the Urals and, as we have seen, in parts of Scotland the birch grows to the greatest altitudes. In the British Isles the margin of stunted timber and scrubby woods which like a tide-line, marks the hillsides at heights of from 1,200 ft. and more makes up one of the largest and most important of the ecotone

TABLE 24. *Total Numbers of Birds Recorded at Newborough Warren, Anglesey, in Winter, 1962–3*

The figures in brackets indicate the number of transects up to a maximum of 8 on which each species was recorded

Species	Mobile Dunes	Grass-land	Early Thicket	
Curlew	2 (1)			
Meadow Pipit	4 (3)	3 (3)		
Raven	3 (2)	2 (1)		
Partridge	6 (1)	6 (2)		
Skylark	1 (1)	12 (3)		
Carrion Crow		5 (2)		
Hen Harrier		1 (1)		
Reed Bunting	6 (4)	5 (2)	5 (2)	10 (6)
Wren	4 (3)		9 (6)	8 (4)
Redwing	2 (1)		2 (1)	2 (1)
Fieldfare	1 (1)			1 (1)
Mistle Thrush		4 (1)		4 (2)
Song Thrush		1 (1)	4 (3)	3 (3)
Short-eared Owl			1 (1)	
Goldcrest			5 (4)	15 (7)
Linnet			2 (1)	2 (1)
Crossbill				25 (5)
Coal Tit				5 (3)
Bullfinch				5 (2)
Redpoll				5 (2)
Yellowhammer				5 (2)
Magpie				4 (3)
Wood Pigeon				3 (3)
Great Tit				3 (2)
Chaffinch				2 (2)
Green Woodpecker				1 (1)
Totals	29	39	28	103

From Jones (1966) by courtesy of *British Birds*

areas. I have already made a brief reference to it in the last chapter. In these hillwoods the commonest birds are willow warbler, chaffinch and tree pipit, but moorland birds also penetrate them and some, like the yellowhammer, seem to be in the process of adapting themselves to another kind of habitat. The willow warbler ranges south from the birch-woods of the Arctic down to the steppes; it appears in many ecotones and may have evolved in one of them. In Europe another bird of birchwoods

TABLE 25. *The Winter Populations of Conifer Plantations, 17–26 Years Old*

(% of population formed by each species; × means present but less than 0.5%)

Species	East Anglian Breckland		Dorset	North Wales		North Tyne	Fife
	Scots Pine	Corsican Pine	Mixed Pine	Douglas Fir	Spruce	Spruce	Scots Pine
Wren	4	1	16	4	1	4	4
Chaffinch	·	·	·	·	·	13	·
Goldcrest	32	49	41	62	61	19	30
Coal Tit	28	23	29	22	16	24	55
Blue Tit	23	4	3	1	20	25	9
Great Tit	×	×	·	·	·	2	1
Willow Tit	2	×	5	·	·	·	·
Long-tailed Tit	6	15	6	1	·	·	·
Treecreeper	4	7	2	·	·	·	×
Robin	×	×	2	10	×	2	1
Total Contacts	2,019	1,109	174	105	273	540	193

From Lack and Lack (1951) by courtesy of *J. Anim. Ecol.*

is the closely-related Arctic warbler which has spread into Europe from eastern Asia since the last glacial period. Although part of their respective ranges overlaps, the willow warbler is a bird of the lower altitudes, not appearing above 4,500 ft., while in eastern Asia the Arctic warbler occurs in subalpine birch and conifer forests well above that height. The chaffinch appears in a vast number of different forest types, but its habit of camouflaging its nest with lichens has led to the suggestion that its nest is cryptically coloured only in the lichen-covered fellwoods, and these are probably its original home. The chaffinch can exploit food over a wide range size and it is a most efficient ground-feeder, so that by taking advantage of a wide ecological niche it has become one of the commonest birds over its distribution limits.

The ecotone formed by woodland and heath, with the latter dominated by *Calluna* or *Vaccinium*, is frequent among the native pine forests of Scotland and on some of the southern heathlands. Here the commonest species are again those of the hillwoods; the tree pipit is essentially a bird of grass or heathland with scattered trees, although it can be found, too, in open oak woods and coniferous woodland. In this tree/heath ecotone, besides the tree pipit, whinchat and yellowhammer are also regular. In Scotland I have also known greenshanks nest in this type of country and perch quite often in the pines. In Europe the green sandpiper is a bird of ancient coniferous forest, while the related wood sandpiper is common in damp tree/heath ecotones with its greatest density in the transitional belt between the taiga and the tundra. Perhaps the wood sandpiper which has bred in Britain was once a regular breeder in this kind of ecotone. In Finland the whinchat and the yellow wagtail, besides the wood sandpiper, are found on peat-bogs mainly near trees and from these they sing or begin their song flights. The black grouse is a bird of swampy heathlands with a little birch and pine and is generally most frequent along the edges of woods, especially those of birch, pine and sessile oak. Magpies are not uncommon in this kind of country while cuckoos often parasitise meadow pipits on heathland. Missing, however, from the British tree/heath is the great grey shrike which appears as a winter visitor in eastern and southern England; in parts of Europe it is often found on heathland with scattered pine and birch. It is not quite clear why this handsome bird does not breed here; there is an English fossil from the late ice age, but this may have been a winter visitor too.

Small fragmentary woodlands often climb up the dingles and crevices in the hills and these are also bounded by open heathland. At the lower levels of these woods in the Welsh hills I have seen pied flycatchers, redstarts and sometimes wood warblers, tits, mistle thrushes, tree pipits, great spotted woodpeckers, buzzards and sparrowhawks. At the upper levels ravens, carrion crows and willow warblers persist to the uppermost limit of growth. The hillside river courses with their woodland fringes are always full of interest. In moorland coombes in Somerset and Devon with their twisted, dwarf oaks there are buzzards, crows and ravens nesting while redstarts, wood warblers, and robins also occur. Merlins were found nesting in an old magpie's and a crow's nests in rowans growing on Exmoor. One small wood on a hillside in the Isle of Skye boasts a May dawn chorus of six birds – a couple of wrens, and single robin, blackbird, whinchat and greenfinch.

The second most important ecotone is a lowland one – that of parkland – and it is composed of trees and grassland. A great part of the English countryside can be classified as parkland since it consists of a landscape which is a patchwork of small woods often enclosed as shelter belts or game coverts, ornamental clumps and groves, garden trees, orchards, avenues, hedgerows and lines of trees as well as the laid-out parks of the manors and country mansions. Much of Ireland, too, viewed from the lower level of a travelling car, seems well wooded, but this impression is due, not to the presence of countless woods, but to the quantity of good timber growing in the hedges. The Forestry Commission's 1953 Report No. 2 separated small woods of from one to five acres in size from the combined amounts of hedgerow and park trees, the groups of trees of less than an acre in extent and the strips and belts less than 66 ft. wide which were left out of the main census of woodlands I described earlier in Chapter 3. The small woods covered by Report No. 2 were very varied and ranged from small patches of scrub to properly maintained high forest on the plains. In 1951 the total area of small woods in Britain was calculated at 178,300 acres of which 63% were in England, 16% in Wales and 21% in Scotland. The total acreage of small woods of five acres or less represented only 5% of the total woodland area. Oak accounted for one third of all the woods surveyed while beech, sycamore and ash together represented another third. The remaining third was composed largely of broad-leaved species including hazel, birch, alder, horse and sweet chestnut, elm, hornbeam, lime, poplar, willow and elder and coniferous trees such as Scots pine, European larch and Norway spruce in particular with smaller amounts of other larches, Sitka spruce, Corsican and Monterey pines, Douglas fir and one or two other species. Of all the trees in the 71,730 small woods recorded in Britain, sycamore and beech were important constituents and the most numerous trees in Wales were alder, oak, ash and beech and in Scotland sycamore, beech, Scots pine, oak, lime and birch in that order. Of course, lime, sycamore and beech were all introduced to Scotland. It is not possible to divide up the Irish woods in the same way, but anyone who has toured Ireland will have noticed the many small isolated woods which appear along the roads, chiefly on the demesnes. Many of these small woods together with the hedgerows, which I shall mention again later in this chapter, the pasture fields and meadows comprise an environment which can be described as parkland. The Census revealed that one fifth of all Britain's timber is to be found in scattered hedgerow, park and policy trees and "when the small woods and the hedgerows are taken together, they hold 27%, or over one quarter, of Britain's timber reserves". Before man began to change the landscape parkland would have been far less extensive and would have been confined chiefly to the woodlands adjoining the hill or downland grasslands.

The birds of parkland as distinct from woodland are those whose lives involve both trees and grassland. Of these, one of the most conspicuous and best known is the rook which nests socially in trees, often in hedgerows or small woods, but whose feeding habits are connected with grassland, and fields. In an extensive national survey it was found that rooks spend at least 50% of their feeding time in almost every month of the year on grasslands. The rook probes below the grassland surface and the main animal food is earthworms, and the period when the young birds are in the nest in April coincides with the period when this food is most available. Rookeries are very characteristic of lowland Britain and Ireland and in hilly country the rooks tend to congregate near the rivers with their meadows and pasture fields. Many rook colonies occur in lines of hedgerow trees and this nesting habit is one of comparatively recent date. Like the rook, the jackdaw also spends about half its feeding time on grassland, but apparently exploits more types of grassy habitat and often forages in the long vegetation on the edges of woods. In bad weather the jackdaw does not move into woodlands like the carrion crow or magpie, and this strongly suggests that woodland is not its natural home. Unlike rooks, which explore the levels below the grassland surface, the jackdaw tends to concentrate much more on food on the surface so that competition between the two species is generally avoided. Jackdaws are also busy feeding their young some six weeks later than the rooks when the surface invertebrates are most abundant. For the jackdaw grassland must be the primary habitat, although jackdaws not only nest in woodland but also search the canopy for defoliating caterpillars, especially *Tortrix viridana* and *Operophtera brumata*. Both rooks and jackdaws gather in winter roosts in tall trees in belts or woods and some of the roosts are quite large. There were over 20,000 birds at a roost near Bishop's Stortford in the winter of 1954–5;

here jackdaws represented between 50% and 60% of the total number. In south-west Cornwall the roosts were smaller with the largest total about 14,000, of which between 75% and 83% were jackdaws.

Another bird of parkland which may also breed in woodland is the starling. This species is dependent upon trees, cliffs and buildings for the holes in which it can breed. A population of starlings near Aberdeen located most of its food in the top layers of soil in some pasture fields. More than 80% of the food brought to the nestlings consisted of leather-jackets and some 16% of earthworms. It seems that the onset of breeding was not closely related to the abundance of food, but there was evidence to suggest that the available food supply was the factor that brought the breeding season to an end. Starlings collect most of their food from grass-land, but they will also visit arable land, farms with hen-runs and wood-land with berries. They feed on the ground by probing into the upper soil layer with a closed bill which is then opened underground and this method leaves characteristic holes in the grass. Such a habit appears in a some-what ludicrous context when starlings tackle slices of bread or lumps of fat on a bird-table. Starlings also roost in great assemblies in small woods, spinneys and plantations. Some roosts I have known have contained perhaps 3 million birds and it has been calculated that the maximum possible size for a roost is between four and five million.

The kestrel can be found in a great variety of parkland habitats nesting in trees and hunting over the grasslands for small rodents, insects and occasional small birds. Another bird of prey – the hobby – often nests in small isolated clumps or lines of trees in central and southern Britain, but I have seen some nests in quite dense woodland. The nests are often on the disused platforms of crows and wood pigeons and may be at quite a height above the ground. In one small clump of trees in Hampshire I was able to watch the food exchange ceremony between male and female hobby and to make a sound recording as well. The hobby's food consists mainly of large insects, small birds and sometimes bats which are all taken in flight. In recent years the breeding population has been under a hundred pairs. Another raptor which likes woodland with wide glades and the open spaces typical of parkland is the honey-buzzard. Once a rare but regular summer visitor to parkland country, especially in the New Forest, the honey-buzzard has maintained a small population of several pairs over the last forty years and has bred across southern England to the Welsh border and possibly in Scotland in 1949. It, too, builds on abandoned nests and its main food consists of wasp grubs, wild bees, humble bees and other insects. Barn and occasionally tawny owls nest in hollow trees in parkland, but the little owl whose voice in many parts was one of the most typical sounds of parkland has, since about 1955, suffered a decline in numbers.

Stock doves often breed in parkland ecotones as well as in dense woodland. The turtle dove likes a certain amount of space and is sometimes common where areas of grassland are interspersed with small woods and dense hedgerows. Of the woodpeckers the green is generally more common in parkland than in woodland. I located more pairs per hundred acres of Fawsley Park in Northamptonshire – a typical parkland habitat – than in the same acreage of Badby Wood nearby. In the New Forest, too, I have often watched this woodpecker in the open, park-like sections of the forest where it feeds on ants. The other two species of woodpeckers can also be found but the wryneck which is essentially a parkland bird is now very rare. Outside Kent there has been no certain nesting since 1959 and the decline in Britain has been catastrophic. Figure 20 shows how the wryneck has declined in numbers as a breeding species. It has decreased in Europe as well, but the reasons for this are not yet known. The mistle thrush can be found in this ecotone in the British Isles as well as in woodland. It has increased in recent years in Ireland and a marked movement of mistle thrushes into the parklands of north-west Europe has been noted. Lightly wooded grassland areas are very much favoured by greenfinches and goldfinches which share very similar habitats of park and farmland. This ecotone may also prove to be a favourable habitat for the serin if it extends its breeding activities in Britain, and it could also be a habitat for the hoopoe if it were able to acclimatise itself. Other ecotone birds of parkland are linnet, yellowhammer, tree sparrow, hedgesparrow, whitethroat, red-backed shrike, woodlark and cirl bunting. Linnet, greenfinch and goldfinch show differences in feeding habits. The greenfinch takes large tree seeds, cereals and the seeds of agricultural weeds which are dealt with by its short bill; the goldfinch with its thin bill probes into the seed heads of *Compositae* and the linnet specialises in the seeds of farmland weeds. Finches are very adaptable and seem to be able to change their feeding habits as the flora of the countryside itself changes. The red-backed shrike, as we saw in Chapter 10, is a bird of thorny bushes and grassland. There has been a marked decrease in its numbers and Fig. 21 illustrates this decline very clearly. The fall in numbers could be due to destruction of habitat, or to wet summers in the present century which have curtailed the numbers of large flying insects. The woodlark is perhaps a bird of a rather special kind of parkland for its distribution in England and Wales matches very closely that of the area which experiences 1,500 hours sunshine a year or a mean January temperature of more than 41° F. Throughout the whole of its European breeding range the woodlark

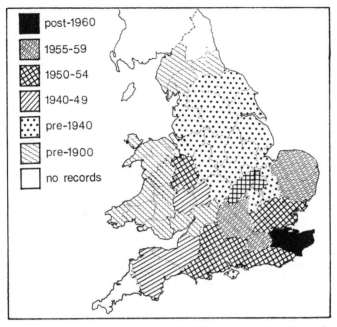

FIG. 20. The decline of the wryneck. The various shadings show the years in which the species is last known to have bred in each county. Emphasis has been placed on the recent near-final collapse of the population which already by 1940 was a shadow of its former strength. Reproduced from *British Birds* by kind permission of J. L. F. Parslow.

has an uneven distribution, but it is not known whether this is due to a dislike of human disturbance or to rather special habitat requirements. It prefers open grassy or heathy country on a dry, well-drained soil and with scattered trees. The land must have short open turf, but the territory also seems to need longer grass or heather for nesting and roosting. Since woodlarks may suffer severely from winter weather, dry, warm sites may help in survival, but the nests usually face north, presumably because the ground temperature on a southwards facing slope might be too high for a species which breeds on the ground. There is a subtle combination of factors at work here. The cirl bunting also seems to prefer warm, dry areas and this with certain requirements of vegetation limits its range in the British Isles. It seems to favour warm escarpments that face the south while high sun, low rainfall and mild winters may all affect its distribution. In England and Wales the cirl bunting is at the northern limit of its range. In the Alps, where its population also seems to fluctuate, it needs dry, warm conditions, but there are other factors which cannot yet be defined.

In the winter months redwings and fieldfares come into the parklands to feed on the pastures as well as the scrub and hedgerow thorns. Many finches also feed in this ecotone and in autumn it is not unusual to see wood pigeons, blackbirds and thrushes from the nearby woodlands in the grassland areas, while house sparrows eat the grass seed in autumn and spring.

Some of the typical parkland birds can also be found along the edge of the forest. These include the magpie, cuckoo and turtle dove, which are birds of semi-open country, and such ecotone species as greenfinch, goldfinch, tree sparrow, yellowhammer, nightingale, lesser whitethroat, robin, blackbird, hedgesparrow and, within their range, cirl bunting and woodlark. There is evidence that some species tend to occur more frequently near the edge than in the centre of a mature forest. Badby Wood was surrounded almost entirely by grassland consisting of pasture and parkland, and there was a tendency for blackbirds and willow warblers to be more common along the edges of the wood. In the great mixed forests of Tennessee there were more birds near the edge than in the centre, but in parts of Africa, where the bird zonation in the trees is often vertical as well as varied, I found that the sharp margin of the forest was not always the most densely populated; here there was an abrupt ecological change similar to that on the edges of many conifer plantations. Observation proved that the borders of mixed forests in Algonquin Provincial Park in Canada carried more birds than the heart of the woods. A nestbox scheme in four oakwoods in Westphalia showed that the nesting densities were higher in each case along the wood edges. The highest densities for the wood pigeon in both coniferous and broad-leaved woods are always recorded round the edges. At Preston Bushes near Preston-on-Stour in Warwickshire most of the nightingale territories were near the northeastern corner; a census made in Gloucestershire showed that nightingales there tended to be found much more on the eastern side of woods. This suggests an avoidance of the more regular and persistent winds which assail the south-western borders. If there is scrub growing along the edge of a wood then the bird community will show a spread through the ecotone, but more information is required about the ecology of forest edges.

When farming imposed its present pattern on the countryside a high proportion of the woodland bird species was able to cross the straggly edges of the forests into the new habitats of parkland, farmland, hedgerow, orchard and garden. The fields of the new farmlands were divided from each other by hedges and wind-breaks and these were soon colonised by

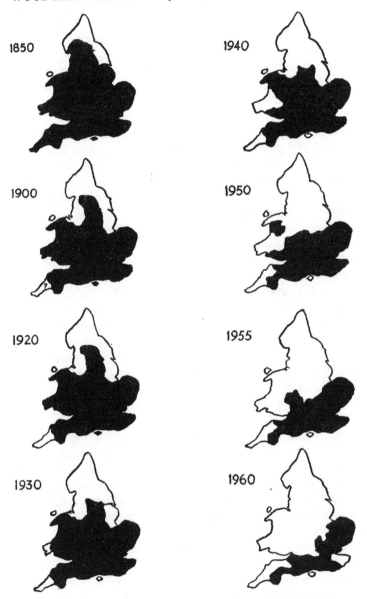

FIG. 21. Changes in the breeding status of the red-backed shrike, 1850-1960. Reproduced from *Bird Study* by kind permission of Dr D. B. Peakall.

birds. Farmland with its fields, small woods and hedgerows is a kind of woodland strip but it is an unstable environment subject to the processes of continuing change with ploughing, harvesting, hedge destruction, sprays and toxic chemicals preventing the establishment of a stable community. There are some quarter of a million acres of hedge in Great Britain which have largely originated from the enclosure movement and consist chiefly of hawthorn. Blackthorn is common in parts of the Midlands and I have also seen hedges of beech and hazel in the south-west, of privet in the south, of copper beech in Fenland, and of gorse and fuchsia in the Outer Hebrides and Ireland. Some of the thorn hedges are large and dense having been allowed to grow naturally without being cut or "laid", and these are often favoured by magpies, turtle doves, bullfinches, lesser whitethroats and nightingales, all of which are typical species of thorn scrub. Some of these hedges may represent what Sir Edward Salisbury called "residual strips of the scrub, left as windbreaks within the agricultural encroachments upon the primitive forest". The hedges that are laid perhaps at about fifteen-year intervals are reduced to low, thin strips from which branches develop to make the thick barrier against cattle. There are perhaps some $1\frac{1}{2}$ million miles of field hedgerow with another $\frac{3}{4}$ million bordering roads, but the last twenty years have seen something like a 10% to 20% decrease. However, the remaining area with some 20,000 miles of British Rail track represents a considerable refuge for birds and other animals. An encouraging step is the 1970 announcement that the Crown Estate Commissioners intend to pay a bonus to their 900 tenants who leave saplings standing when they lay hedges.

Hedgerows often contain standard or smaller trees, shrubs, climbers and a very interesting flora. The number of trees in this situation and in parkland in England is about 55 million and there are 11 million in Wales and 7 million in Scotland. Half of the English hedgerow timber grows south of a line from the River Thames to the River Severn and in the two counties of Gloucestershire and Hereford. Oak is the principal hedgerow tree in the Midlands of England, East Anglia, in the south-west and in the south-east. In the north of England oak and ash are the most important with some sycamore and elm. Lincoln, Bedford and the south-east are also rich in elm, while ash is frequent in the north-east and south-west. In Wales oak is the commonest hedgerow tree, but there are also considerable amounts of ash, beech, sycamore and elm. Hedgerow timber in Scotland occurs only in the lowland belt and consists primarily of beech, oak, ash, sycamore and Scots pine. In Ireland ash, beech and sycamore appear very regularly, often as magnificent and well developed trees. Other trees that can be found in hedges include elder, crab apple and holly. In the autumn spindle tree, buckthorn and guelder rose, which are shrubs of the forest edge, may add brightness to the hedges with their fruit.

When the country was less densely populated, and agriculture took place on a smaller scale, most of our forests were fringed by areas of scrub with a rich and varied flora made possible because the ecotone conditions between forest and grassland allowed many species to flourish that lacked the ability to succeed in those specialised habitats. Many plants of this marginal flora appear in hedgerows – wild rose, bramble, honeysuckle, bryony, greater bindweed, and, on calcareous soils, traveller's joy. The field layer may be composed of umbellifers such as hedge and cow parsley, rough chervil and hogweed besides stinging nettle, white dead nettle, hedge mustard, jack-by-the-hedge, black horehound, goosegrass, cuckoo pint, various vetches and welted thistle. In hedges near the coast, fennel and alexanders are often very common. Many plants of the hedgerow have been brought by birds which have perched in the hedge and then excreted seeds. Seed-eating birds must be quite important in the dispersal of some plant species and viable seeds have been recovered from the droppings of several species of bird. Pigeon droppings have supplied seeds of sheep's sorrel, charlock, ironweed, poppy, plantain and pennycress, while those from sparrows have yielded fat hen, shepherd's purse, ribwort, groundsel, spurry and chickweed.

These hedgerows provide a sanctuary for quite a proportion of our bird population and so far, considering their ecological interest, they have been little studied. Recently work has been undertaken on hedges and their bird-life, showing how serious the destruction of hedges, especially in East Anglia, can be. The Merthyr Report more than ten years ago underlined the importance of hedgerows and farm timber in a balanced countryside. Farmers need more information about tree planting and practical help to appreciate the value of including forestry and forestry practice in their own planning and farm management. Hedgerows create local conditions of temperature, humidity, shade and protection which mark them off very distinctly from the fields or roads for which they provide borders. In any ecological study of a hedgerow it is necessary to know whether it possesses trees and shrubs that penetrate the hedge top as well as finding out their species, height, width, and structure, all of which may influence the birds. A list of typical hedgerow birds would put the following species in order of abundance – blackbird, chaffinch, hedge-sparrow, robin, yellowhammer, linnet and whitethroat. In 1965 the Common Birds Census mapped some 12,000 bird territories in some 35 square miles of farmland and $3\frac{3}{4}$ square miles of woodland. Four species – rook, starling, wood pigeon and house sparrow – were excluded from the survey; it was found that on farmland the blackbird was the commonest species with chaffinch and hedgesparrow in second and third places, but so close to each other that their relative positions might shift from year to year. Yellowhammers, whitethroats, and linnets may take up to 10% each of the passerine total with blue tit, song thrush, great tit, wren, greenfinch and probably starling less than 10%. Blackbirds form between 10% and 20% of the population, hedgesparrows 8% to 16%, but robins and chaffinches, which need trees with their hedges, may reach but rarely exceed 12% of the passerine population. In England, Scotland and Ireland pheasants are on the increase, but the common partridge has decreased in England, Wales, southern Scotland and probably in Ireland, too. Both species use hedges for nesting and for shelter, but the introduced red-legged partridge has shown signs of a local increase in East Anglia. Other species which frequent hedgerows are magpies, long-tailed tits, mistle thrushes, lesser whitethroats, bullfinches, corn buntings, turtle doves, wood pigeons and nightingales. The extensive cutting of the old hedges along the Stratford Tramway in Warwickshire led to the total disappearance of the nightingales, and the laying of hedges around Great Budworth in Cheshire resulted in a reduction in the number of breeding turtle doves. Visitors to hedges may include swallows, cuckoos, and reed buntings as well as other small birds. Sparrowhawks and barn owls often hunt along hedges while stoats, weasels and rats may take a toll of eggs and young birds. Hedges in Ireland are largely made up of hawthorn, blackthorn, gorse and sallow. They are often well developed with big beeches, oaks, ashes, sycamores, wych elms and rowans and have luxuriant field layers. The commonest birds I observed were song thrush, mistle thrush, yellowhammer, magpie and jackdaw. The fuchsia hedges in south-western Ireland were rather disappointing from the bird point of view. Some of the derelict railway tracks of Britain contain long sections of scrub and here there is still room for investigation; the birds tend to be found at the greatest density where the hedgerows and ditches actually impinge on the old track.

In the breeding season birds may occur at an average of one for every five yards of hedgerow, but I have recorded one per four yards near London and one per ten yards in Warwickshire. There must be many differences in density due to geographical separation as well as to the character and type of the hedge. One would expect some species such as the great and blue tits, wren and willow warbler to be more abundant in woodland than on farmland while hedgesparrow and yellowhammer were more common on farms. It has been suggested that English farmland has probably a lower density of nest predators than woodland, but a higher density than gardens, so that its suitability as a nesting habitat could be regarded as intermediate between that of woodland and the suburbs. In species nesting in all three of these habitats more young are produced per pair in direct proportion to the extent to which the environment has been changed by man from untouched woodland to that of suburbia. The birds of the suburbs and built-up areas will be the subject of a separate chapter.

For nearly two years I lived on a farm in south Warwickshire which had an 11 acre orchard made up largely of apple trees with some pears and plums. An orchard is an ecotone of a rather interesting kind and, if it contains old and mature trees, it may be very rich in arboreal birds; if it is newer and managed in the modern style it may be much poorer. The orchard on the farm was mature and unsprayed. In this area of 11 acres there were, in the summer of 1949, some 68 birds of 24 species giving a density of 60 birds per 10 acres. On the rest of the 170 acres of the farm with its 39 species there was a density of 15 birds per 10 acres. In all these calculations I have excluded rooks and house sparrows. Incidentally the figure of 39 species for the farm is comparable to the figure of "about 40" for farmland in the London area given in *The Birds of the London Area*. Of the 24 species nesting in the orchard, magpie, redstart and goldfinch did not breed elsewhere on the farm, while treecreeper, green and lesser spotted woodpecker bred more regularly there than in the farmland's wooded strips where the great spotted woodpecker was well established. One pair of little owls nested in the orchard and a visiting sparrowhawk often hunted through it. In orchards elsewhere I have seen hawfinches and pied flycatchers while some of the last haunts of the wryneck have been in southern orchards.

Between 1939 and 1948 orchards occupied some 270,000 acres in England and Wales, 1,300 acres in Scotland and 9,500 acres in Northern Ireland. These areas represent an important ecotone for birds, but their importance will be affected by whether the orchards have herbage only beneath the trees, or fruit bushes or ploughed land, as well as by the age and treatment of the fruit trees. Orchards are sometimes turned into unstable communities by man's interference with the ecological balance. Although it may be tempting to overestimate the value of birds in controlling pests, a serious break in the ecological chain at the lower levels may render the trees more liable to attack by insect pests. Invasions most often come to cultivated land or to land greatly modified by man's multifarious practices. Orchards are therefore extremely valuable for ecological studies since man's economic needs are also involved.

Market gardens and allotments, which are ecotones midway between those of farmland and garden or suburban habitats, have a bird community rather like that of gardens, although at Dollis Hill in Middlesex during the 1939–45 war, when grassland was turned into allotments, there was an influx of breeding skylarks and a rise in the populations of greenfinches and goldfinches that came to feed on the seeds of weeds and vegetables. Gardens themselves may look like woodland or scrub if they are large with mature trees and shrubberies, or are overgrown and untended. Small suburban gardens contain elements of farmland with their tilled soil, hedges and vegetable plots, of grassland with their lawns, of scrub with their bushes, small trees and herbaceous borders, of parkland with their open spaces and of the woodland/water ecotone with ponds or occasional reservoirs. The difference in the bird-life between the hedgerows of farmland and the gardens of suburbia is less in the number of species to be found than in the relative abundance. The life histories of many of these birds of farm, hedgerow, garden and orchard have been described in E. M. Nicholson's *Birds and Men* – a companion volume in this series. Birds of woodland origin require above all suitable food, a site for the nest and a song post. If these three vital elements are present many species can enter and flourish in the various ecotones that I have described in this chapter. Those that cannot make the adjustment, often indeed a small one, are lacking in the plasticity, sometimes of a psychological origin, that the more successful species possess. In the next chapter we shall see how successfully or not the woodland species have been able to penetrate the most highly sophisticated of all man-made habitats – the town.

CHAPTER 12

WOODLAND BIRDS IN TOWNS

THE story of Britain's woodland birds has brought us from the ice ages to the present day. We have seen how certain species have been able to adapt themselves to the new habitats made by man – parklands, farms, hedgerows and so on. We now come to the most unusual setting for woodland birds – that of suburbs and towns. My upbringing in west London and the fact that I have for some years lived at Dollis Hill – a suburban area of north-west London – have given me unique opportunities for studying the birds of Inner London and of the suburbs; what has basically emerged is that the commonest and the most successful species are those which are the most adaptable. The unsuccessful species are those with rigid demands for specialised habitats which have been destroyed by the coming of the built-up areas or those which are so intolerant of man that they are prevented by his various activities from feeding and breeding near him.

In this chapter I hope to show how the birds whose homes were in woodland or scrub have been able to penetrate the suburbs or the town centres, or both. Where it is possible I shall compare and contrast the behaviour of birds in woodland with that in the man-made environments of towns. A species may also behave differently in similar habitats on the Continent. The bird community of the suburbs and towns with their houses, concrete blocks, streets, parks and gardens is a characteristic one and its permanent species are almost entirely woodland in origin. Since Dollis Hill lies between the ecotones of farmland and of heavily built-up area, I propose to give an account of the bird-life in the suburbs first of all.

The study area in which I live covers some 546 acres, or about five sixths of a square mile, to the west of the Edgware Road and south of the North Circular Road. It takes the form of a shallow cone on the London Clay which rises from heights of 115 to 172 ft. above sea-level on the periphery to 251 ft. in the middle at the highest point; there are some deposits of glacial gravel above the 230 ft. contour. The area contains within its boundaries five major habitats – residential, factory, parkland, allotments and an area of orchards and trees – forming a most interesting ecological unit which is almost entirely man-made. At the time of writing, the last habitat has been cleared and is now being built on. When the

Enclosure Award was made in 1816 this area was open farming land and included a mansion, two farms and 75 fields with hedgerows. The breeding population in the nineteenth century boasted the following lost species: partridge, sparrowhawk, corncrake, cuckoo, wryneck, skylark, swallow, magpie, treecreeper, blackcap, garden warbler, whitethroat, lesser white-throat, bullfinch and yellowhammer. In the last eighteen years there are single breeding records of blackcap and willow warbler (which I imagine was also present in the last century), but all the other species in that list are now missing or occur as very rare vagrants or occasional migrants; they were unable to adapt themselves. At the nearby Brent Reservoir, bird-catchers were taking greenfinches, chaffinches, goldfinches, linnets, redpolls and sometimes twites, bramblings and tree sparrows.

The first serious residential building started in the south-east corner of the area in 1907–8. Then there was a pause and in the middle of the 1920s the Edgware Road was developed and a few houses were built near Dollis Hill Lane. By this time two other landmarks – St. Andrew's Hospital and the Post Office Research Station (which rose on the site of the old Dollis Hill Farm) – had been constructed. The south-west corner had been occupied by a golf course and a large part of the study area therefore still retained much of its rural nature. Then a tide of building swept across the hill between 1928 and 1930 in which period 29 new streets were laid out in the centre with increasing development in the two southern corners. In the next two years the building rash spread to the western side and into the factory area in the north-eastern apex. By 1935 the western half was built over. After 1945 some of the factories were extended and a few small houses and blocks of flats went up. After 1958 two new schools and a block of flats were built on two of the allotment sites. In 1967 a large area of allotments and orchards near Brook Road was cleared and many blocks of flats are going up at the time of writing. This clearance has driven chaffinches, greenfinches, great tits, robins and wrens into the gardens near my own and the displaced population has been satisfactorily absorbed. Figure 22 shows the changes in the area between 1875 and 1961.

The greatest part of the area – some 68%, in fact – is residential in character with slightly more than 3,600 houses in 330 acres. Many of the houses are semi-detached or in terraces with small front gardens, some-times with grass, flower beds or areas of concrete, and these are typically bordered by low walls, railings, fences or privet hedges. The back gardens are about 20 ft. wide and tend to vary from 50 to 100 ft. in length, and are separated from each other by wooden fences, palings, walls or chain-link. The top layer of small tree or shrub growth is about 20 ft. high and in many gardens it is much lower than this. The taller growth is generally

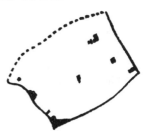

1875   1908

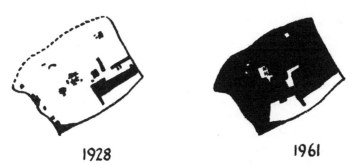

1928   1961

FIG. 22. The study area at Dollis Hill, London, at intervals from 1875-1961, with the built-up parts in black. Reproduced by kind permission of *British Birds*.

made up of ash trees, Lombardy poplars, laburnums, lilacs, flowering cherries, sycamores and assorted fruit trees. A few old oaks and elms still survive from the years before the development began. The roads in the residential area are often tree-lined and among the planted trees are rowan, London plane, horse chestnut, tree-of-heaven, sycamore, false acacia, Norway maple, silver birch, seven species of *Crataegus*, laburnum, lime and several others. As can be seen in Fig. 23 most of the residential area lies in the centre and to the west and here the typical breeding birds are the house sparrow, starling, blackbird and hedgesparrow; this is an avifauna that can be found where a farm and hedgerows join, but this habitat is too disturbed for some farmland species like yellowhammer and whitethroat. Wood pigeons will breed in the roadside trees such as plane, elm, sycamore and horse chestnut and very occasionally in garden trees of sufficient height. Blue tits will use nestboxes as they do in my own garden but they and the great tits are not at all common. Robins and wrens do not often find nesting sites in the gardens and the song thrush rarely attempts to breed since there are not many shrubs or evergreens of sufficient height or thickness. In 1970 there were signs of a real increase.

The second habitat is made up of the factories in the northern part of the area and the complex of buildings forming the Post Office Research Station. These and their environs make up some 15% of the total area. Here the characteristic species are feral pigeon, house sparrow, starling and pied wagtail. Carrion crows often use the buildings for perching and assembling while blackbirds may use their roof-tops as song posts.

The third habitat at Dollis Hill I have called parkland and this includes most of Gladstone Park and part of the grounds of the local hospital; it accounts for 13% of the total area. Here there are tall oaks, elms, poplars, horse chestnuts and smaller flowering trees, a few shrubberies and vast green swards of grass. The breeding species here are mallard, wood pigeon, tawny owl, carrion crow, great tit, blue tit, wren, mistle thrush, song thrush, blackbird, robin, spotted flycatcher, hedgesparrow, starling, greenfinch, chaffinch and house sparrow. A single pair of very shy stock doves held on in the Park until 1957. Sixteen of the eighteen species are regular birds of woodland.

There are three areas of allotments in the district, but one of these is now very largely being developed. Two smaller areas were built on in 1967 and the total amount of this valuable habitat is continuously being eroded away. This is a disadvantage not only for the birds, but also for those of us who feel that the amount of space left is barely sufficient anyway. The surviving pieces of allotment now take up about 4% of the area, but these remnants in varying stages of cultivation with their occasional thick shrubs and clumps of hawthorn, bramble and elder are still important feeding areas for thrushes, wrens, robins, hedgesparrows, wood pigeons, finches and sparrows – both house and tree. Song thrushes and blackbirds breed in the bushes and wrens and robins in the low cover while at the seasons of migration the allotments are always worth searching for migrants such as redstarts, pied flycatchers, blackcaps, lesser whitethroats, willow warblers, chiffchaffs and several other species.

The final habitat makes up only 2% of the area, but it has been very important. This special area consisted of a belt of trees – oaks, elms, sycamore, limes and ashes – with a field layer of cow parsley, nettles, bluebells and ivy; at one end near the Brook Road allotments was a disused orchard with rough grass and several chicken runs. There was an almost rural quality about this strip of land but the Brent Council are now building on the allotments and the whole of the special area. I have recorded the following breeding birds: wood pigeon, carrion crow, jay, great and blue tit, wren, song thrush, blackbird, robin, hedgesparrow,

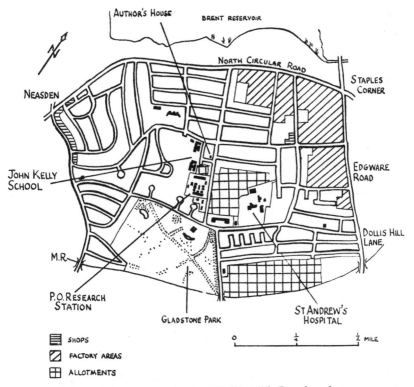

FIG. 23. Map of the area studied at Dollis Hill, London, between 1951-61, showing the major buildings, residential parts, factories, parkland and allotments. Reproduced by kind permission of *British Birds*.

starling, greenfinch, goldfinch, chaffinch, tree sparrow and house sparrow. There are also records of the blackcap and willow warbler as nesting species. A number of the breeding pairs has moved out into the nearby residential part of Dollis Hill.

In Table 26 I have given the species that have bred or been present in the breeding season at Dollis Hill from 1951 to 1968. From this table it can be seen that the average number of breeding species was 20.5 with a minimum of 16 in 1963 and a maximum of 23 in 1954. These figures can be compared to the total of 22 breeding species recorded in 1936 by Rowberry in his census of birds in suburban south-west London and reported in *The Birds of the London Area*. It may be of interest to record that a stable fauna of 18 species was found in a suburban park-like cemetery in France. Of the 26 species that have bred at Dollis Hill, 22 are birds of woodland and woodland ecotone and this gives an idea of how some woodland species have been able to move into the suburbs. When farming land is first turned over to building the effects on the bird population are adverse, but with the growth of trees and shrubs the picture improves. Land which is cultivated and dug provides food in a more accessible form for birds such as mistle and song thrushes, starlings, robins and hedge-sparrows which search for invertebrate life in the soil. The regular cutting of the grass on lawns benefits all the species of thrush, starlings, crows,

TABLE 26. *Species Breeding or Present in Breeding Season at Dollis Hill, 1951–68*

B indicates breeding and p present but not breeding

	1951	1952	1953	1954	1955	1956	1957	1958	1959	1960	1961	1962	1963	1964	1965	1966	1967	1968
Mallard	B	B	B	B	B	B	B	B	B	B	B	B	B	B	B	B	B	p
Kestrel	p			p			p	p	p	p	p	p	p	p	p	p	p	p
Stock Dove	B	B	B?	B	p	B?	B?											
Feral Pigeon	B	B	B	B	B	B	B	B	B	B	B	B	B	B	B	B	B	B
Wood Pigeon	B	B	B	B	B	B	B	B	B	B	B	B	B	B	B	B	B	B
Tawny Owl	B	B	B	B	B	B	B	B	B	B	B	B	B	B	B	p	B	B
Swift	p	p	p	p	p	p	p	p	p	p	p	p	p	B	p	p	B	B
Skylark	B	B	B	B														
Carrion Crow	B	B	B	B	B	B	B	B	B	B	B	B	B	B	B	B	B	B
Jay												p	p	p	p	p	B	p
Great Tit	B	B	B	B	B	B	B	B	B	B	B	B	B?	B	B	B	B	B
Blue Tit	B	B	B	B	B	B	B	B	B	B	B	B	B	B	B	B	B	B
Wren	B	B	B	B	B	B	B	B	B	B	B	B		B	B	B	B	B
Mistle Thrush	B	B	B	B	B	B	B	B	B	B	B	B		p	B	B	B	p
Song Thrush	B	B	B	B	B	B	B	B	B	B	B	B	B	B	B	B	B	B
Blackbird	B	B	B	B	B	B	B	B	B	B	B	B	B	B	B	B	B	B
Robin	B	B	B	B	B	B	B	B	B	B	B	B	B	B	B	B	B	B
Blackcap		B?			B?	B?		B										
Willow Warbler					B?	B?	B											
Spotted Flycatcher	B	B	B	B	B	B	B	B	B	B	B	B	B	B	B	B	B	B
Hedgesparrow	B	B	B	B	B	B	B	B	B	B	B	B	B	B	B	B	B	B
Pied Wagtail	B	B	B	B	B	B	B	B	B	B	B	B	B	B	B	B	B	B
Starling	B	B	B	B	B	B	B	B	B	B	B	B	B	B	B	B	B	B
Greenfinch	p	B?	B	B	B	B	B	B	B	B	B	B	B	B	B	B	B	B
Goldfinch	p	B?	B	B	B	B	B	B	B	B	B	B	B	B	B	B	B	p
Chaffinch	B	B	B	B	B	B	B	B	B	B	B	B	B	B	B	B	B	B
House Sparrow	B	B	B	B	B	B	B	B	B	B	B	B	B	B	B	B	B	B
Tree Sparrow	p	p	B	B	B?	B	B	B	B	B	B	B	p	p	p	B?	p	B
Total of Species Breeding	20	20	22	23	20	21	22	22	21	20	21	21	16	20	20	19	22	19

pigeons and hedgesparrows while greenfinches, goldfinches and tree sparrows find seeds in gardens and allotments where the husbandry is erratic or absent. There are also many potential nesting sites provided by man as well as an abundance of nesting material. In less well developed suburban areas where the human pressure is not quite so great as that at Dollis Hill it is possible to find redpoll, treecreeper, nuthatch, great spotted woodpecker, coal tit and sometimes bullfinch, while in Ireland the magpie is frequent in suburban areas and reaches almost to the heart of Dublin. Jackdaws appear in the quieter older suburbs and even rooks may breed there as well. I saw the first magpie at Dollis Hill in 1969.

In Inner London the number of species of woodland origin again drops and although there are more birds in the parks and squares the City itself is low in species. In the closely built-up zone the commonest birds are feral pigeons and house sparrows although there is evidence that the latter species has been declining in recent years. Kestrels breed in very tiny numbers but wood pigeons, starlings, blackbirds and even jays attempt to breed in the middle of the concrete desert. In the London squares blackbirds and a few mistle thrushes may survive and spotted flycatchers, great and, more commonly, blue tits bring off broods in the most unlikely places. In Ladbroke Square in Kensington I have found nests of jay, wood pigeon, blackbird, mistle and song thrush, robin and great tit, while chaffinch, hedgesparrow, carrion crow, tawny owl and great spotted woodpecker were present at various times during the breeding season. Similarly in the small gardens of the central area like that at Lancaster House it is possible to find blackbird, robin, wood pigeon, hedgesparrow and jay all nesting.

There are several aspects of woodland bird ecology in towns that deserve a somewhat closer look. Perhaps the best known bird of woodland origin in towns is the blackbird, but this is a comparatively recent development. Thomas Bewick in 1804 described the blackbird as "a solitary bird frequenting woods and thickets" and it was not until the 1830s that there are records of birds coming near towns and gardens, but this habit was confined to the winter months. By the end of the nineteenth century the blackbird had become a regular garden bird, but its general spread into the large towns has only been in the last forty or fifty years. Its invasion of the central districts of London did not occur until late in the mid-1930s. In eastern Europe the blackbird is just beginning to penetrate towns as the species expands its easterly range. Blackbirds have low densities in the Polish woodlands, but they are becoming common in towns. It was found that in Slovakia and Poland the blackbird at the limits of its range is much more of a woodland bird. Near Stockholm, blackbirds used to spend the early part of the year in town, but they retired to the nearby forest to roost.

At Dollis Hill the total number of blackbird pairs breeding at least once each year varies normally between 185 and 200 although it may rise to as high as 212 or exceptionally drop to 86. The breeding densities of the blackbirds can be seen in Table 27; the drop in 1963 was due to the effects of the severe winter immediately before the nesting season in that year. There are many more blackbirds at Dollis Hill per acre than in Badby Wood. The breeding density in the oakwoods at Wytham near Oxford was only one-tenth of the density of blackbirds nesting in the Botanic Garden. Parkland is less well populated than gardens, and farmland supports a population about one-twentieth that of the best gardens while woodlands also have low numbers. British gardens are more heavily populated than many Continental ones due to the presence of thicker and more luxuriant cover. In Czechoslovakia town blackbirds were four times more abundant than in the forests and a similar situation was also found in Poland.

Woodland blackbirds begin breeding later than those in gardens, sometimes as much as a fortnight later. A comparable trend has been found on the Continent where garden blackbirds bred ten days earlier than those in the woods. The clutches are also on average smaller in gardens than in woodland and many nestlings seem to die in garden nests. Yet, on the whole, nesting success among blackbirds is relatively high in gardens, fair on farmland and very low in the woods. The woodland population suffers fairly severely from predation. At Dollis Hill the cat is the most important predator and there is one cat to every twelve houses. In 1951 the figure was one cat to every five houses so that there are now some 400 fewer cats than there were seventeen years ago. Of other predators there are a few rats, some grey squirrels since 1964, carrion crows and tawny owls and very occasionally a boy with a catapult. Cats at Dollis Hill seem to fill the ecological niche that adders and our native carnivores do in the woodlands and open countryside. There is quite a high adult mortality among garden blackbirds and predation can have an appreciable effect during the breeding season.

In densely populated gardens blackbirds are very territorial in their behaviour and at Dollis Hill the territories tend to have as their nuclei traditional, often annual, breeding sites. The severe weather during the winter of 1962–3 broke down this territorial pattern since there was a drop of 55% in the blackbird population. An attempt has been made to show that, since there were no apparent changes in blackbird numbers in an area of south London, this drop at Dollis Hill was atypical, but numbers

TABLE 27. *Breeding Densities of Blackbirds at Dollis Hill, North-west London, 1951–68 compared with some Recorded Densities in Other Habitats*

(a) *Dollis Hill*

Year	Males in March	Pairs Breeding	Pairs per Acre
1951	198	185	0.338
1952	199	188	0.344
1953	198	191	0.349
1954	197	190	0.347
1955	196	186	0.340
1956	199	187	0.342
1957	198	189	0.346
1958	218	212	0.388
1959	194	188	0.344
1960	195	187	0.342
1961	200	194	0.354
1962	199	192	0.351
1963	93	86	0.157
1964	244	200	0.366
1965	206	198	0.363
1966	216	204	0.374
1967	199	195	0.357
1968	209	185	0.338

(b) *Other Habitats*

Overgrown garden, south Wales (Campbell 1953)	2.771
Botanic Garden, Oxford, 1954 (Snow 1958)	2.660
Botanic Garden, Oxford, 1955 (Snow 1958)	2.160
Botanic Garden, Oxford, 1953 (Snow 1958)	1.830
Dublin suburb (Jackson 1954)	0.724
Oxford University Parks, 1954–6 (Snow 1958)	0.485
Oxford University Parks, 1953 (Snow 1958)	0.442
Ladbroke Square Garden, 1936 (Simms unpubl.)	0.428
Surrey oakwood (Upper limit) (Beven 1952)	0.283
Oxfordshire farmland (Chapman 1939)	0.161
South Wales farmland (Campbell 1953)	0.121
Surrey oakwood (Lower limit) (Beven 1952)	0.089

seemed low in other parts of north London – Neasden, Stonebridge Park, Hendon and Wembley. There were, however, some instances of apparent residents being recovered in their areas in January and February 1963. Territorial behaviour was very strong in 1964 when there was an excess of male birds, and this helped to limit the breeding density. When the area becomes saturated the density remains fairly stable and certainly it has altered little at Dollis Hill over eighteen years. In 1964 breeding success was low, due primarily to the disturbances arising from competition among local birds; in an urban park in Switzerland high density also resulted in very strongly-marked territorial activity which brought a low breeding success. The density in woodland communities is more likely to be regulated by the survival of adults over the previous winter and perhaps also by the numbers of young birds produced in the previous breeding season. The power of the territorial urge varies at Dollis Hill throughout the year, but in winter the old pairs tend to keep their established territories while some of the young birds capture and hold small domains. In Denmark many urban blackbirds were found to hold winter territories while woodland birds do not. Density is influenced not only by behaviour but also by the amount and nature of "cover" which can regulate the numbers even in an area with plentiful supplies of food and a good provision of potential nesting sites. Although woodland was the blackbird's original home, it now finds a man-made habitat more favourable to it.

In contrast at Dollis Hill there are only seven to ten pairs of song thrushes. At the beginning of this century, in north-west London the song thrush was the commonest thrush; today its status is different and it is outnumbered by the blackbird by between 20 and 27 to 1. The song thrush is scarce in Inner London, but rather more frequent in the larger parks with some good cover and in those big suburban gardens with lawns and shrubberies. There has been a definite decrease in numbers since C. L. Collenette from 1904–11 recorded near Woodford 97 nests of the song thrush to 94 of the blackbird, but after the First World War the balance shifted to a proportion of 5 blackbirds to 1 song thrush. The smaller thrush is certainly less hardy than the blackbird, has a more restricted diet and is more conservative in its choice of nesting sites. All the song thrush nests at Dollis Hill, with only two exceptions, have been in hollies or hawthorns and from 5 to 15 ft. above the ground. Table 28 gives a clear idea of the wide choice of nesting site and the great height range that blackbirds will exploit.

The smaller, more timid song thrush is less tolerant of disturbance than the bigger, bolder blackbird and suffers more total loss through the breeding season than does the blackbird. It seems to dislike the increasing pressures inherent in urban development and, although many suburbs and parks of fifty years ago were attractive to it, those of today certainly seem less favourable. It is interesting to note in passing that it is only during the present century that the Continental song thrush has become a familiar

TABLE 28. *Heights and Situations of 611 Blackbird Nests at Dollis Hill, London, 1951–61*

0–5 ft.	5–10 ft.	10–15 ft.	15–20 ft	20–25 ft.	25–30 ft.
4 In trees and bushes	510 In creeper on walls	56 On pipes on walls	22 On ledges of fences	16 On stacked ladders	3 In sheds and buildings
497	16	15	76	3	4

bird in parks and gardens in Germany. Its larger relative the mistle thrush is a marginal species at Dollis Hill having decreased from two pairs in 1951–4 to a single pair that does not breed every year. There has been some increase in Inner London and the inner suburbs since 1929 and the mistle thrush is now regular in most of the parks and squares. A census made in Kensington Gardens from 1948–9 revealed that both blackbird and mistle thrush were more numerous than in 1925–6. In 1965 there were at least ten pairs or singing males in the parks of Inner London.

Robins are not all that common at Dollis Hill; in fact, only some 7 or 8 pairs nest within half a mile of my house, and these breed chiefly in the park or on the allotments since they rather avoid the private gardens which are lacking in suitable nesting places. A pair bred in my garden for the first time in 1968, but some robins will take up purely winter territories in the gardens from August to March and I have not been without one of these since 1951. Robins have bred in Ladbroke Square and they can be found in most of the central parks, but they suffer rather heavily from the attentions of cats. In parts of Europe, of course, the robin is a shy bird of woodland that has not found towns at all attractive. The redstart is only an autumn passage migrant to Dollis Hill and, although it cannot be described as a garden bird, it has undergone some change of fortune in Britain. In Bromley in 1901 it appeared to have the same kind of habitat as the Continental redstart since it bred in some of the town gardens. Since then there has been a marked drop in numbers as a result of local building, and there has also been a more general decline in the rest of southern, central and eastern England.

The kestrel is one of the British falcons which has adapted itself to life in towns, and its increase in the London area after the war of 1939–45 coincided with a fall in the amount of gamekeeping in the surrounding rural countryside. Kestrels have bred on towers, chimneys, gasholders and spires as well as in old crows' nests in Inner London. In 1963 film camera-man Geoffrey Mulligan and I were able to film one of the kestrels nesting in an old ventilator on the north front of the Langham Hotel in Portland Place. In recent years there has been a setback in numbers, but I still see birds over Dollis Hill; in 1967 I watched one take a house sparrow from my bird-table and another strike a sparrow from a roof-top. In that same year I watched a kestrel capture another hapless victim in a busy street in Ealing. The sparrowhawk nested in Holland Park in Kensington in 1953, but I have not seen a bird of this species at Dollis Hill since 1960. Another predator which has managed to hold on in many towns, although with some signs of a decrease, is the tawny owl. Where there is mature timber in suburban areas and the large central parks the tawny owl can maintain some sort of foothold. At Dollis Hill from 1951–6 two pairs nested in Gladstone Park and one pair in the grounds of St. Andrew's Hospital. A fourth pair appeared in 1957 and bred then and in the next two years, but after that the number settled at three pairs and finally dropped to two in 1967 and 1968. All the nesting holes have been in elms and from 20–25 ft. above the ground. In 1959 tawny owls were present in fourteen places in Inner London and I have been in other large towns such as Birmingham and Bristol where owls live quite successfully feeding regularly on house sparrows. Calculations revealed that 93% of the food of tawny owls in Holland Park in west London consisted of birds, especially pigeons, thrushes, starlings and house sparrows.

Of the doves, wood pigeons have increased at Dollis Hill threefold in the ten years after 1951. More than forty pairs breed in the area in the taller trees. Wood pigeons are common in the central parks and will also breed in the more closely built districts, occasionally nesting on buildings and rain-water pipes. Today they are the third most numerous species in the public squares of Inner London. The increase in the central area began in the late 1880s and the wood pigeon's newly-acquired tolerance of man is one of the more remarkable ornithological developments of modern times. A single pair of stock doves survived at Dollis Hill up to 1957 and this is rather a marginal species in urban habitats. Yet there has been a decrease in most of southern and eastern England in recent years, due perhaps in some measure to the effects of toxic chemicals. In March 1951 W. G. Teagle and I counted 25 stock doves in Kensington Gardens and, after a spread into other parks during the 1950s, the numbers collapsed and in recent years they have not been known to breed regularly.

About 1900 the carrion crow was rather scarce in rural southern England, but it managed to hold on in the unkeepered London suburbs.

From here it later spread into Inner London nesting in tall trees in the parks and squares and occasionally on gasholders and buildings. Two or three pairs nest each year at Dollis Hill in elms, sycamores and black poplars. In central London tall planes are often chosen. In October 1967 I counted 26 crows on the grass near the Round Pond in Kensington Gardens and the species seems to be doing very well. In northern Britain the hooded crow can be seen scavenging in many towns although it may nest outside in more open country; in Stornoway and Lerwick it is common in the streets. Outside the heavily built-up districts the rook can still survive in some suburban areas. A rookery was in use in Inner London until 1915, but the growth of building and the consequent increase in the distance the rooks had to fly to ferry in food led finally to its abandonment. Rooks can therefore breed in towns provided the sources of food and the open fields are not too far away, and I have seen rookeries in Bristol, Oxford, Scarborough and other towns. Like the rook, the jackdaw does not nest at Dollis Hill with its fairly modern houses, but it finds the older dwellings of parts of north London like those at Crouch End to its liking. An old colony in Kensington Gardens was deserted after 1957, but birds are still reported there from time to time.

The jay is a very interesting example of an essentially woodland bird that has colonised both the suburbs and the central parks of London where it can often be seen foraging in litter baskets or hopping boldly about in trees with no shrub layer underneath. Jays spread from Holland Park in Kensington to some of the Royal Parks during the 1930s and although I had seen jays at Hampstead, in Paddington Cemetery and near the Brent Reservoir, they did not appear at Dollis Hill until 1961; since then they have bred, but in 1968 they seem to have become very rare. Jays are a familiar sight in many parts of Inner London and their nests are not usually as conspicuous as that built in 1965 on a ventilator at No. 222, Old Brompton Road. The magpie has not yet penetrated London on any scale although I saw a single bird in Ladbroke Square in 1927 and there was one in Regent's Park in October 1965. Magpies occur near the Brent Reservoir and there is some evidence that the species is using gardens more regularly and may be about to advance into London. It has successfully colonised many Continental towns and I have seen it in Dublin. In 1969 advance birds reached Stonebridge Park, Dollis Hill and Kilburn.

Only two species of tit nest regularly in my suburban area – great and blue. The blue tit will use nesting boxes in gardens, but the great tit is almost entirely absent from the residential parts during the summer. In winter both species forage through the gardens and in autumn there may also be some immigrants as well with a coal tit or two. Great tits have nested in some of the private squares in Inner London, but they have never been very common. The blue tit has always seemed slightly more adaptable and is certainly commoner at Dollis Hill and also in the inner built-up regions of London. The coal tit nested in Holland Park from 1958–60 and again in 1962, but it is to some extent dependent on conifers. I have never recorded the long-tailed tit or the marsh tit at Dollis Hill, but I saw a party of long-tails in Ladbroke Square in 1938, and during the autumn and winter birds may reach the inner suburbs. The marsh tit is missing in summer from most of suburban London since it requires woodlands, but I have seen a bird in winter in Kensington and in 1937 I watched an adult feeding young in the grounds of Holland House.

The wren in summer appears at Dollis Hill primarily in the parkland, on the allotments and in a few of the older, larger gardens. The population was reduced to nil from seven pairs after the severe weather during the winter of 1962–3. Wrens will regularly wander through the gardens in winter although they do not find them attractive enough to nest in. "Wrens find densely built-up areas uncongenial" (Armstrong 1955), but birds have bred at Cripplegate in Inner London in 1961 and 1962. They have also nested in Kensington Gardens, Regent's Park and Battersea Park.

Warblers of woodland origin have met with limited and varying success in their penetration of the built-up areas. In 1958 a pair of blackcaps built in an elder not far from my home and in 1957 a pair of willow warblers bred in some rough grass in the special area. Blackcaps have also nested in large, overgrown gardens at St John's Wood and, since they do not need such thick cover as the garden warbler, they have been able to breed at Charlton, Blackheath, Greenwich, Streatham, Camberwell, Barnes and Holland Park. The willow warbler has nested in the grounds of Holland House and here in 1937 I also found a nest of the chiffchaff. Both species of leaf warbler may occur in large suburban gardens as breeding birds. In autumn they will also pass through my area in north-west London as migrants with whitethroats, lesser whitethroats, blackcaps and garden warblers.

The spotted flycatcher has not changed its status in north-west London during the last sixty years and its breeding population remains constant. Pied flycatchers appear in August and September at Dollis Hill and I have seen as many as 11 in Regent's Park. Two pairs of pied wagtails breed in the study area and numbers have also nested on many of the bombed sites of Inner London.

PLATE 15. Beechwoods. *Above*, open canopy with shrubs and field layer, Toys Hill; *below*, close canopy, Cotswolds.

PLATE 16. Scots pine. *Above*, native trees growing in Glen Affric, Inverness-shire; *below*, naturalised trees and birch colonising heath,
Frensham, Surrey.

The hedgesparrow is very widely distributed around my home with some 45 to 50 pairs breeding within half a mile of my house; 99.5% of the nests are in privet with the remainder in hawthorn or lilac. Some 85% of all nests have been from 3 to 5 ft. above the ground and the hedgesparrow in suburban areas is very much associated with the privet hedge. It is a common bird of parks, gardens and shrubby areas and has adapted itself well to man-made environments. Hedgesparrows sing from television aerials and rooftops, but in eighteen years I have only once seen a bird on my bird-table even in the severest weather. As a species it prefers to creep round the base picking up particles knocked off by other birds. Hedge-sparrows occur in Ladbroke Square, but in Hyde Park, for example, they are uncommon.

A bird of ecotones fully adapted to urban life is the starling. I have from 250 to 275 pairs nesting each year within half a mile of my home giving a density of 50 nests per 100 acres. If one compares this figure to that of 7 nests per 100 acres for Badby Wood it is clear that man has provided the starling with a habitat much more favourable and attractive than wood-land. Some 92% of the starling nests at Dollis Hill are in houses and factories while the remainder are in holes in trees. In 1951 some 3,500 starlings from the flightline along the Edgware Road from Stanmore to the central London roost chose to spend the nights from August until October in some Lombardy poplars at Dollis Hill. A review of the urban roosting habits of the starling shows that they have spread steadily over the last 140 years. Most of the roosts on masonry in urban areas are in the northern industrial districts, and there is no large roost of this type in southern or eastern England except for London and Bristol. On the Continent there are similar roosts in Munich, Hamburg, Amsterdam and Rome. A pair of starlings regularly spend the night in the roof of my house, after breeding there; it has been suggested that not many adults begin to roost in their nesting holes as early as November, but my pair comes in every night summer and winter.

Three species of finch nest at Dollis Hill in very small numbers. Three or four pairs of greenfinches are confined to high hedges and shrubberies, one or two pairs of goldfinches occur in thorns or apple trees and three pairs of chaffinches nest in thorns, almonds or apple trees. These three species occur, with one exception, only in Gladstone Park and the hospital grounds, and they are marginal in their status. The exception is the chaffinch pair which nested in the residential area after the destruction of the greater part of the special area. Both the greenfinch and the goldfinch have increased in Inner London since the beginning of the present century, but they are more birds of the suburbs than of the built-up districts.

Greenfinches have bred in Hyde Park and Regent's Park and goldfinches with young have been reported from Battersea Park, Chelsea Hospital and Regent's Park. The chaffinch is fairly common in many of the outer suburbs and, although it breeds in most of the central London parks, it is missing from the central squares. The linnet has never colonised the suburbs, and it has been suggested that its avoidance of built-up districts is adaptive; it certainly has a lower breeding success in partly built-up regions than in rural ones. The hawfinch may appear in well-wooded parts of the London suburbs such as Dulwich, Wimbledon Common, Kew and Hampstead, but it is not really a suburban bird. Redpolls nest in some of the outer areas with orchards or large gardens, particularly those in Surrey, but they avoid the more developed areas of London. In Ireland redpolls are common in many town gardens and I have seen them in summer in the middle of Armagh, Omagh, Carrick-on-Shannon and other towns. The bullfinch is a very uncommon winter visitor to Dollis Hill and Ladbroke Square, but a pair managed to nest in Regent's Park in 1959. The yellowhammer, too, is a bird that has been unable to adapt itself to life in towns. One pair of tree sparrows, sometimes two, can be found at Dollis Hill nesting in old oaks, and this marginal colony is the nearest to the centre of London in this direction.

Occasionally great and lesser spotted woodpeckers appear at Dollis Hill outside the breeding season. During the 1920s the first of these species increased and colonised quite a number of suburban areas, eventually penetrating Inner London itself. Great spotted woodpeckers bred in the grounds of Holland House from 1922 onwards and I recorded two breeding pairs there from 1936–9. From here the species spread into the nearby parks where pairs bred or attempted to breed in most years, but it seems that it is now on the decline. It has been a commoner species than the green woodpecker in the London area and has bred at Greenwich, Wandsworth, Kew and Hampstead in the suburbs, and at Kensington and Regent's Park in the central region. The lesser spotted woodpecker remains in the outer ring of suburbs at about the same limit as the green. The initial increase of woodpeckers in London may have been due to the ageing of the timber, most of which had been planted in the nineteenth century and which now provides enough rotten wood for finding food and nesting sites. The nuthatch is another species which requires mature woodland and parkland and so it is missing from Dollis Hill. However, following the irruption of tits and other species, the nuthatch bred in 1958 in Holland Park and Kensington Gardens, but, like the treecreeper, it is not very happy in built-up districts. The tiny colony of creepers in Kensington Gardens has finally disappeared and it is necessary to go to

Hampstead and similar parts to find them now. Of course, insectivorous birds find urban life difficult and atmospheric pollution must deter all but the hardiest and most adaptable species.

Perhaps it may be useful to summarise now this review of the woodland birds in towns. It is clear that only a restricted number of species can exist in the built-up areas, but the greater proportion of these originated in woodland or ecotones. These species are house sparrow and feral pigeon, and, from woodland, starling, wood pigeon, and more rarely kestrel and jay. Where public and private squares appear in the built-up zone it is also possible to find blackbird, mistle thrush and blue tit. In the quieter squares there are also small numbers of song thrushes, great tits, robins, carrion crows, spotted flycatchers and hedgesparrows. The larger parks like Kensington Gardens and Regent's Park generally have all the species I have mentioned so far, with the addition of tawny owl, wren, chaffinch, and sometimes greenfinch, while a list in recent years for Regent's Park shows that willow warbler, blackcap, whitethroat and bullfinch have attempted to breed. In some of the smaller open spaces and larger private gardens goldfinches may breed as well.

The limiting factors in the establishment of any species in a town are threefold – the availability of food, of nesting site and the ability to tolerate the close presence of man. Wrens, treecreepers, coal tits and warblers of woodland origin may therefore be restricted, whereas hedgesparrows favour privet for nesting, can change their diet according to the season and can tolerate man cutting the privet hedges periodically during the breeding season without becoming over-familiar or too confiding for their own safety. There has been a great increase in the last ten or fifteen years in the feeding of birds and more nesting boxes have been provided. At Dollis Hill, apart from a campaign against the wood pigeon, the influence of man on the bird-life has been almost wholly beneficial. Miss E. P. Brown's very interesting study of the birds of Holland Park has shown that human interference in tidying up and maintaining an area of woodland that had been converted into a public park with enclosures resulted in the loss of sparrowhawk and green woodpecker, a decrease in robins and song thrushes, but an increase in the tameness of the population as a whole.

The typical breeding birds of the outer suburbs number some thirty species and of this total five are cliff-nesters, four nest in trees or cliffs, two are commensals of man while the remaining twenty are characteristic of woodland and scrub. These twenty species are tawny owl, rook, jay, starling, wood pigeon, great spotted woodpecker, mistle thrush, song thrush, blackbird, robin, wren, hedgesparrow, great tit, blue tit, coal tit, spotted flycatcher, greenfinch, goldfinch, chaffinch and tree sparrow. This list shows the wide range of genus and species capable of sharing part of man's environment. Some woodland birds have been unable to make this transition and these include sparrowhawk, long-eared owl, woodcock, pheasant, cuckoo, turtle dove, redstart, nightingale, tree pipit, garden and wood warblers, whitethroat, lesser whitethroat, goldcrest, marsh, willow and long-tailed tits, redpoll and hawfinch. If these species are found in gardens these are usually large and mature and in close proximity to well-grown woodland. These may then be the home of the other two species of woodpecker as well as nuthatch and treecreeper. The less adaptable species seem to find the absence of shrub and field layers and the presence of buildings and human disturbance too daunting for them. If many of our parks were given more shrubberies and areas to which public access were forbidden, we could create more sanctuaries not only for passing migrants, but also for those species which need some privacy and quiet during the breeding season.

My eighteen-year study of the birds of Dollis Hill has revealed a very stable community altering little from year to year with a density of some 520 birds of 21 species per 100 acres. Only the severe weather of 1962–3 temporarily upset the balance and this had been restored by 1965. This density can be compared to that of 190–220 birds per 100 acres in Regent's Park and my own records of 480 birds per 100 acres in one area of north Oxford gardens, 980 birds per 100 acres in the Ladbroke Square district of Kensington and 286–383 birds per 100 acres of Badby Wood. The high figure for Kensington suggests that some built-up areas may be more attractive to birds than some suburban areas, but here we need more figures to work from. Despite the growth of building the number of breeding species in central London has increased in the last fifty years, and some woodland species have derived great benefit from man's activities as we have seen – the blackbird, for example. In every change that man makes to the environment there must be a corresponding change in the bird-life, and it is this quality of change that makes the study of birds in towns so fascinating. Do we know, for example, what proportion of birds in London dies from Vitamin B deficiency compared to the proportion that survives each year only because of artificial feeding? The greater the variety of habitats the more diverse the bird-life will be. Lord Hurcomb, in the Report of the Committee on Bird Sanctuaries in the Royal Parks, 1959–60, expressed concern about the decline of the central parks as bird habitats and pointed out that "Only by maintaining the essential conditions necessary for the encouragement of the more unusual and interesting species will it be possible to maintain the existing level of bird-life in the Royal Parks in the face of the changes arising from the diversity of development that is now going on around them." Our environment needs to be varied and diverse and, if this thought can be carried in the minds of those responsible for the planning of our future urban communities, it would be to the advantage not only of the birds, but of man himself.

CHAPTER 13

POPULATIONS AND PRESSURES

THE long-term study of the birds of Dollis Hill has shown that the suburban bird community there is, on the whole, comparatively stable with periodic but generally quite small fluctuations in numbers. Only the severe weather of 1962–3 seriously disturbed the blackbird population, but in a comparatively short time the stable pattern was restored. The starling, after its introduction to the New World, increased at a tremendous rate, but the population finally levelled off and any further changes were quite small. This kind of phenomenon was described a long time ago by Charles Darwin. An eventually stable population could only be achieved as the result of strong pressures or checks on numbers, and in this chapter I shall explore those factors which may control the numbers of woodland birds. Inside the woods different species occur side by side, but occupy different ecological niches and each species can show certain characteristics of abundance and behaviour. Marginal habitats outside the woodlands may help to absorb the overspill from the optimal habitats. The distribution and relative abundance of some birds can be accounted for by preferences for certain kinds of habitat as well as other factors resulting from natural selection. Several factors may interact and the analysis of these factors and the way in which they may be interwoven is one of the newest of the sciences. In as complex an ecosystem as a wood it is an extremely difficult task to try and unravel the threads.

In the course of this book it has slowly become clear that food requirements, the physical and vegetational background to the breeding habitat and psychological preferences for particular environments may all determine whether a species of bird can be found in a certain wood or not. Food, of course, is of the very greatest importance. Birds may feed on plants, on animals or on both, but few species are restricted to vegetable food alone in the way that some mammals and many insects are. Many birds have a wide range of foods while some invertebrates are confined to a single plant species. Some kinds of bird are able to change their feeding habits according to the season, switching, like some of the warblers, from insects to fruit as the summer advances. Hawks, buzzards and owls prey on mammals and other species of bird, while crows, magpies, jackdaws and jays that take some vegetable material may also take their toll of the eggs and nestlings of other birds. All the inhabitants of a wood are dependent in one way or another on plants for their food, while some rely for their very existence on animal food in association with plants; of these, aphids are, according to Elton, "the key industry". Aphids often feed on the sap of oakleaves and themselves provide the main nourishment for many birds and carnivorous insects. The addition of parasitic insects, and even of insects that parasitise the parasites, to the woodland ecosystem shows the complexity of the inter-relations between different organisms in the community. Some of the food chains in woodland communities are extremely involved. Below is a plan of some food chains, based on the principles of the Eltonian pyramid in which each species comprises a lower biomass than that of the next lower link, culminating in the green leaves at the base of the pyramid.

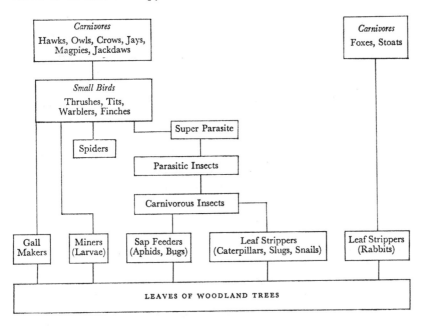

Even this table is not complete since I have not included the links between the trunk or bough, fungus and insects that feed on fungus. It nevertheless helps to underline the difficulties involved in attempts to unravel woodland food chains. And, of course, the figure of man should also be considered as well.

The feeding habits of birds really have two major aspects – the first being the characteristics of the food and feeding techniques found in the order or the group, and the second the special preferences and methods which distinguish a species from and permit it to survive alongside a closely-related species. This notion, known as the Volterra-Gause principle, has figured quite prominently in recent discussions on the feeding habits of birds since it maintains that two species cannot live side by side indefinitely if the same factors limit their population size. In those examples which have been very closely studied it has been found that there are clear differences in feeding site, in feeding behaviour, in the size of the food taken or in the combination of all three factors. Each species learns to take the food that it can deal with most efficiently and to which it is structurally adapted. A study of the habits of the Eurasian tits has shown that the bill and other features used in feeding are generally adapted to the conditions of the region in which the tits live, and to the feeding sites and nature of the food for each species. In Britain the various species of tit occupy feeding niches which can vary between species and from season to season. There can be overlap and competition between species if two kinds of tit should take the same insect but at different stages of growth and at different seasons. Only by discovering which insect species are taken, by recognising the stages of development they have reached and by finding out what proportion they represent of the total food consumed, is it possible to establish a clear foodchain and so decide on the amount of competition between the two species of tit. It is here in research of the most complex and sophisticated kind that the key to the solution will lie. Without it we cannot judge the economic importance of many woodland bird species. Ecological separations can, of course, disappear during temporary gluts of food, but separation again follows when the food supply has been used up.

Each species of tit has a characteristic height distribution which can vary seasonally and can be modified when food is abundant or in short supply. Figure 24 shows the height-frequency distributions obtained for five species of tit in Wytham Great Wood in 1948. The great tit is a ground-feeder in winter and goes up into the trees for the caterpillars of early summer; it then forages in the lower woodland foliage in high summer and in autumn feeds high or low, according to the availability of food. The blue tit ranges through a wide zone of heights and deserts the highest levels in mid-summer. The coal tit keeps fairly high in spring and summer, but drops to lower levels in mid-winter. The long-tailed tit is a forager in the top of the shrub layer and the lower canopy, while the marsh tit has a clearly defined height distribution in the shrub layer and around the lowest levels of big trees. In winter other insect-eating species also show preferences; the robin tends to remain below 10 ft. and the wren below

6 ft. Tits are not the only birds which show structural adaptation to their feeding habits. Woodpeckers use their tails for balancing and their stout bills to hammer out wood-boring and bark-eating organisms, while tree-creepers are able to explore the crevices in the bark with their thin, curved beaks and extract creatures too deep for the shorter bills of the tits.

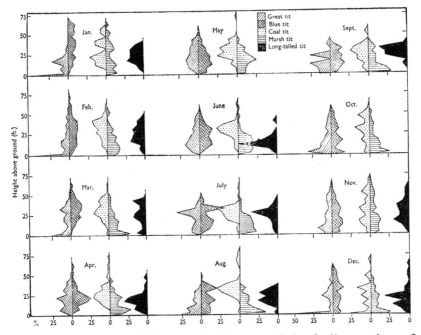

FIG. 24. The height-frequency distributions of the feeding stations of titmice in Wyham Great Wood, 1948. Reproduced from *Journal of Animal Ecology*, 1953, by kind permission of the Rev. Peter Hartley.

Although some organisms in the crevices may well be the same as those living on the rest of the tree and accessible to the tits, others may be quite different. No two species therefore have identical diets or feeding zones all the time, but some overlap does take place, for example, great and blue tits will take the larvae of the same moth. We have seen already that some tree species are richer in insects and invertebrates than others, and in mixed woods competition between bird species would therefore tend to be less than in a monoculture. A study of bird populations in different types of forest in America showed that the stability of the total population increased with the growing diversity of species in the forest types.

At the present time hawks are scarce or absent from many British woodlands, but in Ireland quite a few woods still have their resident pair of sparrowhawks. It is interesting to speculate upon the effect that a pair of these predatory birds would have on a small bird community. It has been suggested that a pair of sparrowhawks to satisfy the needs of their young and themselves would need some 2,000 small birds a year, and this would mean a maximum density for sparrowhawks of one pair per square mile. Should the hawks be taking only diseased or abnormal birds in preference to healthy ones, then the final result could be a rise and not a decrease in the prey population. After a study of the hunting behaviour of several species of birds of prey it was estimated that only 5% of sparrowhawk attacks were successful; there was also evidence that out of 23 successful strikes 7, and possibly 9, were upon birds abnormal in behaviour or condition. The high rate of failure provides some support for the theory that there is a selective effect upon the prey species. It is obviously of no advantage to the predator to reduce the level of prey numbers too severely in the area. Unfortunately we do not yet know how effective predators are in limiting the numbers of birds. Owls, crows, magpies, jackdaws and jays may affect the numbers of young birds reared. In the case of the song thrush, predation is the most usual cause of nesting failure and it is reported that only 14% of the blackbird nests at Wytham resulted in fledged young, due to predation, compared with 50% of the nests in the Oxford Botanic Garden. On the whole, predator-prey relationships seem unlikely to be the most important factors regulating bird numbers, but they cannot be ignored.

Since predators that specialise in rodents may have a greater density in woodland than hawks, the relationships between tawny owls and their prey have been intensively studied, also at Wytham. Here up to 30 pairs bred in an open broad-leaved wood stretching over some 1,000 acres of countryside. This was a self-contained population of owls in which the adults were strictly sedentary and the young wandered only a very few miles away. Their diet was noted throughout the year by analysing the small mammal remains in the regurgitated pellets; the most important prey species were the wood mouse and the bank vole which together made up in roughly equal proportions nearly 60% of the total prey. The rest of the mammal prey consisted of short-tailed voles, common shrews and moles. A variety of other foods was taken when mice or voles were scarce, and included beetles, earthworms and small birds such as chaffinches. Southern in a classic experiment demonstrated that the owls were very territorial by marking the mice with leg-rings and mapping both their place of release and the recovery point of the ring at one of the pellet stations. The breeding success of the owls varied with the density of the wood mice and the bank voles. The proportion of breeding owls was higher in the years when mice were abundant than in years when they were scarce. In 1958 no pairs out of the thirty present in fact bred, and this was a bad year for small mammals. In contrast, in 1949, 1950 and 1956, when rodents were plentiful, over 75% of the owl pairs bred. The clutch size also varied from 2.0 in a bad year to 3.0 in a good year. The average number of owls raised was three times as high in years when rodents were fairly common as in years when they were very scarce. Although there was a rise in the population numbers during the period of the study, the population at Wytham remained fairly stable. This comparative stability has been attributed to territorial behaviour since the number did not fluctuate with the density of wood mice and bank voles. Table 29 gives the breeding history of the tawny owls at Wytham from 1947–59. The correlation between bad years for rodents and poor breeding success in the owls is very clear, and the lack of food would seem to be directly responsible for the high loss of eggs and chicks. Mortality may be an important factor in the control of numbers and Southern has concluded that density-dependent mortality is an important regulator even in populations which appear to control their own levels by a territorial spacing.

We have seen how food supply can influence the breeding success of the tawny owl, but what factors determine the actual breeding seasons of birds? In Europe there is certainly a correlation between breeding seasons and the clearly defined, annual changes in the habitat; in fact, breeding begins generally in spring and summer, but there are a few exceptions in which species breed sporadically through the year, like the house sparrow, or start before the end of winter, like the crossbill. Length of daylight and temperature are part of the direct influences of climate and the natural gonad cycle of the wood pigeon is controlled through hormones by the seasonal changes in day length. More important still are the biological changes in each species that accompany the physical changes. In a general review in the *Ibis* Sir Landsborough Thomson stated that the breeding seasons are "adapted to the environmental cycles in such a way as to secure that the maximum supply of appropriate food will be available when the young are hatched and for a sufficient time after they are first on the wing". Although there are quite a few instances in which the correlation has not been proved so far, the exceptions appear to be few and can sometimes be explained in terms of other factors known to apply. It is generally believed now that breeding seasons are determined by natural selection, operating through complex proximate factors of physiology and

TABLE 29. *Breeding History of Tawny Owls in Wytham Woods, Oxford,*
1947–59

Year	Number of Pairs	% Pairs Breeding	Mean Clutch	Number of young fledged	Young fledged per pair	Abundance of rodents on arbitrary scale
1947	16	69	(2.5)	20	1.3	?
1948	20	65	(2.0)	19	1.0	?
1949	20	90	2.8	25	1.3	5
1950	21	81	2.7	27	1.3	6
1951	22	50	2.0	6	0.3	3
1952	24	70	2.6	20	0.8	5
1953	25	60	2.1	19	0.8	4
1954	26	69	2.4	16	0.6	5
1955	27	15	(2.0)	4	0.1	2
1956	29	79	2.2	23	0.8	6
1957	30	60	3.0	20	0.7	7
1958	30	0	—	0	0	1
1959	30	—	—	29	1.0	8

Mean clutch is based on a sample of the nests (at least 11 a year; except for only 2 in each year where the average has been placed in brackets).

The arbitrary scale ranges from 8 (extremely abundant) to 1 (extremely scarce); intervals do not necessarily correspond to equal differences in density.

Reproduced from *Population Studies of Birds* by Dr David Lack (1966) by courtesy of the author, Dr H. N. Southern and the Clarendon Press.

environment that make sure that the individual is ready to breed, and ultimate factors of food, breeding site and cover which tend to be more favourable at one time of the year rather than another.

Of the ultimate factors food is most likely to be the predominant one. The size of clutches tends to increase with increasing day length since parent birds can usually carry more food to the nest each day to bring up more young. The clutch size is adjusted by natural selection to a figure which gives the best chance of producing the largest number of fledged young. In passerine birds the limit to clutch size is finally set by the increased mortality in large broods due to the lack of food. The size of clutches may also be above average in March and April if the weather is fine and warm. After the mild winter and spring of 1957, seven resident passerine species as well as tawny owls, were recorded, laying eggs some 6 to 12 days earlier than usual; temperature here seemed to be acting directly upon the birds since some species even laid in February when there was no change in the amount of vegetative growth. Annual variations in the breeding season of the rook near Oxford could be correlated with the mean air temperatures before egg-laying. The influence of temperature could be adaptive, but more research is needed to see how widely temperature and clutch size can be related.

There is close correlation in normal years between the breeding season and the availability of food. Robins and tits of the *Parus* family feed their young in British oakwoods primarily on the caterpillars of the geometrid moth *Operophtera brumata* – the winter moth. The season for the nestlings of robins and some tit species matches very closely the peak of the caterpillar abundance in May. This suggests that the breeding season in these species is adapted to the caterpillar season, although how this is actually regulated is another problem. Pairs of great tits which laid early in the main period were found to produce a greater proportion of surviving offspring than those which laid later in the main period; the factor affecting the time of laying was probably the time needed by the hen great tit to collect enough food to form a clutch of eggs. Some species which feed their young on adult rather than larval insects, such as the nightjar and the spotted flycatcher, do not breed before late May or June. Pied flycatchers breed earlier when the springs are warmer and this, too, suggests that the hens start laying when they have enough food reserves to form their eggs and food is more plentiful in a warm spring. For the wood pigeon and the bullfinch there is also evidence that the onset of breeding is determined by the hens obtaining enough food. The feeding of female tits in the genus *Parus* by the males nourishes them so that they have sufficient food for the task of producing a number of eggs on successive days. The clutch size of the great tit becomes smaller as the season wears on and the numbers of caterpillars decline – this is almost certainly adaptive. The clutch size is adjusted, according to Lack (1954), by natural selection to produce the greatest number of offspring that the parents can, on average, adequately feed and bring up to a healthy fledgling stage. His argument is that food supply is the most frequent factor in regulating the numbers of birds although predation and disease must not be ignored. Nobody can yet tell how all these factors may and do interact; some species show modifications and lay clutches of different sizes according to season and habitat. Table 30 shows variations in the breeding of great and blue tits in southern England. Clutches of the pied flycatcher tend to be smaller later in the season at higher population densities, but generally clutch size does not appear to vary very greatly with population density. It has been noted that some variations in fecundity among great tits could be related to density, but density-dependent fecundity rates in birds were not large enough to be the cause of natural stability in a population. The chief regulation of numbers was thought to occur through density-dependent variations in mortality and here the commonest factor among birds is shortage of food outside the breeding season. For the starling there may be an acute lack of food in the early autumn, at a time when birds are moulting and their weights are low. At this time mortality could act as a density-governed factor maintaining the stability of the breeding population. It has been established that the size of the wood pigeon population in early winter depends, not on the success of the previous breeding season, but on the amount of grain available in the autumn when poor stocks affect the juveniles. Thus

TABLE 30. *Breeding of Great and Blue Tits in Different Habitats in Southern England*

Habitat	Mean Density per 10 hectares	Mean Date of Laying (d=Mean for the Great Tit)	Mean Clutch	Nestling Weight	% of nestlings dying (not predation)
Great Tit First Broods					
Pure oak and mixed	10–20	d	9.8	18.9	5
Scots Pine	2.5	d	10.0	14.6	38
Corsican Pine	1.3	d+8	9.1	14.0	40
Gardens	c. 6–12	d−4½	7.6	16.0	44
Blue Tit First Broods					
Pure oak	20+	d−3	11.5	—	4
Mixed	9+	d−3	10.7	10.6	8
Scots Pine	1.2	d−3	10.4	10.4	29
Corsican Pine	0.6	d+?	9.3	9.5	38
Gardens	—	d−3	8.8	—	31

Reproduced from *Population Studies of Birds* by Dr David Lack, by courtesy of the author and the Clarendon Press

fecundity variations are thought to be unimportant. The effects of food shortage may be modified by the birds undertaking local dispersals or by larger scale movements and migrations. An emigration attributable to a food shortage may be triggered off by a behavioural response to large numbers even before the shortage of food begins to take effect.

The theory put forward by Dr Lack has not gone unchallenged. Several authors have claimed that animal populations contain within themselves the power to regulate their own numbers. Andrewartha and Birch considered that numbers fluctuated irregularly from year to year through factors such as climate in particular which operate quite independently of density. Wynne Edwards (1959) accepted that "food is almost always the critical or limiting resource" and he suggested that animals can regulate their own density below the upper limit set by the food and that group selection accounts for the delayed breeding in some birds and the lowered clutch size in others. Animals have thus become adapted to controlling their own population densities. Instead of competing directly for food animals compete instead for such substitutes as territory or position in the group which provides a ceiling density at the optimum level. These protective conventions thus prevent the overfishing of the food resources.

We know quite a bit already about one of the ways in which population density is controlled, namely, territory. When birds compete for food they can do so in one of two ways – scramble or contest. In a scramble for an inadequate food supply most, if not all, the animals die, whereas in a contest although some will not survive others will come through without any major ill-effects. A scramble would be accompanied by quite violent fluctuations in populations and so it is essential for this activity to move forward into a ritualised context – the very basis of the territorial system. Some research workers believe that it is this system which gives stability to bird populations. Territory has been defined as "a defended area" – the result, in fact, of two distinct tendencies in the territory holder. The first is the attachment to a site and the second hostility towards a certain category of other animals, usually members of the same species and the same sex. Either tendency can occur without the other.

The function of territories is to space out the individuals, pairs or larger units of populations. Most woodland species are territorial. A now classic experiment has been described in which 81% of 148 males of certain territorial species in about 40 acres of spruce-fir forest in America were killed off. From 15th June until 8th July the numbers were kept down to the new level, but this resulted in the shooting of 455 new birds which had settled, including twice as many males as were present before the experiment began. In the following year 79% of 154 pairs in the same wood were shot and numbers held at the same level as before; this time 528 new settlers were killed. This showed beyond doubt that the presence of settled birds acted as a deterrent to would-be settlers; the effect was density limiting. Unoccupied sites were also more readily colonised than occupied ones. The breeding population was higher and more stable in mixed than in pinewoods. However, an increase in the number of tits in the area did not have any appreciable effect on the numbers in the preferred habitat and this was attributed to territorial behaviour regulating the numbers in the mixed woods. Territories have been compared to rubber discs – the more they are compressed the greater becomes the resistance to compression. In this way population densities can be limited by territorial activity. There is evidence that territories are elastic and can grow or shrink according to the pressures and the nature of the habitat. Marsh tit territories can vary from one to sixteen acres in size.

Attachment to a site can convey positive advantages to a bird since there must be survival value in knowing intimately the topography and resources of an area. The value to tawny owls of finding food in familiar regions has been shown, but the direct evidence is not strong. The exact value of spacing birds out in this way has been widely debated particularly where territories often vary according to size and season. Some species have very specialised breeding demands and this applies very strongly to hole-nesting birds. Of the thirty-six species that have bred in Badby Wood sixteen are breeders in holes. Of the sixty or so species recorded at Wytham Woods eighteen or nearly one-third were wholly or partly dependent on dead or dying timber for their nest sites. These species were stock dove, barn, little and tawny owls, three species of woodpecker, jackdaw, five species of tit, nuthatch, treecreeper, redstart, starling and tree sparrow. The reservation of nest sites for the families of these birds is important and their overall number will depend upon the age and the nature of the wood. In the selection of such a site there may be strong competition between members of different as well as of the same species. I have watched great and blue tits fighting for the same hole, and in Yorkshire I once saw great and blue tits struggling with a pied flycatcher for possession of one nest site. There are reports of a great tit building its nest on top of one built by a redstart and of a blue tit usurping the home of a great tit. Great tits usually dominate blue tits in my own garden and they may eject them from boxes and holes already occupied. Green and great spotted woodpeckers have been known to use the same hole. Starlings are very fond of woodpeckers' holes which they often requisition after the rightful owners have finished their work of excavation. There is often a shortage of holes and competition may be high. In one view the limited number of nesting holes is the main factor controlling the population density of the pied flycatcher and competition causes a certain number of young birds to move on. The territory of the pied flycatcher tends to be small since the male is primarily concerned with the defence of the nesting hole. In some species it was found that territorial behaviour developed only after a hole was obtained and fighting occurred at the hole rather than on the boundaries of the territory. The great tit's aggressive behaviour is centred around its breeding hole and it has been shown that the critical

PLATE 17. Developing conifer plantation. *Above*, spruce in early establishment stage, Loch Maree, Ross-shire; *below*, spruce in thicket stage. Kielder Forest.

PLATE 18. Two birds of coniferous woodland. *Above*, redpoll, an increasing bird with reafforestation; *below*, goldcrest. A common bird of mature plantations.

density-dependent mortality in this species was not caused by disease, predation or territorial behaviour. Tits of the genus *Parus* can often be seen inspecting holes during the winter months but, since they often roost in the same holes as those they use the following spring for breeding, they may be selecting roosting places in the first instance which become nest sites later on. Many species have developed elaborate ceremonies in which one member of the pair attracts the other to the nest hole, and these include the redstart, pied flycatcher, blue and great tits. In the case of the blue tit it was thought that the hole inspection display was primarily to maintain the pair-bond. In these rituals the advantages must outweigh the disadvantages since the behaviour itself must make the birds more conspicuous and obvious to predators such as hawks. Some species can hold territory all the year round and territory-holding marsh tits will travel so far with a nomadic flock passing through their ground, but drop out at the borders of the territory.

Territorial behaviour in many passerines is of value in acquiring mates and indeed in the case of the blackbird it is essential for a male bird to have a territory in order to obtain a mate. For blackbirds territory is not used chiefly as a source of food, for many of them around my home feed outside their territories for long periods. Yet breeding pairs of birds are disposed broadly in relation to food supplies as a result of behaviour arising from natural selection. Possession of a territory may eliminate direct competition for food and a system of food territories could well be the primary function of the territory habit. Therefore social species such as rooks hold food territories communally, and possession of a nest site in the colony gives the rooks membership of a limited society. On the other hand in some cases it is unlikely that territory is of much food value. Dr Lack agrees with Professor Wynne-Edwards that conventional patterns of behaviour provide a secondary limitation to density, but he differs from Wynne-Edwards by holding the belief that natural selection provides a sufficient explanation for any relationship between this type of behaviour and the survival of the individuals concerned. Much more information is needed on the feeding habits of birds according to habitat and season so that the functions and value of territories to individual species can be correctly worked out.

In a favourable habitat like the gardens at Dollis Hill territorial behaviour certainly limits the breeding density of the blackbird. The average number of pairs breeding within half a mile of my home between 1951 and 1962 was 191, but after the cold winter of 1962–3 the number dropped to 86 pairs. In the following year 244 males appeared in March – a number far in excess of the previous territorial strength. The final number of blackbird pairs settled at 200, but intense fighting contributed to a low breeding success.

The selection of the site for a territory is in response to a number of different stimuli, some of which may be innate and others acquired in an early process of conditioning. These stimuli include both general and specific topographical features, song posts, nest sites and perhaps an overall "psychological" factor. The presence of cover may be important to several species. The two essential parts of territorial behaviour are those of escape and attack, and these two activities, sometimes in conflict with each other, may lead to many interesting pieces of behaviour. The marking out of a territory may be accompanied by various threat displays, special calls and territorial song. Some species seem to have preferences for high song posts and these probably play some part in the selection of territories.

Animal populations are normally in a state of balance. There are density-dependent factors which tend to suppress the population at high levels and to increase it at low densities. The chief factors are those which we have been considering already – the reproductive rate, death due to shortage of food, disease, predation and self-regulating behaviour inherent in territorial systems. Woodland bird communities are unlikely to be very much affected by disease and it is improbable that disease is a major factor in regulating the numbers of wild birds. In an examination of the causes of death of wild birds in Britain, it was found that infectious diseases accounted for only 18% of the sample. Out of 605 wood pigeons shot between 1959 and 1961 only 3.1% were obviously diseased, and in a sample of 122 taken with narcotic baits only 1.6% were diseased. It seems likely that the sick birds were removed selectively by shooting. Diseased birds cannot cope so well, fail to compete and often die first in bad weather when food is short or fall easy prey to predators. The direct influence of disease is not great, but there is some effect from accidents since along the edges of some woods certain species such as blackbirds, song thrushes and robins may be killed by passing road vehicles.

To what extent do climatic conditions affect woodland bird populations? There are undoubtedly fluctuations, but these tend to be appreciable only as the result of severe weather. The very cold winter of 1962–3, with an army of ornithologists ready to collect the information, provided a unique opportunity to assess the effects of the severe weather. The winter was the coldest recorded in central and southern England since 1740 and had a serious effect on the numbers of many species in the British Isles. The woodland species most reduced were goldcrest, wren, long-tailed tit and green woodpecker in that order. Wood pigeons were badly affected and there were also reductions in the numbers of song thrushes with less marked drops in the totals of treecreepers, mistle thrushes, robins, goldfinches, chaffinches and linnets. About half the population of one quarter of our indigenous species died during the cold spell. On the other hand, members of the crow family as well as nuthatches, hedgesparrows, starlings, greenfinches, redpolls and bullfinches did not fare too badly. The blackbird was one of the species "apparently" not adversely affected by the weather, but the numbers of the suburban population at Dollis Hill were reduced by 55%. Up to 1963 there was no evidence that blackbirds left the woodland at Bookham Common in winter, but in the exceptional weather of January 1963 some probably did so. A smaller breeding population of blackbirds generally followed a cold winter at Bookham, but birds remained in the area. The blackbird population at Dollis Hill left the district altogether and either met disaster somewhere else or found that as a normally sedentary group they had no ability to home. The treecreeper suffered badly in many areas in the winters of 1940 and 1947 as well as in 1962-3. The long-tailed tit is also very vulnerable during cold winters. The population of herons was reduced in 1947 to the lowest total since 1928. The nuthatch was more badly hit in 1947 than in 1963. The loss of body weight in some of the affected species in 1962 was severe – up to 50% for redwings and fieldfares, 44% for chaffinches, 33% for greenfinches and 30% for starlings and wrens. Populations can be sadly reduced, but in many species recovery is often rapid. In the second breeding season in the London area after the bad winter of 1962-3, green woodpeckers had recovered in some areas but not in others, while the wren was doing well; the goldcrest was still scarce. Robins, song thrushes and hedgesparrows returned to their usual numbers in the following year, but it was not before the third breeding season at Dollis Hill that the populations of great and blue tits and greenfinches were back to normal.

Apart from these exceptional periods of severe weather, winter cold does not seem to have a very marked influence on population numbers. Birds may vacate woodland at the onset of bad conditions and the survivors return later for the breeding season. In the winter of 1946-7 great tits were the first of the tits to leave Marley Wood at Wytham, followed by blue, coal and long-tailed tits. Some of these and marsh tits often leave the woods for farmland and other more favourable habitats. Annual fluctuations in the weather may be reflected to a small extent in the bird populations. Figure 25 shows the density of breeding pairs of the great tit in three English localities and in one in Holland. Since it was important to know whether the yearly fluctuations taking place in Marley Wood were due entirely to local factors or to some wider influence it was necessary to plot them against the figures for several other areas. This has been done in Fig. 25. The four localities are the mixed broad-leaved wood at Marley, a mature oak plantation in the Forest of Dean, some pine plantations in the Breckland of East Anglia and a rather poor mixed coniferous/broad-leaved wood in the Veluwe, near Arnhem, in Holland. The population changes are shown in terms of pairs per hectare. It is possible to see increases between 1947–9, 1956–7, 1960–1; the rise from 1947–9 is reflected in the figures in Table 15 on page 98 for Badby Wood where similar fluctuations occurred not only for the great tit, but also for the population of chaffinch, blue tit, robin and wren. Dr Lack has pointed out that the increases visible in the graph only occur occasionally and from this he deduces that, as the fluctuations are around different average levels, climatic factors are probably responsible. He would have expected much bigger fluctuations if density-dependent factors had not been in operation. Light and warmth together with other factors such as food supply, territory, nest site and building materials can accelerate the sexual cycle while cold, rain and hunger can inhibit it.

If we look at the population dynamics of another species – the blackbird – over about the same period, we find that throughout the decade from 1951 there has been a decrease in annual mortality from about 50% to 32%. There were some fluctuations with higher mortality figures reflecting the colder winters so that climatic factors were visible here, but the general and long drop in the mortality rate cannot be accounted for solely in terms of weather conditions. There are other factors at work. The effect on the numbers of blackbirds would depend on the recruitment rate over the same period. If this had stayed constant at the level which satisfactorily maintained the population, then the total would have gone up by about 70% over the decade. Unfortunately the figures available on the population levels are very incomplete, but it does not look as if there has been a marked or general rise in numbers. This suggests that the level of recruitment has fallen and so the level of numbers has been maintained. The blackbird may be in the process of extending its range, and it has been suggested that this combined with an increase in some of the blackbird's more marginal habitats may be absorbing the surplus numbers. Nobody can give any reason for the reduced mortality, and it is clear that a great deal still remains to be discovered about the factors which control and regulate the numbers of birds.

A useful indication of the success of any breeding season is in the percentage of juvenile birds that can be found in the autumn population. It was found that the variations between different years were greater than could be accounted for by breeding success and this seemed to suggest that

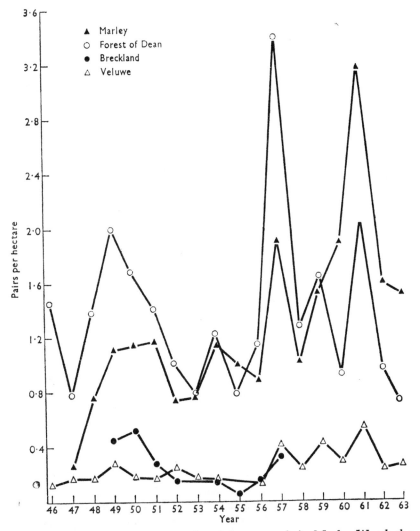

FIG. 25. Density of breeding pairs of the great tit in Marley Wood, the Forest of Dean, the Breckland and the Veluwe (Holland), 1946-62. Reproduced from *Population Studies of Birds*, 1966, by kind permission of the author, Dr David Lack, and of Dr C. M. Perrins. Original drawing loaned by Clarendon Press.

the differences in the rate of post-fledging survival were the critical factors. In the hot, dry summer of 1959 survival after leaving the nest was less than half as high as in the following two years. The mortality of young blackbirds is probably determined by what has been called "the carrying capacity" of the environment. Since there is generally a high figure of young birds in March, a correspondingly high figure in the autumn before suggests that the level of numbers breeding is almost certainly influenced by the success of the breeding season before. It would appear that the critical density-dependent factor influencing the annual fluctuations in the breeding population of great tits at Wytham is mortality among the juveniles. If this is so then weather must again play an important part in controlling numbers.

It would be inappropriate in this book to go too deeply into an examination of the current controversy running through the present-day study of ecology on the importance of density-dependent and density-independent factors. We have seen already how many factors may influence numbers and that density-dependent factors are those which vary with the density of birds in an area. When populations are reduced it is thought that some other factor may become less severe so that recovery is made possible in the following year. The evidence that density-dependent factors are important is impressive, but it is not easy to assess the effect of food shortages on birds. It may be a series of limiting factors which determines the population of a species; numbers are held down because food supplies or nest sites are taken up to the limit. Any drop in the numbers is restored by adults and young birds which can now avail themselves of the food and nesting places. In this way the introduction of nestboxes to an area can increase the overall numbers, provided that the habitat remains unchanged. After studying the distribution of blackbirds at Dollis Hill since 1951, I have come to the conclusion that their spread and general stability are due not so much to food supplies which are provided or guaranteed by man's activities, except in very severe weather, as to the availability of nesting sites, which is limited. The greatest concentrations are in the areas of gardens and parks with trees and bushes, and as 84% of all blackbird nests are in trees, bushes or creepers, these play an important part in the ecology of the species. These sites lie within territories which are assiduously defended, but the birds often feed outside them. The evidence that food shortage is an important factor in limiting bird numbers is strong, and it would be even more important in pure woodland where artificial feeding does not occur. It is possible that the apparent stability of many bird populations is due to density-dependent tendencies to disperse into marginal habitats, to remain as non-breeding birds or even to leave the area altogether. These factors could work alone or in concert, but the effect on the numbers of the birds would be very like that of density-dependent mortality. A great deal of ecological study remains to be done in this field and it may well be that the attempts to explain the regulation of bird numbers should exclude neither functional nor evolutionary ecology. It is in the field of population dynamics that the hardest work and greatest rewards still lie. As long ago as 1963, an editorial in *British Birds* pointed out that such work besides advancing knowledge, "will form a most practical means of aiding the conservation of our bird-life in face of such growing threats as those of destruction by toxic chemicals on the land." The Census of Common Birds begun by the British Trust for Ornithology may help to provide some of the answers.

Indeed, one of the points that has clearly emerged from the controversy about the use of pesticides is really how little is known about bird populations. After all, it is not possible to decide whether pesticides are affecting bird numbers if little is known about the normal fluctuations in bird populations. However, the application in Britain after the Second World War of the chlorinated hydrocarbon insecticides has caused conservationists a great deal of concern. It was between 1956 and 1961, particularly in eastern England, that numbers of birds from many different species were found dead. In one piece of woodland of nearly 1,500 acres it was thought that 5,688 wood pigeons, 118 stock doves, 59 rooks and 89 pheasants died. The highest casualties tended to be among the seed-eating birds, but predatory birds also seemed to suffer. These incidents, occurring chiefly in the eastern parts of England where cereal crops were widely grown, suggested that the most likely cause was the use of seed-dressings, especially dieldrin. Dressed seeds were actually dug up by birds which in time accumulated lethal doses. Wood pigeons were able to replace their losses quickly; in fact, after a kill of at least 8% in one locality in Cambridgeshire in 1961, the population had completely recovered by the following breeding season. Birds that bred more slowly were in danger of extinction. The bird victims of dieldrin passed on their toxicity to any animals that devoured them so that predatory mammals and birds were also poisoned. A voluntary ban was imposed on the use of dieldrin which helped to reduce the deaths among seed-eating birds, but since there appeared to be other important but less direct effects on many bird species, there was pressure to prohibit the use altogether. The two important groups of pesticide are the organo-phosphorus – highly toxic but non-persistent in the tissues – and the organo-chlorine which possess high toxicity and persistence so that sublethal amounts can grow cumulatively through a food chain to the predator at the end.

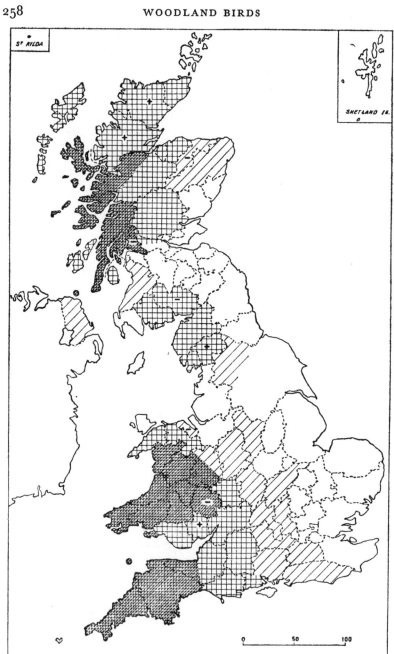

In the last eighteen years there has been an undoubted drop in the numbers of peregrines, kestrels and sparrowhawks in many parts of the British Isles. This reduction, with that of some smaller species as well, has coincided with the use of persistent chlorinated hydrocarbons on the land. Organo-chlorine residues appeared to cause sterility as well as affecting chick survival. There is sometimes abnormal and adverse behaviour in nesting birds. A ban on the spring use of the three most toxic chemicals – dieldrin, aldrin and heptachlor – came into force in January 1962. Dieldrin as a sheep dip was banned in 1966 and this may help the golden eagle, which has been badly affected by a reduction in the number of successful nestings, to recover some of its lost ground. A further decline in the buzzard population of Lakeland may have been due to the same cause, and it will now be interesting to see whether numbers begin to pick up again. In Britain the dangers were seen early by the conservationists who proclaimed clearly that reasonable control was imperative. A Code of Conduct drawn up late in 1967 between the Association of Manufacturers of these chemicals and the conservationists marked a welcome convergence between two opposing sides.

The use of these chemicals in Britain has coincided with a number of agricultural trends which in their turn have been responsible for the destruction of many wildlife habitats. We have already seen how countless miles of hedgerow have been removed while others have suffered from drifting crop sprays. The application of insecticides has occurred along with habitat destruction, the increase of traffic on the roads and a new

FIG. 26. The breeding population density of the buzzard in the British Isles in 1954. Highest density occurs in areas shaded darkly.

KEY: Double Cross-hatch. Average breeding density=1 or more pairs per 10 square miles.

Cross-hatch Average breeding density=more than 1 pair per 100 square miles, but less than 1 pair per 10 square miles.

Diagonal Hatch. Average breeding density=less than 1 pair per 100 square miles.

White. No breeding Buzzards.

+means that breeding density may be higher than indicated.
—means that breeding density may be lower than indicated.

Reproduced from *British Birds* by kind permission of Dr Norman Moore.

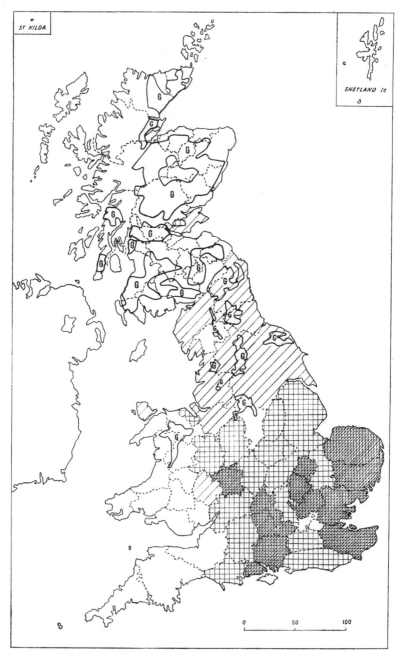

growth of fences of wire and cables which may all cause death among birds. As there are also cumulative and sublethal side effects of some of the chemicals, it is very difficult to assess the full impact of the chemicals themselves on bird populations. It is not fully clear how pesticides can change ecological relationships although an attempt has been made to do this in America. What, may we ask, are the indirect effects of toxic chemicals on the numbers and range of the small plants, invertebrates and soil fauna of the ground zone? There may still be concealed long-term results which we do not yet know about.

At the moment comparatively little spraying goes on in British forests and woodland, but no exact figures are available. According to some statistics kindly supplied to me in 1968 by the Forestry Commission, insecticides were used on a total of 2,560 acres of nurseries and plantations in the Forest Year 1966. This figure does not imply 100% treatment of that area and it includes the use of pre-dipped plants; the insecticides employed were almost exclusively DDT, BHC and Malathion. The dipping of plants before planting against *Hylobius abietis* and *Hylastes* spp. is the most important regular use of insecticides, and for this purpose BHC is replacing DDT. BHC is also used against Ambrosia beetle, *Trypodendron lineatum* and *Tomicus piniperda*. Populations of *Bupalus piniarius* may occasionally reach plague proportions and these are controlled by aerial spraying with DDT at 1 lb. active ingredient per acre. The last occasion was at Cannock in 1963 when 1,400 acres were treated.

Unlike the fruit-grower, the forester's attitude to his trees and fungal diseases is philosophical, and he prefers to grow and harvest trees which are resistant to pests and disease. The annual fruit crop is of greater overall value than the long-term timber harvest and so the fruit-grower is willing to grow trees that, although susceptible to disease, produce a heavy crop.

FIG. 27. Game preservation in the British Isles in 1955. Most game-preservation occurs in shaded areas.

KEY:	Double Cross-Hatch	3-6 gamekeepers per 100 square miles.
	Cross-hatch.	1-2 gamekeepers per 100 square miles.
	Diagonal hatch.	1 gamekeeper or more per 200 square miles, but less than 1 gamekeeper per 100 square miles.
	White.	Less than 1 gamekeeper per 200 square miles.
	G.	Principal grouse-preserving areas.

Reproduced from *British Birds* by kind permission of Dr Norman Moore.

The use of fungicides containing copper in East Anglian orchards resulted in the total destruction of earthworms in the soil. British orchards are very heavily and regularly sprayed and although the surviving worms and insects may cause the death of some birds the evidence of widespread mortality seems to be lacking. Dr Kenneth Mellanby in his most instructive book in the New Naturalist series, *Pesticides and Pollution*, suggests that in relation to orchards it is probable that "a comparatively small increase in pesticide use might have more serious results."

Much of what appears to be wild Britain is artificial, and man's continuing alteration of habitats is one of the more important influences on bird numbers. In the last two hundred years there has been a slow and then rapidly accelerating growth in small gardens in association with houses. More recently the Forestry Commission has been replanting vast areas with coniferous trees and the conversion of a bare moor with a small population of heathland birds into a plantation must inevitably lead to an increase in the number of woodland birds that come in with the developing trees. On the other hand, the loss of woodland to housing, airfields, motorways and factories must lead to some diminution. Should the gardens of the new housing estates be capable of supporting mature trees and shrubs then the final density may be higher than it was in the original woodland. Where broad-leaved woods have given way to coniferous plantations then the density may well drop. Yet for the wood pigeon the provision of conifer plantations in farming and previously unwooded areas, such as Buchan in north-east Scotland, has been an unmixed blessing. In some birds an increase in the number of suitable nesting places may be followed by an increase in the breeding, but not necessarily in the total population. The provision of nesting boxes may also increase local populations and man may increase winter food supplies and introduce birds to new habitats. Yet, however attractive nestboxes and a new habitat may appear to be, pied flycatchers, for example, will not stay unless all the biological requirements are met in the area.

A species whose distribution has been closely studied and whose history sheds some valuable light on the factors controlling its numbers is the buzzard. The total population of buzzards is probably limited by different factors in different parts of its range or by various combinations of these factors. Six have been listed – the relative abundance of prey species, the availability of nest sites, serious changes in the habitat, persecution, disturbance and contamination of the environment by organo-chlorine pesticides. As an unspecialised species the buzzard is capable of considerable adaptation, but its history in the last two hundred years can be closely linked with game preservation. The attempts to preserve game animals in

Britain has sometimes had catastrophic effects on our predatory animals – foxes, stoats, polecats, hawks and owls. Figures 26 and 27 illustrate very clearly the correlation that Dr Norman Moore was able to achieve between gamekeeping and the decline of the buzzard. Persecution may still go on today in the more remote parts of Britain. Myxomatosis, disturbance and polluted habitats may have helped to accelerate a process started earlier by the gamekeepers. The effects of game preservation on many of our other animals have never been properly examined.

Considerable evidence has been amassed to show that, because variations in the reproductive rate of many birds are small, bird numbers are controlled by mortality factors which are density-dependent and when numbers are high these increase in their effectiveness but when they are small decrease in their severity. Some causes of death operate quite independently of population density. Food is most likely to be a limiting factor and the stability of a natural community probably depends on the elaborate food chains and food webs acquired by that community over a long period of evolution. We have yet to discover what the long-term effects of breaking these chains may be. Modern methods of agriculture and forestry together with the growing destruction of habitats and the use of chemicals on the land may in the end lead to an environment which is in a permanent state of instability. For hundreds of years prey and predator have managed to exist side by side in a stable environment. We are clearing, planting, managing, cementing, polluting and flooding and we are more and more regarding the countryside as something which can produce good short-term profits. The key-words are efficiency and intensification, but if these always mean the ravaging and spoliation of our beautiful land then we may pass the point of no return without noticing it.

CHAPTER 14

BIRDS AND FORESTRY

LANDOWNERS and foresters are usually pleased to discuss not only their own local methods of sylviculture, but also the wild life to be found in their woods. All of them recognise that they have a duty to improve the production and quality of the timber that they grow, and many feel that they also have a responsibility to conserve the wild life and provide a refuge for those species increasingly threatened by the human pressures on other environments in which they occur. Some of these pressures were outlined in the last chapter. It is important that land should be used with a proper regard for fundamental ecological principles and with a sincere desire to understand the relationships that exist between living things in their surroundings. We have already seen that when vegetation becomes more complex a greater variety of habitats for animals is created, and that the later stages in successions are noteworthy for the high number of species present. A climax woodland where the annual rate of change is small is ecologically very stable. We can only become fully conscious of our environment when its true character and diversity form an integral part of our daily thinking and awareness. We need to know a great deal more about the feeding habits of birds including those of woodland. *The Handbook of British Birds* is a useful guide to the food of many woodland species but classification is difficult due to a lack of information. Table 16 was an attempt to separate species according to habit.

Birds in woodland seem to exploit the available food supply fairly well although the total amount of vegetable matter taken is comparatively small. Birds do not feed on actual wood but they may take shoots, twigs, leaves, berries and seeds. Bullfinches and some of the tits will sometimes feed on the buds of deciduous trees. Wood pigeons from April to June will take tree buds and flowers especially those of beech, ash and hawthorn, and in southern England I have often seem them feeding on elms in March. The winter food of the capercaillie consists almost entirely of pine twigs, needles, buds and unopened cones and control of this species will depend on local conditions. When mature woods have been felled capercaillies have sometimes been driven into young plantations and control became necessary to prevent a loss in timber production. However, this fine game-bird may balance some of this damage by feeding on the pine weevil which flourishes in felled clearings from which it may threaten new plantations. Black grouse have often been condemned for the damage that they do to young conifers. However, the District Officer of the Forestry Commission in one of the counties of north-east Scotland has suggested that damage to lodgepole pine by black grouse may in the long run not be harmful. In Echies and Teindland Forests three compartments were badly eaten back at one time but in 1966 they were of good form. Lodgepole pine can be subject to a condition known as basal sweep caused perhaps by the root system being unable to carry the weight of the heavy crown in the first eight to ten years. The suggestion is that black grouse check this early top growth while the roots are still spreading. When the damage to buds and shoots ceases the tree is well balanced and the form of the stem is improved. The District Officer went on to say (*in litt.*): "It may well be that Scots pine is affected in the same way but due to the normally good stem form, the 'improvement' is not noticed. I must say that I have not come across rough Scots pine where the poor form can be attributed to Black Grouse damage." It is not the policy of the Forestry Commission in any case to exterminate either capercaillie or black grouse.

Many birds such as robins, thrushes and some of the warblers take soft fruits, and a research project carried out by the Royal Society for the Protection of Birds showed that the berries most frequently taken by birds were those of elder, hawthorn, yew and holly. Blackberries were especially favoured by blackbirds, bullfinches, starlings and great and blue tits. Birds, of course, can denude a tree of its entire crop of fruits and I once watched a party of fieldfares in Ladbroke Square in London strip three hawthorns in six days. The seeds may survive and be dispersed elsewhere, and seed storage can result in the spread of many tree species, even uphill! Woodland can even be self-maintaining in this way. Conifer seeds are also eaten but it is unlikely that this is on a serious scale and the numbers of crossbills and crested tits cannot be great enough to constitute a threat to the pine-forests. Dr F. J. Turček, who combines the respective skills of forester and ornithologist, has written a comprehensive book describing his researches into the kinds of seed taken by European woodland birds and into those species of bird which feed on the vegetable matter of the trees including leaves, shoots, galls and even the sap. The attacks of woodpeckers upon trees is an indication of the presence already of insects harmful to timber. In Europe great spotted woodpeckers and green woodpeckers have drilled the trunks of trees, particularly pine, fir and yew to drink the sap, but it was found that the attacked trees were already damaged or foreign to the area. Woodpeckers chiefly take insects including various wood-boring and bark beetles, weevils, moths, flies, ants, wood wasps and gall makers, but the vegetable matter covers nuts, acorns, beech-mast, pine and spruce seeds, berries and fruit. Nuts and cones are fitted into cracks in trees, held tight with one foot and hammered very effectively by great spotted woodpeckers. Although woodpeckers might be responsible for spreading some virus diseases of trees they may well reduce the number of some insects by passing on other viruses inimical to them. They are handsome and striking birds to have in a forest and any damage must be of the slightest and most infrequent kind.

It has often been suggested in the past that birds constitute a useful check on the populations and numbers of insect pests. Opinions still differ about the economic importance of some birds in woodlands and some of the ecological aspects are still unclear. It is beyond question that many birds eat insects that are harmful to growing trees, but it is also certain that they consume other insects which may provide checks on the harmful ones by parasitising them in turn. It has even been suggested that the beneficial work of birds is cancelled out by their taking of these useful insects. Some observers believe that birds eat only a small fraction of their food reserves, but Gibb (1960) showed that the density of certain insectivorous birds such as coal tits and goldcrests was governed chiefly by the amount of food available to them in the winter. These species sometimes ate a high proportion – up to 50% – of the eucosmid moth *Ernarmonia conicolana* and Gibb's findings suggested, but did not prove, that bird predation is important in the natural control of forest insects. He considered that predation by birds was "a force to be reckoned with." In North America from 50% to 100% predation by woodpeckers was claimed and woodpeckers were found to reduce the winter population of the spruce beetle *Dendroctonus engelmanni* by from 45% to 95%.

One of the problems of animal ecology is discovering which of several factors in an ecosystem decides how many individuals of a species may occur in one place. Some interesting work has been carried out on the aphid *Acyrthosiphon spartii* on 120 broom bushes growing along the edge of a piece of mixed woodland in Silwood Park. This research showed clearly that insect predators and parasites had little effect on the aphid numbers, whereas the two most important influences were attack by birds and the normal departure of the surviving fully-grown aphids. Some of the broom bushes were protected by cages from birds and the abundance of aphids fell by 56% in 20 days; this could be compared to 98% on the uncaged bushes. Blue tits, chaffinches and less commonly hedgesparrows and lesser whitethroats were responsible for the attacks which occurred mainly in the morning and late afternoon, but which went on all day when the numbers of aphids were at their peak. On the other hand the invertebrate predators

PLATE 19. Brashed plantations. *Above,* Corsican pine with fallen brashings. Mundford, near Thetford; *below,* sitka spruce being brashed.

PLATE 20. Broad-leaved and mixed plantations.
The *top* picture is the young oak plantation.
Micheldever, Hampshire;
below, European larch plantation under-planted with beech.
Tollymore Park, Northern Ireland.

– hoverfly larvae, ladybird larvae, larval bugs and a parasitic wasp – were not in sufficient numbers at the aphid peak to have much effect. This suggests that the birds were proving more useful in taking the aphids and that this advantage was not cancelled out through the birds' predation on useful insects. The birds tended to take the bigger mature aphids so that their predation also slowed down the rate of reproduction already adversely affected by the emigration of the winged adult aphids.

If predators took weakly specimens the result of the predation could be an increase in the population of the prey. We have just seen that the biggest and best-developed aphids were taken off the broom bushes. From 34,315 food samples from ten bird species feeding on the larvae or pupae of *Tortrix viridana* in an oak/beech forest it was found that the birds showed no preferences for parasitised insects. It has been seen that birds actively preferred the non-parasitised caterpillars of the moth *Liparis dispar*. Other research revealed that from 50,000 samples of food collected by neck-ring technique from 12,000 nestlings "the insect-eating birds feed chiefly on harmful insects, often in large quantities." Although work in Britain, Germany and Holland demonstrates that it is possible for birds to consume quite sizeable quantities of harmful insects, it should not be assumed that birds can either prevent an insect plague or make a truly significant assault upon it once it has broken out. Birds such as tits, rooks, jackdaws and starlings often gather in oakwoods to eat defoliating cater-pillars when they are abundant enough to constitute a plague in the woodlands. An individual bird may appear to be taking a really impressive quantity of insects – great tit and lesser whitethroat some 300 caterpillars a day – but a plague can increase the total number of insects a hundred-fold or more. Even over a period of several weeks a bird can only consume a tiny proportion of the total. The effect of the birds is likely to be at its smallest. Calculations show that during a plague of insects in the Canadian spruce forests predation accounted for only 5% of the larvae. This con-trasts with the claim made by Baron von Berlepsch that woods where birds had been encouraged to nest remained green, while the surrounding woods were stripped by defoliating insects. Another experiment demon-strated that in a seventy acre wood with nestboxes there were only 50 caterpillars per tree of the moth *Bupalius piniarius*, whereas there was an average of 5,000 caterpillars per tree in nearby unprotected areas.

There is some evidence that birds consume a higher proportion of insects when these occur in small numbers. Predation by tits on *Ernamonia conicolana* larvae went up with a rise in the number of larvae per cone. Insects do not, of course, appear in plague numbers all the time but at low endemic population levels and the sustained predation by birds in these circumstances may be of considerable importance in keeping the woodland ecosystem stable. The limited reproductive capacity of birds compared to that of most insects implies that they cannot effectively combat major insect plagues. It is during the winter that birds may take more appreciable proportions of the stock of insect food, and at this time they may provide a check particularly if such species as tits take the wingless and adult female winter moths *Operophtera brumata* when their numbers are low. This could mean that our resident birds which are still present in winter may have a greater influence in controlling insect numbers than the summer visitors. If this is so, then tits and goldcrests could have a more significant part to play in the war against pests than the warblers and flycatchers which come to us for the summer months. The constructive encouragement of these resident birds can reap worthwhile if not necessarily decisive results, and tits, on the whole, are thought to be beneficial to forests. On strictly economic grounds it is unlikely that tits in Breckland, although eating sometimes more than 50% of the over-wintering larvae, could regulate the population of *Ernarmonia*. Whether insect-eating birds in forests should be actively encouraged or just tolerated is open to question but in Germany and Russia the contribution of these birds is considered to be important enough to warrant special measures.

On the Continent the question "How can bird-life in woodland be enriched?" was asked some years ago. Economic forests are often monocultures of even age in which there is a striking absence of trees with natural holes. Here hole-nesting birds are unable to breed, except for those few which may be able to use holes in the ground. The ecological balance and stability in an uneven-aged forest with old timber is lacking from the monocultures. Artificial nestboxes have been used to remedy the lack of natural holes with some very interesting results. Dr H. Bruns has described in some detail reservations about the possibility of increasing bird numbers in an area above a certain figure, due to limitations set by the birds' territorial behaviour and a failure to occupy all the nestboxes available. Experiments in Germany showed that it was possible to increase the population of birds by from five to twenty times. The Institute of Bird Protection at Frankfurt-on-Main obtained, with the exception of the starling, populations of twenty-five or more breeding pairs per acre where according to informed opinion eight pairs was regarded as the maximum number. The prior condition for this kind of increase was the availability of suitable breeding sites and not the food supply. These spectacular results were attributed to the use of new concrete and sawdust nestboxes which provided better insulation, easier handling and resulted in fewer parasites and a longer life than the old style wooden ones. These boxes were made in different styles for flycatchers, tits, starlings, redstarts and so on, and, when provided with vertical slots, were suitable for tree-creepers. There were disadvantages of cost and sometimes weight and the boxes tended to overheat in some situations but they were considered to be impervious to attacks by great spotted woodpeckers. In Britain wooden boxes have been attacked and this has resulted in the death of nestling tits, and great spotted woodpeckers have even made assaults on concrete ones in England. In the German trials the old belief that a 65% occupation of boxes meant that it was useless to increase their number was disproved since the absolute density could be raised even if the percentage used was reduced. Dr Bruns discovered that a concentration of nestboxes was essential to persuade the semi-social pied and collared flycatchers to colonise a new area while widely scattered boxes proved quite ineffectual. The percentage of used boxes also rose with an increase in the number of boxes. Spare ones were widely used by male flycatchers for roosting and these were defended even against breeding females. The extra empty nestboxes were also preferred to the old ones by tits embarking on the second brood of the season. Other European countries have used nestboxes very widely indeed and in Russia 10,000 were placed in nine different areas in 1953. Eighteen species nested in some 40% of these boxes. In Sweden pied flycatchers nest in boxes in the towns, and in the schools there the making of a nestbox is one of the very early handwork lessons!

Nestboxes have also been considered in Britain as a means of increasing the populations of hole-nesting birds but a distinction has to be drawn between a real increase in the population as a whole and a purely local increase at the expense of surrounding areas. The increased density of coal tits in Thetford Chase after the provision of nestboxes was believed to be due to birds being drawn from the immediate district. Nestboxes affected the local distribution in Breckland of great and blue tits, but the overall population was determined by the winter food supply. On the other hand, the use of such boxes has resulted in a remarkable and real increase in the population and range of the pied flycatcher in Britain, which suggests that the numbers of this species are not entirely controlled by density-dependent mortality. Boxes were first put up in the Forest of Dean in 1942 when 84 were fixed in a mature oakwood in readiness for that breeding season. The boxes were set up on trees some ten or eleven feet above the ground to avoid disturbance. Eventually the number of boxes was increased to a maximum of 260. Since 1948 Dr Bruce Campbell and students from the Forester Training School, Parkend, have made regular observations on these boxes which are primarily used by five resident species, of which great and blue tits are numerically the most important, and two summer visitors – redstart and pied flycatcher. There was some competition between the species for nestboxes. Table 31 shows how these nestboxes in the Forest of Dean have been used by pied flycatchers; it may also be indicative of more general populations trends over the whole period.

TABLE 31. *Occupation of Nestboxes (First Layings) by Pied Flycatchers in an area of the Forest of Dean, Gloucestershire, 1942–62*

Year	Layings	Year	Layings	Year	Layings
1942	15	1949	67	1956	60
1943	33	1950	87	1957	54
1944	35	1951	100	1958	71
1945	34	1952	98	1959	71
1946	37	1953	85	1960	58
1947	54	1954	76	1961	62
1948	56	1955	67	1962	59

(The figures for 1942–7 are not as accurate as later ones and in 1958 and 1959 the holes were blocked until the flycatchers arrived to reduce competition from resident species. In 1950 the number of boxes was increased to 260.)
Reproduced from *Bird Study*, Vol. 12, by kind permission of Dr Bruce Campbell.

I have been informed by the Forestry Commission that in 1966 there were approximately 4,350 nestboxes on their land in England, Wales and Scotland. There are, for example, some 200 boxes in Grizedale Forest in Cumberland used especially by pied flycatchers, and great, blue and coal tits; it is hoped that the local ornithological group will take over responsibility for the boxes. There are certain requirements that nestboxes should meet as well as specifications and these are clearly listed in a guide published by the British Trust for Ornithology. This guide not only describes a nestbox suitable for mass production, but also gives details of precautions that ought to be taken in their construction and erection. These include lids or roofs that overlap the sides to reduce the effects of rain, an absence of projections including perches which predators could use and the positioning of the hole itself at such a height up the side of the box that enemies could not reach it. Boxes should not be placed facing the sun at its hottest or near branches and twigs from which predators could reach the box. It is also a good idea to place the box at a height of no less than ten feet above the ground where it is free from human disturbance. An entrance hole of no more than 1⅛ inches is useful for tits and will exclude sparrows but there are also designs available with front panels adapted for robins, spotted flycatchers and other species which prefer a more open

PLATE 21. Male redstart. This is a bird of open-canopy broad-leaved woods, pine forest, heath and parkland.

type of box. The Royal Society for the Protection of Birds has designed one dual-purpose nestbox suitable for hole-nesting passerines which has a removable front to accommodate robins, spotted flycatchers and pied wagtails; an aluminium front can be fitted to prevent the hole being enlarged by woodpeckers and squirrels.

The West Midland Bird Club has been co-operating with the Forestry Commission in a project to increase the tit population in Cannock Chase by providing nestboxes. It is hoped that in this way a natural means can be found to control *Bupalius piniarius*. In 1962 some 540 nestboxes were set out and broods were successfully reared that year in 20 of the boxes. Coal tits were already present but great and blue tits were regarded as "gains." Observations at one coal tit's nest showed that the brood would consume between 10,000 and 20,000 caterpillars, but it was not clear how many of these belonged to *Bupalius piniarius*. It will be interesting to see the results of this experiment when they are completed. The Herefordshire and Radnorshire Nature Trust was responsible for 462 nestboxes in nineteen areas of woodland; 245 of the boxes were occupied in 1965, chiefly by blue tits, great tits, redstarts and pied flycatchers. Only three clutches of pied flycatchers nesting in 65 boxes failed.

It has been pointed out that if birds are to be attracted to woodlands as a means of checking insect numbers, a wider range of insects will be taken if the whole community and not just the hole-nesters are encouraged. One way in which potential nest-sites for passerines can be increased in conifer stands where ground cover and shrub layer are absent is the use of old brashings. Left on the ground they can provide sites for species that nest low down but when tied in bundles and lashed to the trees may be used by thrushes, blackbirds and wrens which would not otherwise nest in that area of woodland. Artificial low cover is, of course, only a substitute for natural shrub layers. If woodland can include some natural cover then it will contain a wider range of bird species and this will contribute both to the amenity value of the forest and to the number of insect-eating birds present.

Natural forest is full of variety and is comparatively stable. Artificial coniferous woods with their few tree species, usually also of even age, represent simple environments which are less stable and where the natural control of populations is uncertain. Since insectivorous birds may help in this control their increase is desirable and, as we have already seen, nestboxes can have some effect. Since winter food is so important, it has been suggested that it may be helpful to plant or to leave *in situ* a wide variety of trees when the conifer plantations are first begun. In broad-leaved woods coal tits, for example, feed on a variety of foods through the winter months and the addition of beech, birch, oak, hazel, maple and other cone-bearing species to the coniferous monocultures would have several desirable effects – it would give the tits the variety they need as well as ensuring a greater stability in the ecosystem and enhancing the appearance of the countryside. Monocultures are sometimes subject to insect plagues and the work more than forty years ago of a forester named Freiberger (1926–7) near Baden, has shown the value of a systematic increase by deliberate means of birds in a large pinewood which had undergone a whole series of insect plagues; in fact, Freiberger found that the plagues originated from the comparatively bird-less monocultures while the areas artificially enriched with birds were spared. One experiment over thirty-three years showed how a pinewood with an increased number of birds remained comparatively undamaged despite several insect plagues in the area. It would be very difficult to prove that a serious plague had been positively prevented in the absence of a control area, but the claims of many of the European observers are impressive and cannot all be lightly dismissed. Conifers may be used as nurse trees for broad-leaved species such as oak and beech and here the woods are rich in birds since the canopy tends to remain more open and shrubs are able to grow. In some situations only certain species of conifer will grow anyway and it would not be possible to establish hardwoods. Where varied cultures are possible the bird-life and the appearance of the woods are both improved. In a Norway sprucewood in Ireland which was underplanted with beech there was a secondary growth of hollies and rowans with a good shrub layer. Wrens, robins, blackbirds, chaffinches, hedgesparrows and chiff-chaffs were common and there were also more expected species such as coal tit, goldcrest, wood pigeon, treecreeper and sparrowhawk. Besides actual underplanting, the provision of broad-leaved trees as screens or shelter-belts around conifer plantations where this is practicable will also attract numbers of insect-eating birds. The inclusion of some berry-bearing trees or shrubs in these strips will help to feed the birds during the winter. It is possible to exploit the immediate surroundings of many forests and it has been shown that the provision of nestboxes among the alders which flourish along the streams flowing out from the moorland forests of Durham has resulted in an increase in the population of tits, redstarts, treecreepers and pied flycatchers.

Dr H. Bruns believes that the artificial winter feeding of birds – its ethical value aside – should be necessary only during periods of prolonged frost or snow since the birds should not be kept away from their most important task of controlling insect numbers during the winter months. We have already seen that some birds leave the woodlands at the onset of cold weather and forage for food in gardens, parks and on farms and once away from their wood they may not go back for some time. By providing food in the really severe weather, numbers of these birds may be retained in their home woodlands where their economic value is at its highest.

The Russians have tried to increase the numbers of useful birds in some of their newly planted forests by the deliberate introductions of adult or nestling birds. The pied flycatcher was one of the first species to be used in these experiments in acclimatization which began in 1952 since it was regarded as an important bird in the defence of the forests against insect pests. Some of the displaced birds settled and also bred in succeeding years. Dr Bruce Campbell has suggested that we should carefully consider whether at the same time as we are creating vast new forests we should perhaps add new species which are both beneficial in feeding behaviour and sedentary in habit. He believes that we ought to be able to assess the effects of this kind of introduction and his likely candidates included the European crested tit in the pine plantations of England, as well as some of the European woodpeckers and perhaps even the goshawk which would help to keep the numbers of wood pigeons down. Some past introductions such as the pheasant have settled down without too much trouble, but I am not sure that the ecologists have yet sufficient information about how animals succeed or fail in adapting themselves to a new habitat to be able to defend such introductions against their opponents. In the case of the crested tits their numbers would be controlled to a considerable extent by the nestboxes available. Attempts to supplement the impoverished bird fauna of Ireland with such woodland species as nightingale, nuthatch, hawfinch and crossbill did not meet with success.

Some of the German foresters believe that there are other allies of the birds and of these the most useful are bats, parasites and ants. Dr Bruns has recommended settling wood ants to provide a winter food reserve for birds as well as supplementing predation on such pests as *Tortrix viridana*. In three samples of oakwoods it was recorded that defoliation by this insect was least in the plot where ants and nestboxes occurred together, more severe in the second area where there were boxes and no ants, and most severe in the piece of woodland without either ants or nestboxes. In Britain the wood ant occurs in woodlands, but especially where pines prevail.

We cannot yet pass absolute judgments on the economic significance of many of our British woodland birds, although the almost total destruction of a plantation by roosting starlings or the forages from the sprucewoods by marauding wood pigeons are clearly on the debit side. Birds may take the insects that prey on harmful ones but they also feed on many enemies of the trees. When an insect plague reaches its peak the numbers of birds may rise, but their nesting may be adversely affected when the trees lose their leaves through defoliation.

Birds clearly form part of a complex balance in woodland ecosystems and the foodchains and foodwebs in natural communities have been built up over a long period of evolution. This balance should be continued or re-established by more mixed plantings of woodlands. In a structurally simple community with rather few species the numbers of the herbivores tend to fluctuate considerably and the use of blanketing insecticides makes the community even more simple. Birds cannot make much of an impression on a plague but if they are present in proper numbers before its occurrence their effect could be significant. Other factors apart, a forest rich in birds and other wild life has its own attraction, for here man can refresh his thoughts and forget his material needs. How much more welcome is this than even a tree-filled landscape without birds or their songs! For this reason such research projects as those of the Nature Conservancy into the ecology of our hedgerows, our native woodlands and artificial plantations are especially welcome. Forest policy will eventually ensure, as the first generation woodlands become ripe for replanting, that the new forests will become more mixed both in age and where possible in species. In the past the policy has not always been guided by ecological principles. Trees have often been man's rivals for space on the earth, and their real contribution to the quality of the landscape has not always been appreciated. Too often they have been regarded as inanimate objects, which merely provide timber or are nuisances to be eliminated, while scrub has been called "an affront" to good husbandry. We have not always taken much notice of the forms of life that do not seem to serve our immediate purpose. Every organism in a wood from the giant oaks down through the birds to the fauna of the soil occupies a niche in the ecosystem, and each must play some part in the harmonious working of the whole. Some of these balanced patterns evolved long before man and they helped to create a favourable environment in which we ourselves could finally flourish. When we more fully understand these patterns we shall also take more regard for them, and in so doing relegate ourselves to a less arrogant, less aggressive place in the whole scheme of nature.

SYSTEMATIC LIST OF WOODLAND BIRDS

I have chosen to end this book with a chapter on the distribution of the woodland birds which will provide a summary of what is known of their geographical distribution and the habitats which they occupy in the British Isles. It is not possible to give detailed life-histories or behavioural accounts of the species involved since much of this information is available elsewhere. Despite some gaps *The Handbook of British Birds* is still an invaluable guide to the ornithologist and Dr David Bannerman's impressive book *The Birds of the British Isles* provides eminently readable accounts of the general biology of individual bird species. The projected work on *The Birds of the Western Palearctic* will be awaited with great interest as well. It is fortunate that prior to the publication of this book a survey by J. L. F. Parslow (1967–8) in the magazine *British Birds* became available giving the status of all the breeding birds in Britain and Ireland up to and after 1940. I am especially indebted to this fine work of scholarship. The European distribution of our woodland birds is broadly sketched in the species notes by James Fisher to *Thorburn's Birds* (1967) and there are very useful species summaries in Dr Voous's *Atlas of European Birds* (1960); this describes the breeding range in terms of climatic zones and gives accounts of habitats, food, nest materials and sites which can all affect the distribution of birds.

In this systematic list some generalisations are inevitable and there is still a great deal that we do not know even about quite common species. In this respect the census work of the British Trust for Ornithology now going on will eventually reap a rich reward.

The details for each species are given in the form of paragraphs which it is hoped will make for easy reference.

Paragraph 1. The status of the species in the British Isles, e.g. resident, summer visitor, etc.

2. A brief summary of the European distribution, where known.

3. A summary of the distribution in the British Isles.

4. The habitats in which each woodland species occurs in the British Isles.

5. Any other information.

The species are listed with their Latin names under families and in an order known as the Wetmore Order since this is the system of classification most widely used in present ornithological practice. This method is employed not to stereotype a system but because it seems likely to have the widest understanding at the present time. The abbreviation R A is used for any figures of Relative Abundance that I quote.

ARDEIDAE

Heron (Grey or Common) *Ardea cinerea*

British herons are largely resident and sedentary but young birds tend to disperse; also passage migrant and winter visitor.

This is a palearctic species with a tendency to spread north-west but its range in Europe is discontinuous due to disturbance and the felling of its nesting trees. Apart from isolated groups in the Iberian Peninsula, Corsica and Italy its range becomes more continuous from central France, Switzerland and the Balkans north to the British Isles, western Norway, southern Sweden and Finland.

Herons nest every year in all but nine of the counties of Britain and Ireland; the exceptions are Denbigh, Flint, Northumberland, Shetland and five in south-east Scotland. Considerable decreases may occur after hard winters. Many heronries have been lost through disturbance and tree-felling, but new ones have also been established. In 1961 there were 200 heronries in England, Wales and Scotland with 3,363, 114 and 119 nests respectively, while at least 213 were reported in Ireland with 939 pairs. In south Scotland there seems to have been some persecution of young birds. There has been a notable decrease in north-east England. Many of the heronries contain fewer than 10 nests. Large heronries are generally near water.

The heron is a bird of pools, lakes, riverbanks, even ditches as well as the coast, feeding extensively on fish, amphibians, small mammals and aquatic and land insects. The nests are platforms of sticks built usually colonially in tall trees, both broad-leaved and coniferous – I have records of oaks, elms, hawthorns, sweet chestnut, Scots pine, Sitka and Norway spruce – or more rarely in small trees, bushes, reed-beds, on cliff-faces or the ground. Herons nest close to London and I have seen them fishing in the central parks.

Breeding begins in February, but many birds do not lay before March. Incubation is by both sexes and the young are fed by regurgitation. The natural history of the heron has been extensively treated in a New Naturalist monograph by Lowe.

ANATIDAE

Mallard *Anas platyrhynchos*

Common resident, passage migrant and winter visitor.

A Holarctic species to be found throughout most of Europe.

Mallard breed in all parts of the British Isles and in Scotland up to 2,000 ft.

The habitat is almost anywhere in which fresh and brackish water is to be found, including quiet forest pools and streams. Nests are sometimes in holes in trees and even in the abandoned nests of crows and birds-of-prey quite high in the trees. Although not a typical bird of woodland I have surprised mallard in many British woods. Mallard also breed in towns and suburban areas.

Mallard normally breed from March onwards but they may start earlier and carry on into the autumn in artificial environments.

Goosander *Mergus merganser*

Resident and winter visitor to the British Isles.

A Holarctic species breeding in Europe south to about 50° North.

This sawbilled duck has spread south from the central Highlands of Scotland, where it bred for the first time in 1871, into south-west Scotland and northern England; there are some signs of a decrease in north-west Scotland. It does not breed in Ireland.

The goosander is a bird of lakes and rivers, especially in areas of coniferous woodland but also in treeless regions. Much of the breeding in Britain occurs within partially wooded areas and it nests frequently in hollow trees. In Scotland the population density on two rivers was calculated at 2 to 3 birds per 10 miles of river.

FALCONIDAE

Golden Eagle *Aquila chrysaetos*

Scarce resident in Scotland; has bred in Northern Ireland in recent years.

A very rare vagrant to England and Wales; bred Lake District in 1970.

In Europe the golden eagle breeds in the Iberian Peninsula, the Massif Central in France, the Apennines, the Alps, the Balkans, northern Russia, Finland and Sweden, Norway and Scotland.

The headquarters in the British Isles are in the Scottish Highlands and the Hebrides with a small group in south-west Scotland. In the early 1950s the Scottish population stood at about 190 pairs. In the early 1960s the breeding success had fallen considerably; in a sample population in west Scotland the number of pairs rearing young dropped from 72% during 1937–60 to 29% from 1961–3. It was considered that the decline was due mainly to the residues of chlorinated hydrocarbons, particularly dieldrin (used for sheep-dips), in both birds and eggs. The breeding population seems to be decreasing. Nests have been built in the Lakes and in 1970 1 young was reared. The golden eagle became extinct in Ireland about 1914, but a pair nested in Antrim from 1953 to 1960 though without success in 1956.

Eagles frequent wild mountainous country, sometimes forested, and each pair may need 16,000 acres of deer-forest. Nests are often on rock ledges, but the eyries are sometimes in old pines in the forest and occasionally in birches. The natural history of the golden eagle has been described by Seton Gordon.

Buzzard *Buteo buteo*

Resident in Britain; occasional vagrant.

The buzzard, a bird of woodlands, is missing in Europe primarily from the far north, Ireland and eastern England.

In Britain it suffered a severe decrease in the nineteenth century owing to persecution, but it staged a recovery during the last half century. This trend was reversed about 1954 by the appearance of myxomatosis among rabbits. After a slow recovery the population seems to have stabilised itself but at a lower level. It is not uncommon in the Scottish Highlands, the Hebrides, Wales and the western parts of the Lowlands and England. It has withdrawn from the Midland counties of England which it had penetrated between about 1948 and 1955. The buzzard first bred in Orkney in 1966. Breeding stopped in Ireland about 1915; a small recolonisation begun in about 1951 had failed by 1964 but I saw a pair in Antrim in 1969 and 1970. The history of the buzzard in Britain has been reviewed and maps showing the correlation between the distribution of the buzzard and game preservation are reproduced on pages 258 and 260.

The buzzard is a woodland bird and its presence on open moorland may be the result of past persecution and an indication of the bird's adaptability. It can be found in both dense and open canopy woods. It is regular in many of the sessile oakwoods of western Scotland, Wales and western England but is missing from many pedunculate woods. In the

PLATE 22. Capercaillie, Europe's finest game-bird; re-introduced to Scottish pine forests in 1837.

Speyside pine-forests the buzzard had a relative abundance of 1 in 1967 and the species can also be found in some of the older coniferous plantations. I have also found buzzards in 2 of the 6 Scottish alderwoods I visited, as well as some ashwoods.

Sparrowhawk *Accipiter nisus*

Resident and passage migrant; the native stock is sedentary.

Widely distributed throughout the whole of Europe except for the extreme north. Its limits are bounded roughly by the July isotherms of 53° F. and 86° F. There has been a decline in recent years.

The sparrowhawk breeds throughout the British Isles except for the Outer Hebrides and the Northern Isles. Heavily persecuted by gamekeepers, the species recovered everywhere during the 1939–45 war except in South Wales. From 1955 onwards a serious general decrease occurred with an almost complete disappearance from much of eastern England as well as a serious decline in parts of Scotland and the eastern counties of Ireland. Only in the New Forest, the extreme south-west of England, parts of Ireland and in South Wales have numbers remained relatively unchanged. This overall decrease has been attributed to the use of toxic chemicals.

The sparrowhawk is a bird of well-wooded areas of broad-leaved trees, especially oak and birch, of coniferous and mixed woods sometimes with open ground nearby. It shows a preference for conifers, especially spruce, in mixed woods. I have on occasion seen sparrowhawks in Scottish pine plantations and I watched many soaring over conifer plantations in Ireland in 1967. Twenty years ago birds often hunted through north Oxford gardens and if woods of sufficient size survive it can live in many suburban areas. A pair attempted to breed in Holland Park in London in 1953.

Its food consists largely of small passerines and larger species such as wood pigeon, jackdaw and magpie. In 1895 D'Urban and Matthew regretted the disastrous increase in the blackbird due to the destruction by gamekeepers of "his natural enemy the sparrowhawk." The nest is usually built by the birds themselves, sometimes on the top of an old nest of crow, magpie or jay.

Goshawk *Accipiter gentilis*

Rare vagrant; has bred (but some nests are those of escaped birds).

Widely distributed in Europe but exterminated by man in many places, particularly in France, parts of the Low Countries and Portugal.

The goshawk nested on occasions in the nineteenth century and perhaps more regularly in earlier times. Eyries were often built in pines. A pair attempted to nest in Lincolnshire in 1864 and a pair bred in Yorkshire in 1893. Three pairs bred in Sussex from 1938 (perhaps even from 1921) to 1951 but they were eventually disturbed. Goshawks may have nested since in one or two other areas. It is not known how many of these breeding birds may have been released or escaped.

This is essentially a bird of the coniferous taiga. From examples I have seen in Germany and Switzerland there seems a preference for woods adjoining open country. According to *The Handbook*, goshawks will breed in mixed and broad-leaved woods including beech.

Kite *Milvus milvus*

A very scarce resident; perhaps also a vagrant from the Continent.

Widespread in Europe north to about the July isotherm of 62° F. It has been exterminated in many areas during the last hundred years.

The resident population is confined to about 20 pairs in a few counties in Central Wales. In the nineteenth century the kite bred in nearly every county in England and Wales (e.g. "the kite was abundant" in parts of Oxfordshire in the 1820s). Kites also bred in a number of mainland counties of Scotland, but not Ireland. Sporadic nesting has occurred this century in Devon and Cornwall. The surviving colony in Wales was down to about 9 birds at the beginning of the present century but protected now by the Royal Society for the Protection of Birds as many as 11 young were reared in 1965; the future of this colony must remain in doubt. The decrease has been attributed to deliberate persecution and the disappearance of carrion. It is possible that some Continental kites may come across to England; there appears to have been a small immigration in 1958 when I saw a bird over the BBC Television Studios in Shepherd's Bush on 20th May.

On the Continent the kite is a bird of well grown broad-leaved forest and forest edge adjoining grassy plains and parkland. In Wales the kite often nests in tall sessile oaks in hanging hillside woods but it has bred in ash, birch, beech, Scots pine, spruce and larch. Before it was exterminated in Scotland it regularly nested in Scots pines. Winter roosting can take place in coniferous and broad-leaved woodlands.

Honey-Buzzard *Pernis apivorus*

Formerly a rare but regular summer resident; now an occasional breeder or very irregular bird of passage.

Breeds on Continent north to southern Norway, Sweden, Finland and North Russia and south to south-eastern Portugal, Central Spain and much of the Mediterranean shore. England is on the limit of the bird's range.

The breeding population is probably somewhere between 1 and 9 pairs. Nesting has taken place during the last 40 years from southern England north to the Welsh Borders and probably in Fife in 1949.

The habitat consists of well-developed woodlands, often broad-leaved such as oak and beech, as well as mixed and coniferous forest, with open glades, or near open patches of grassland.

The main food consists largely of wasp grubs, wild bees and honey, humble bees, hornets, ant pupae, small mammals, nestlings and eggs.

Hen Harrier *Circus cyaneus*

Scarce resident and winter visitor in small numbers.

The hen harrier is widely distributed in Europe from northern Spain, Central France, Central Italy and Yugoslavia north to North Norway, Sweden, Finland and Russia.

Probably more than 100 pairs breed in Scotland, in six Irish counties and three counties in England and Wales. The species has increased again after almost total extinction.

This very adaptable harrier was formerly confined to moorland and moorland valleys in Britain with a preference for old, tall heather for the actual nest site. It has shown a tendency in recent years to enter young conifer plantations which are not keepered and where it can breed undisturbed. For this reason it must be included as a species colonising the early stages of these plantations.

Montagu's Harrier *Circus pygargus*

Very scarce summer resident and vagrant.

Very local in Europe from the Iberian Peninsula and Central Europe north to about 58° N. Its decline has been due to the reclamation of moorland and marsh.

About 20 pairs breed annually. The Montagu's harrier has bred every year in probably three counties of England and Wales and almost annually in three others. From 1956–65 it bred at least once in from 12 to 14 counties in England and Wales. One or two pairs breed in Ireland.

This is a species of marshlands, reed-beds, heaths and commons. In south-west England, north-east England and North Wales it has increased and the favoured habitat has been that of young conifer plantations (*cf.* the hen harrier). The ultimate growth of these woodlands and the exclusion of the harriers may be responsible for some of the sporadic breeding records.

Osprey *Pandion haliaetus*

A very rare summer resident and regular passage migrant.

Ospreys breed in the Mediterranean area, Scandinavia and eastern Europe; in the past they have been widely exterminated.

Birds last bred in England in 1847 and in Scotland (before recolonisation) in 1908 and possibly later. The return to Scotland took place in 1954 or the years immediately before. Since then 2 or 3 pairs have attempted to breed with varying success. The recolonisation has coincided with an increase in Scandinavia. The species has not been known to breed in Ireland or Wales. A very full account of the osprey's return to Britain has been given by Brown and Waterston.

In the breeding season ospreys are to be found in the neighbourhood of lakes and rivers; in Scotland the eyries are built in living or dead Scots pines but in the past they have usually been on rocky islets or occasionally buildings.

Hobby *Falco subbuteo*

A very scarce summer resident.

The hobby is widely distributed in Europe from the Mediterranean area north to England, Denmark, the extreme south of Norway and Sweden, Central Finland and northern Russia.

This species decreased in the nineteenth century like many other birds-of-prey as the result of human persecution. It is estimated that there are now 75–100 pairs breeding largely in southern England. Its chief stronghold is in Hampshire with probably more than 25 pairs and in Sussex, Surrey, Wiltshire, Berkshire and Dorset. From 1 to 2 pairs also breed quite often in Devon, Gloucester, Hereford, Oxford, Buckinghamshire and Kent while sporadic nesting is known from Radnor, Cornwall, Somerset, Warwick, Northampton and Huntingdon and five other counties. Breeding has taken place as far north as Cheshire and Yorkshire.

In the breeding season the hobby is to be found on downland, heathland, open country with scattered belts or clumps of trees as well as fairly open woodlands, in wide river valleys and similar country. Birds hunt for flying prey over open countryside and avoid close woodland.

PLATE 23. Scrub..*Above*, high scrub of hawthorn and blackthorn; *below*, hazel scrub on Burren, Ireland.

PLATE 24. Sparrowhawk. A woodland predator.

Hobbies commandeer the unoccupied nests of crows, rooks, sparrow-hawks, wood pigeons and those of other large birds as well as squirrel dreys. In southern England many of the nests are in pines but farther north they tend to be in broad-leaved trees, often in river valleys or near marshy ground. In 1957 I was able to make the first sound recording of this species at a nest in Hampshire in an open canopy wood on a hill slope where the birds could be easily overlooked but another pair in Warwick-shire I found to be very elusive. Since many nests are in groves, clumps and belts of trees this species seems to be a bird of the ecotone and in Europe it is predominantly a bird of parklands.

Peregrine *Falco peregrinus*

I have included this species of mountains and sea-cliffs only because it may have nested formerly in small numbers in woodland sites. A list has been made of 570 known peregrine eyries in the British Isles of which 71.2% were on coastal cliffs and only 28.8% on inland cliffs. Since 1955 there has been a serious decline that has been attributed to toxic chemicals (Ratcliffe 1965), but the population has stabilised itself at 40% of its pre-war level (Ratcliffe 1967). On the North German plains peregrines regularly nest in trees and in earlier times they may have done so in Britain with some regularity. Peregrines may build in "an old nest of a Raven, Crow, Heron etc. in rocks or trees (usually pines)" (Saunders 1899). They were also reported as breeding in trees in Co. Antrim. In Warwickshire starling roosts I have found peregrines roosting, with sparrowhawks, in the thorns among countless thousands of starlings.

Merlin *Falco columbarius*

This species typical of upland country, moors and coastal dunes has suffered some decline due to the encroachment of new forests on the moors. The nest is usually on the ground but there are records of breeding in trees in the old nests of other species. In some upland areas, following afforestation, merlins "commonly nest in trees" (Prestt 1965). Here there are signs of an increase and birds often hunt through the plantations – a habit already noticed in a Cumberland wood.

Kestrel *Falco tinnunculus*

Fairly common resident, passage migrant and winter visitor.

The kestrel is widespread throughout Europe but missing from Iceland and the tundra regions.

Breeding takes place in every county of the British Isles except Shetland where it last nested in 1905. Its status has changed little over the years but there have been local changes. There was a very serious decline in numbers in eastern England in the early 1960s, especially in agricultural areas from Nottingham and Lincoln south to Kent, Sussex and Hampshire. This decrease has been associated with the use of toxic chemicals. A less severe drop in numbers was also noted in parts of central England, south-east Scotland and eastern Ireland. There are now some signs of recovery. The population and breeding success of the kestrel appear to change with the abundance of short-tailed field-voles – the kestrel's chief prey.

The kestrel is very much an ecotone bird and can be found in well-timbered open country, parkland in cultivated areas, open woods, tree clumps and hedgerow trees, moors, marshes, rocky coasts, quarries and ruins. It is the commonest bird of prey but is scattered thinly throughout the country and is nowhere common. Twenty six kestrels I saw in Buchan in half an hour in August 1965 were clearly Continental immigrants. After 1930 kestrels began to nest regularly in urban areas; in 1950 five pairs laid eggs in less than 10 square miles of central London. As the bombed sites have been developed there has been some decline in numbers. Kestrels also breed in the suburbs. In 1966 some 29–32 pairs bred in the London area. The penetration of London is probably due to the cessation of gamekeeping in the rural areas outside.

Eggs are laid in wooded areas in the old nests of crow, magpie, raven, rook, buzzard, sparrowhawk, heron or squirrel. Sometimes hollow trees are used, holes in ruins and other buildings, and ledges on church towers, chimneys, gasholders and other constructions.

TETRAONIDAE

Red Grouse *Lagopus lagopus*
This moorland species can survive for several years in the establishment stage of coniferous forest and I have found these grouse in a number of Scottish plantations where the trees are up to 3 feet or so in height. I have a few records in Scottish birch.

Black Grouse *Lyrurus tetrix*
Resident in Britain.
Black grouse breed in Britain, Scandinavia, the Low Countries, eastern France and the Alps south-east to the Carpathians and east to Siberia.
They are fairly numerous in Scotland, northern England and Wales

with smaller numbers in the Pennines, the Quantocks and on Exmoor. Black grouse were probably well distributed throughout Britain in ice age times, but a marked decrease has been occurring for many years; in most southern English counties the species was extinct by 1900. As we have seen earlier there is evidence of an increase in the new conifer plantations of Wales and Scotland.

This is a bird of swampy heathlands and moors, often with thin scrub along the forest edge and sometimes with growths of pine and birch. According to one account, in Europe the black grouse ecologically replaces the capercaillie along the edges of forests and in more open, less wooded districts. In Britain it is not so much a moorland bird as one of scrub. It feeds on birch catkins and buds and coniferous buds so that in places its numbers have been controlled. In the Pennines it occurs on hill slopes with heathery moors and hawthorn and rowan scrub. Its "leks" or display grounds are always in the open, but generally with pine or birch nearby. In Scotland I have seen it on the edges of sessile oakwoods, in birch scrub, in the old Speyside forest and the mature plantations of Scots pine. In Wales it favours the conifer plantations from their first establishment. Its natural history has been described by Palmar (1968).

Breeding can take place up to 1,400 ft. in the Highlands generally on the ground, but sometimes in old trees up to 20 ft. On the other hand some nests are quite far from the nearest trees.

Capercaillie *Tetrao urogallus*

Extinct resident before 1800; re-introduced from 1837 onwards.

The capercaillie breeds in the coniferous woodland that stretches from Norway through to Siberia with isolated, or nearly isolated, populations that can be regarded as glacial relics in the Pyrenees, the Cantabrian Mountains and the Alps.

This fine game-bird probably survived in England and Wales after the ice age. After persecution it was exterminated in Ireland about 1790 and Scotland about 1762. Birds of Swedish stock were reintroduced to Perthshire in 1837-8 and their descendants have colonised the eastern Highlands from Stirling north to Sutherland. A decrease occurred after both World Wars, but there has been some recovery since 1950 with birds entering younger plantations and even broad-leaved woods. Foresters may exercise some measure of control.

In Europe its habitats are those of extensive coniferous or broad-leaved forest with dense undergrowth, forest glades and occasional bogs. In Britain it favours mature coniferous woodland as in Scotland, either natural as in Rothiemurchus or Abernethy or in pine, larch or spruce plantations when they reach a height of 25 ft. or so. In 1967 I found a greater density in Abernethy, where the juniper scrub was thick and the shrub layer damp and often impenetrable, than in the more open conditions of much of Rothiemurchus. Near Dunkeld birds were very common in the bigger hybrid larch plantations. Oak, beech and birchwoods may be visited outside the breeding season.

Capercaillies will build their nests from near sea-level to heights of 1,500 ft. or so. The site of the nest is usually in a scrape at the foot of a pine in the forest. Occasionally nests have been found in a tree and a falcon's eyrie and, according to *The Handbook*, at heights of from 10 to 15 ft. above the ground. The history and habits of the capercaillie have been described by Palmar.

Hazel Hen (or Hazel Grouse) *Tetrastes bonasia*

A late ice age fossil of this European woodland species has been listed from Devon.

Red-legged Partridge *Alectoris rufa*

This introduced species is not a woodland bird and is more typical of scrub vegetation; however, in Castile I have often found it in woods. In East Anglia I have seen red-legged partridges nesting twenty or thirty feet inside broad-leaved woodland and in the same region I have found them persisting in conifer plantations up to the thicket stage, as well as along pinewood verges in southern England.

Partridge *Perdix perdix*

This species can be found occasionally in the establishment stage of conifer plantations.

Pheasant *Phasianus colchicus*

A resident introduced to England possibly by the Romans and again in immediately pre-Norman times, and to Scotland and Ireland some 500 years later. The original stock was the black-necked but there has been much interbreeding with other introduced races.

The pheasant is preserved as a game-bird in much of Europe also after ntroductions.

It can be found in nearly all parts of the British Isles and has bred in every county except Shetland. Since about 1900 numbers have increased in England, Scotland and Ireland, but not Wales, as a result of better management and some restocking. In the West Highlands and some other wetter, more exposed areas it depends for its future on restocking.

The pheasant occurs in woods of many types as well as along forest edges, in parkland, on farmland with hedges, game coverts and belts of trees, in large gardens and in reed-beds. It is regular in English pedunculate oak, beech and mixed woods, in Irish sessile oakwoods and mixed hardwoods and has an RA of 4 in Scottish sessile oak; it was found to be completely absent from the fellwoods and its upper nesting limit seems to be about 1,000 ft. It also had an RA of 4 in mature Scots pine plantations, 3 in Scottish conifer thickets and mature beech, and I have records in English and Scottish birch, ash, alder, and spruce. In Breckland the golden pheasant (*Chrysolophus pictus*) is feral.

RALLIDAE

Corncrake *Crex crex*

I found this bird very regularly in the establishment stage of many conifer plantations in Ireland.

Moorhen *Gallinula chloropus*

This bird of freshwater marshes of almost unlimited kind can often be found on pools and slow-running streams in wooded areas and can be seen foraging among the trees. It will nest in thorns and other trees and has been known to take over the old nests of rook, jay, magpie, wood pigeon and sparrowhawk.

CHARADRIIDAE

Lapwing *Vanellus vanellus*

This species will sometimes persist on newly afforested moors and heaths for the first year or so.

SCOLOPACIDAE

Snipe *Gallinago gallinago*

Like the last species the snipe may also remain for two or three years in the establishment stage of new plantations.

Woodcock *Scolopax rusticola*

Resident, summer resident, winter visitor and passage migrant.

A woodland bird nesting primarily in Europe from the Pyrenees, the Alps and the Balkans east to Japan and north to Central Scandinavia and about 64° N.

The woodcock is widely distributed throughout a great deal of Britain and Ireland but not in south-west England, Pembroke, Anglesey, the Outer Hebrides, Northern Isles and perhaps Donegal. There has been some decrease recently in southern England due to woodland destruction, but an increase has been reported in numbers in Ireland, East Anglia, North Wales and south-east Scotland due to the spread of new coniferous forest.

It is largely a bird of open, damp woods, particularly those of oak, birch, Scots pine, larch and spruce often with swampy hollows, rides and spaces as well as a good field layer of brambles and bracken and a shrub layer of evergreens. A ground zone of wet, decaying leaves often forms part of the habitat. Young conifer plantations and broad-leaved scrub also prove attractive. I have an RA of 1 for Irish sessile oakwoods and a slightly lower figure for Scottish sessile oak, birch and Scots pine. It appears in English and Scottish ash and alder and will also nest in beechwoods.

Curlew *Numenius arquata.*

Sometimes present in the establishment stages of new plantations on moorland.

Green Sandpiper *Tringa ochropus*

This wader from the swampy forests of Scandinavia and eastern Europe nested in Westmorland (1917) and Inverness (1959). Since it generally lays its eggs in the old nests of other species it could be overlooked but it is unlikely to have bred often in the British Isles.

Wood Sandpiper *Tringa glareola*

This is less of a woodland bird than the green sandpiper but on occasion has the same habit of breeding in the disused nests of other species. There are breeding records for Northumberland in 1853 and for one pair in Sutherland between 1959 and 1965, of another pair in 1962 and possibly of a third in 1961. Other pairs bred in 1960 in Inverness-shire and in Perthshire in 1966. The species may well have nested elsewhere in the north of Scotland.

Common Sandpiper *Tringa hypoleucos*

The habitat of this freshwater species may, in both Europe and Britain, include coniferous forest. In Speyside I have found nests in hollows well inside quite dense pinewoods and it is a common enough sight to watch birds displaying between the pine trunks.

Greenshank *Tringa nebularia*

During my stays in Strathspey I had many opportunities of watching this lovely bird on the swamps and moors partially covered in trees. Here hen greenshanks often took up station on the highest spur of the tallest tree in the vicinity and I have one sound recording of a bird giving the beautiful alarm call. This is one of the three habitats listed for the Spey Valley, and described as "a forest-bog or clearing, wet, tussocky marshy ground planted thinly with a natural growth of trees" (Nethersole Thompson 1951).

COLUMBIDAE

Stock Dove *Columba oenas*

Resident, partial migrant and winter visitor.

In Europe the stock dove breeds from Portugal east to the Caspian Sea and Persia, north to Fenno-Scandia and south to the Mediterranean.

In the early nineteenth century the species was restricted to southern and eastern England. A considerable expansion of range then took place to the west and north, reaching Ireland in 1875 and south and east Scotland by the end of the century. Further expansions then followed. Breeding now takes place in almost all the counties of Britain north to Argyll and Easter Ross. In Ireland it did not reach western Kerry and Mayo until after 1951; in western Ireland it prefers wooded country. A sudden decline in much of England and eastern Scotland took place from about 1957 to 1963, but there is some evidence that this trend has been reversed. The earlier increase has been attributed to an increase in the spread of arable farming while the decrease in the late 1950s may have been associated with toxic chemicals.

The stock dove is a bird of broad-leaved and mixed woods and parkland with old mature timber, as well as rocky coasts where it may compete with the rock dove, and arable districts with hedgerows where its habitat appears to be similar to that of the wood pigeon. However, stock doves and wood pigeons select mainly different feeding sites in the same habitat throughout the year. I have seen stock doves in many kinds of broad-leaved wood with nests in oaks, elms, beeches, ashes, willows and other trees. Other nesting sites include buildings, cliffs, quarries, sand dunes and holes in sandy or chalky plantations. Stock doves on the Continent nest in gardens in quite large cities but here they have colonised towns in only small numbers. The stock dove appears to be an ecotone bird rather than one of true woodland.

Wood Pigeon *Columba palumbus*

The natural history of this species has been described very fully in a monograph in this same series by Dr R. K. Murton, and I propose to give here only some of the relative abundance figures that I have collected in various habitats. The highest figures – 47 and 38 – are for mature Sitka spruce and Norway spruce plantations in eastern Scotland. Other figures are 17 for unbrashed Scottish conifer thickets, 16 for mature mixed plantations in Ireland, 11 in Irish beech, 10 in Irish sessile oak, 8 in Scottish beech, 7 in Scottish ash, 6 in English pedunculate oak, 4 in English, Welsh and Scottish sessile oak and Scottish birch, 3 in Scottish alder, 2 in English ash and 1 in Irish birch. Murton recorded a peak breeding density of 5.6 per acre for coniferous woodland, 4.4 for hedge-rows and only 1.5 for broad-leaved woodland. There has been a great increase in numbers through agricultural development and increases have also taken place in urban and suburban populations. The wood pigeon is a woodland species now living in very close association with arable farming and other forms of cultivation. It breeds in every county.

Turtle Dove *Streptopelia turtur*

Summer resident and passage migrant.

The turtle dove breeds north from the Mediterranean to south-east Scotland, Denmark and the southern Baltic.

From 1800 it has spread from southern, central and eastern England west to Wales, north to south-west Scotland and East Lothian. Small numbers breed occasionally in eastern Ireland. It has been shown that the distribution of the turtle dove matches closely that of its favoured food plant *Fumaria officinalis*.

This is very much a bird of woodland edges and more open country with scrub, dense hedgerows and small woods. I have found it commonly in thorn scrub in the south Midlands, in the Breckland overgrown hedges and in numbers of coniferous plantations in East Anglia. It has decreased in parts of Suffolk with hedge destruction. Turtle doves avoid dense woodland, but, although they may breed in large gardens with plenty of shrubs or small trees, they do not come very far into towns.

CUCULIDAE

Cuckoo *Cuculus canorus*

Summer resident.

Breeds throughout Europe from the Mediterranean north to Lapland.

The cuckoo breeds in every county of the British Isles but not very regularly in Shetland. A decrease has been reported from Ireland and in England since the 1950s.

This species can be found in a wide variety of habitats from open canopy woodland, scrub and wooded cultivated land to treeless moors, reed-beds and dunes. It occurs in open broad-leaved woods from the pedunculate oaks of southern England north to the Scottish and west to the Irish birchwoods; it is less frequent in coniferous woodlands. The cuckoo is commoner in the heathy areas of south-west Ireland and Scotland than anywhere else I know which suggests it is a bird of the tree/heath ecotone. I have found it in scrub and since its chief hosts in Britain are the meadow pipit and the hedgesparrow this tends to confirm that it is an ecotone bird. In woodland robins are frequently victimised. The normal inner limit of suburban breeding in London is 9 to 10 miles from the centre, perhaps because of a shortage of potential fosterers, but it has been recorded on the Continent as a bird also of city parks and gardens.

STRIGIDAE

Barn Owl *Tyto alba*

This owl has generally decreased perhaps owing to changes in land use, disturbance and toxic chemicals. It is closely associated with man favouring farms, old buildings, church towers and so on but it may also occur in wooded areas and parkland where it nests in hollow trees. Birds sometimes hunt over young plantations and I have often found them roosting in thorn scrub in East Anglia.

Little Owl *Athene noctua*

This tiny introduced owl breeds in every county of England and Wales as well as Berwick, but has suffered a recent decline in numbers. It is an ecotone bird of open country with old hedgerow timber, orchards and farms and it avoids woodland although it may frequent wood edges as I have noticed several times in Northamptonshire.

Tawny Owl *Strix aluco*

Resident.

The tawny owl breeds from the Mediterranean north to the British Isles and southern Fenno-Scandia.

In the British Isles this owl is missing from Ireland, the Isle of Man, Orkney and Shetland and from most of the Hebrides although it does occur at Stornoway in the Isle of Lewis. There has been some increase this century.

This is essentially a bird of broad-leaved or mixed woodland, but it can also be found in groves, parkland, and suburban and city parks and gardens. I have found it in both types of oakwood as well as alder, ash, birch and beech. It is not uncommon in the old pine-forests and the spruce plantations of Speyside as well as the pinewoods of the Borders. Tawny owls have been recorded in the South Down yew-woods. In Europe this species appears only rarely in coniferous woodland.

Long-eared Owl *Asio otus*

Resident.

This species breeds through Europe from Spain and the Mediterranean north to about 64° N.

Has bred widely but thinly over most of Ireland, Scotland, northern England and more locally south in England and Wales. There has been a decline in the present century in Wales and southern England due perhaps to the destruction of its habitats and also in northern England and the Lowlands perhaps for the same reason. There is some evidence of changes in Scotland and Ireland where the species appears to have increased with the spread of conifer plantations.

This owl favours coniferous woodland especially of pines and spruce as well as quite small clumps and belts of the same tree species. In areas where it is not uncommon it may also be found in broad-leaved woods and groves. Although generally regarded as nocturnal I have seen it hunting by day many times in Northern Ireland. I have records from as far apart as the Speyside pine-forests and many mature Scottish and Border pine plantations, from small clumps of spruce in Suffolk, on Salisbury Plain and Dorset heaths. In Ireland I found it quite often in sometimes large sessile oakwoods from Co. Antrim west to Co. Mayo as well as spruce plantations throughout much of Ireland. Long-eared owls have been known to breed in oaks in England.

Short-eared owl *Asio flammeus*

This owl has taken advantage of the planting of new conifer forests which it occupies in the establishment stages. Noticeable increases due to afforestation have been reported from Wales, Yorkshire and Scotland. Population changes are often associated with vole numbers.

CAPRIMULGIDAE

Nightjar *Caprimulgus europaeus*

Summer resident.

Breeds throughout most of Europe north to southern Fenno-Scandia.

The nightjar occurs widely throughout most of Britain and Ireland north to south-west Scotland and very sparsely farther north. The species has lost ground widely in recent years. Figure 18 gives the distribution of the nightjar from 1957–8. The decrease may be due to some climatic change as well as increased disturbance and destruction of its habitat since its distribution is probably linked to the persistence of heaths and dry bracken areas. It is not yet clear to what extent the nightjar may have generally benefited from new conifer plantations.

The habitat consists of fairly open or glade broad-leaved and coniferous woodland, areas of felled timber, commons, brackeny heaths and heathy hillsides and occasionally sand-dunes and coastal shingle. In the West Midlands the two most favoured habitats were dry tree/heath with birch and bracken and young conifer plantations. The nightjar is probably a bird of the tree/heath ecotone. I have recorded nightjars in oakwoods, birch, beech, mixed broad-leaved woods and natural woods and plantations of Scots pine.

Hoopoe *Upupa epops*

This passage migrant has bred, generally in the south coastal counties of England, roughly once every decade since the 1830s but slightly more frequently at the turn of the century and in the 1950s. Its English habitat has been described as "low and moist situations near woods." Breeding has taken place in ashes, willows and in Surrey a yew. It has been recorded in the breeding season from a wood in Devon and orchards as well.

Green Woodpecker *Picus viridis*

Resident.

The European range stretches from the Mediterranean north to southern Norway and Sweden and the region of Leningrad.

This woodpecker is widely distributed and breeds in every county of England and Wales and locally in southern Scotland as far north as Clackmannan and possibly Perth. The species is missing from the Isle of Man and Ireland. The numbers are sometimes much reduced by hard winters.

The green woodpecker occurs in light, open broad-leaved woodland, especially pedunculate oak and beech, but it can also be found in sessile oakwoods, ash and occasionally birch and yew. It is even more regular in parkland with well-grown timber, orchards and large gardens even in suburban areas and in some of the inner suburbs and parks of London. I have found it in mixed woods, but it is very scarce in coniferous woodlands.

Great Spotted Woodpecker *Dendrocopos major*

Resident.

Breeds in Europe from the Mediterranean north to mid-Fenno-Scandia.

The great spotted woodpecker breeds in every mainland county of Britain except perhaps Caithness and is absent from the Hebrides, the Northern Isles, the Isle of Man and Ireland. A considerable extension of range in northern England and Scotland took place about 1890 after the species had become extinct in these areas early in the nineteenth century; it is not known why this spread should have taken place. The species also penetrated the inner suburbs and London parks in the 1920s and I have seen it in such suburbs of Birmingham as Handsworth Wood, Harborne and Moseley.

This is primarily a woodland species, but it can also be found in small woods and groves, parks and gardens and trees bordering roads but it is not really a bird of the ecotones. In central and southern England it favours broad-leaved woods, especially those of pedunculate and sessile oak, beech, ash, fen alder and birch; in the north it is frequent in coniferous woodland, especially Scots pine plantations as well as the natural pines of Speyside. It is also regular in some of the European conifer forests and I have seen it in good numbers in mixed conifer and beech-forest in Canton Vaud. It does have, however, an RA of 2 in Scottish beechwoods and is also regular in many Scottish birch and sessile oakwoods.

Lesser Spotted Woodpecker *Dendrocopos minor*

Resident.

The European range is similar to that of the great spotted woodpecker but it does not include Denmark.

It does not breed in Scotland, Ireland and the Isle of Man and perhaps only irregularly in the Isle of Wight, Pembroke, Anglesey, Durham and Northumberland. The small population is fairly stable.

This is a shy species of open woods, isolated clumps and groves, parkland with old timber, orchards with decayed trees, avenues, belts and roadside trees. It is to be found in pedunculate and sessile oakwoods, in beech, ash and alder carr. In the Midlands and East Anglia it often nests at about 20 ft. in roadside ashes, willows and more rarely birch and elm; it seems to avoid conifers. Like the green woodpecker it reaches only so far into the suburbs and prefers to avoid the more built-up districts.

Wryneck *Jynx torquilla*

Summer resident.

It breeds in Europe from northern Portugal and Spain, France, Italy, Yugoslavia and northern Greece north to mid-Fenno-Scandia.

A very scarce species now, the wryneck has undergone a huge decline in Britain and is confined to a few pairs in Kent and elsewhere in southern England. The breeding population in 1958 was thought to be between 100 and 200 pairs, only 15 of which were proved to breed. In 1967 it was thought that, including birds in Kent, Surrey and perhaps a few other places in southern England the entire British population numbered not more than 25–30 breeding pairs. A decline has also taken place in much of western Europe. Figure 20 is based on the year in which breeding was last proved in each county. The wryneck has not bred in Scotland or Ireland. The reasons for the decline are not known, but climatic factors may be responsible.

The wryneck was once very much a bird of parkland, heaths with old timber, open broad-leaved forests, groves and forest edge – in fact, a bird of the ecotones. This may explain its present restriction largely to orchards and gardens. One author described it as "a common bird" and said that "it frequents small copses, plantations, orchards and fields enclosed with tall hedges." Larchwoods are given as one habitat on the Continent, but it seems unlikely that it ever favoured conifer woods here.

ALAUDIDAE

Woodlark *Lullula arborea*

Resident.

The European range of the woodlark stretches north from the Mediterranean to Britain, Denmark, southern Sweden and Finland.

This is a scarce bird, now breeding in most counties south-west of a line from Merioneth to Kent and in Nottingham and East Anglia. Since about 1954 there has been a decrease; only about 100 occupied territories were known in 1965, although the actual number was greater. The species formerly bred in Ireland. It has been suggested that there is a correlation between the bird's distribution and that part of England and Wales with a mean January temperature of more than 41° F. (5° C.). Since the woodlark is on the edge of its range, its position may be precarious and certainly its numbers have fluctuated widely over the last hundred years. There may be special habitat requirements, since the bird is fastidious in its choice of breeding site.

Woodlarks can be found in varied country that includes grassy or heathery patches with scrub, bracken and scattered trees, scrubby hillsides, sandy heaths, thinly timbered parkland, derelict and felled woodlands, and wood edges all usually on dry, light soils. Weather, a song post, and dry, well-drained soils may be important in the choice of nest site and of 26 localities near London nearly all were on chalk, sandstone or glacial and fluvial gravels. In East Anglia the vicinity of overhead wires was found to be a feature of most woodlark territories.

Skylark *Alauda arvensis*

This species often persists in conifer plantations all over the British Isles from the establishment stage until the trees are several feet high or six to seven years old.

ORIOLIDAE

Golden Oriole *Oriolus oriolus*

Spring visitor (rarely autumn); has bred.

In Europe breeds from Mediterranean north to mid-Denmark, south Sweden and Finland.

The golden oriole bred fairly often in Kent in the nineteenth century and it bred once or twice in about 10 counties in southern England and East Anglia between 1840 and 1890. Breeding has been proved in Somerset (1949), Devon (1951), Lancashire (1958–61) and Shropshire (1964) as well as perhaps Pembroke, Cardigan and five other English counties after a decline earlier in the century. An extension northwards in Europe has been linked with a rise in the mean spring temperatures in northern Europe; it is probably climatic factors which limit its breeding in Britain. In Ireland it is largely an irregular visitor in May.

Its habitats include broad-leaved and mixed woods, riverine woods with poplars, well-timbered parks and gardens, areas of scattered woods of oak, and in East Anglia the fen alder carrs. I have found its nest in riverside poplar forests along the Rhône, in roadside trees in the Camargue, among cork oaks and eucalyptus in the Coto Doñana and in oak, beech and maple in Switzerland.

CORVIDAE

Raven *Corvus corax*

Resident.

In Europe ravens can be found in Spain, Portugal, north-western and southern France, the Alps, Italy, the Balkans, eastern Europe and much of Fenno-Scandia; birds have been exterminated in much of their range.

In early historical times ravens probably bred in all the counties of Britain and Ireland but by the nineteenth century they were extinct in much of England except the south-west and the north. Now it is widely distributed in the coastal and hillier parts of western and northern Britain and Ireland. There have been signs of an increase in Wales and the West of England. A survey of the raven has been made by Ratcliffe.

Ravens now mainly haunt mountainous and hilly country, with or without trees, and coastal or inland cliffs. Ravens could once be found in the wooded lowlands where they regularly nested in trees. During the period of persecution ravens nested almost entirely on cliffs. From the 1920s, however, tree-nesting began to increase again in Wales and south-western England with a further spread of the habit after 1945 in north-west England and south-west Scotland. In Ireland, too, there have been more reports of tree-nesting ravens. Nests may be in both broad-leaved and coniferous trees. Ravens may also resort to communal roosting in trees.

Carrion/Hooded Crow *Corvus corone*

Resident; winter visitor. Carrion and hooded crows are only racially distinct and interbreed where their ranges overlap.

The carrion crow breeds in Europe in Britain as far north as the south-east Highlands and in western Europe north to Denmark and east to the Alps and very roughly 15° E.; elsewhere it is replaced by the hooded crow.

The hooded crow occupies Ireland and the Scottish Isles and is dominant over the carrion crow in the Isle of Man and most of the Scottish Highlands. The carrion crow fills the rest of the country. The hooded may have moved east after the last glacial period to Scandinavia and then to Scotland and Ireland before the carrion crow came up from the south-west. The zone of hybridisation in Scotland has moved north at the expense of the hooded. The carrion crow has increased in Scotland, bred recently in Ireland, but, except near large towns, shows signs of a decrease in southern and south-eastern England.

The carrion crow is a bird of fairly well-timbered country, often cultivated, of groves and sometimes quite large woods, of moors, heaths and coasts. It can be found in pedunculate and sessile oakwoods, birch, ash, alder as well as mixed and coniferous woods. It nests in the outer and inner suburbs of London and there are 4 nests within half a mile of my house some 5 miles from Marble Arch. In 1966 eight pairs bred in Regent's Park and six pairs in Hyde Park and Kensington Gardens. Carrion crows have penetrated the outskirts of other large towns as well as very open country in the south where they nest on pylons, posts or in small bushes.

The hooded crow I have found in Scotland quite regularly in Norway spruce (RA 5), mature coniferous plantations of the mixed kind (RA 3), native Scots pine (RA 2) as well as plantations of Scots pine, Sitka spruce and other conifers. It was also regular in Scottish sessile oak, birch, alder, sycamore and mixed hardwoods, but it was absent from Scottish beech

PLATE 25. The patchwork quilt of the English countryside. A typical scene composed of small woods, hedges, hedgerow trees and fields. View from Long Mynd towards Corndon Hill, Shropshire.

PLATE 26. Suburban habitats. *Above*, view northwards along Brook Road, Dollis Hill, North-West London, September, 1960; *below*, front garden with privet hedges, small shrubs and grass area. Dollis Hill, June, 1960.

and ash. In Ireland it was frequent in sessile oak, mixed woods and conifer plantations and thickets but it was missing from all beech and ashwoods and some birch and mixed broad-leaved woods. These records from Scotland and Ireland seem to show a preference of the hooded for conifers and sessile oak, but a dislike of ash and beech.

Rook *Corvus frugilegus*

Resident, partial migrant and winter visitor.

In Europe the rook breeds from about 46° N. to the British Isles, south Fenno-Scandia and North Russia with populations also in Yugoslavia, Bulgaria, southern Russia and northern Spain.

The rook is abundant in the British Isles and breeds in every county, but less commonly in the extreme north-west and the Scottish Isles while it is restricted to single localities in Shetland and the Outer Hebrides. There has been some increase in England since the 1930s followed by a decrease as cereal production dropped; there has also been some withdrawal from many towns and suburbs as these have been further developed.

The rook favours agricultural country, both arable and more importantly grassland, and tends to avoid heavily wooded country. Rooks nest colonially usually in fairly tall trees, but occasionally in smaller ones and even bushes. Large woods are not often used and most rookeries are in hedgerow trees, small woods, groves and clumps, especially in England, of elms and oaks. I have seen rooks' nests in many different species of tree in Britain including ash, beech, oak, elm, Scots pine, larch and in Ireland sessile oak, ash, sycamore, wych elm and Scots pine. Near Pomeroy, Co. Tyrone, I have seen 25 nests in dead Scots pine as well as nests in horse chestnuts in Donegal and holm oaks in Carrick-on-Shannon. As we have seen earlier, rooks may also nest in towns and suburbs provided that they do not have to fly too far for food. In Chichester they have nested on gasholders. The Hatton Castle rookery near Turiff in Aberdeenshire held 6,697 nests in 2,570 trees in 1957. On average beech-trees held about 5 nests each, spruces and elms about 3 and pines about 2; other nests were in sycamores, horse chestnuts, birches and Douglas fir. This rookery was probably the largest breeding colony of any land bird in Great Britain. A rook's nest has been recorded on the ground in Kent. The life of the rook has been described by Yeates. In winter large tree roosts are often shared with jackdaws and both species may enter woods in summer to feed on defoliating caterpillars although they are ecotone and not true woodland species.

Jackdaw *Corvus monedula*

Resident, partial migrant and winter visitor.

The European distribution of the jackdaw extends throughout western Europe as far north as central Norway, Sweden, southern Finland and northern Russia; it is irregularly spread through Spain.

The jackdaw breeds in every county after a considerable increase and spread in Scotland and Ireland; it is very common everywhere except north-west Scotland and the Outer Hebrides.

British jackdaw colonies are "either crag-based, structure-based or tree-based, or a blend of two or three types." Jackdaws forage chiefly on grassland, are mainly ecotone birds and can be found nesting in wooded areas, parkland, on cliffs and old buildings. Four or five pairs nested in my 200 acre pedunculate oakwood in Northamptonshire; its RA for woods of this type was 1, which compared with 3 for Scottish sessile woods. In Ireland, on the other hand, I had only one contact in 17 sessile woods. I found jackdaws commoner in Scottish and Irish beech than in English. They can often be found in Scots pine and birch, but often in association with inland cliffs or rocky outcrops. The nest is usually in a hole in a tree, cliff, building or burrow but jackdaws will also construct open nests of sticks; these are sometimes roofed. It was noted that of six open tree-nests four were probably old crow or rook nests and two were in ivy growth on trees. Open nests have been built in conifers on occasion. The jackdaw will breed in suburbs and towns with old buildings and chimney stacks, but it has largely withdrawn from the central London parks.

Magpie *Pica pica*

Resident; some evidence of migration on the east coasts.

The magpie is widely distributed in Europe, but is absent from Corsica and Sardinia.

It is common and widely distributed in every county of Britain and Ireland north to the line of the Forth-Clyde, but with the exception of those in south-east Scotland. Breeding goes on in small numbers in the eastern Highlands as far north as Easter Ross. It suffered a marked decline in the nineteenth century as a result of gamekeeping. Since the 1930s it has increased and this trend was accelerated by the 1939–45 war. Since the late 1950s a decrease has occurred in the rural, though not suburban, areas of eastern England due perhaps to hedge destruction and the use of toxic chemicals. I have seen magpies in Dublin, near the centre of Birmingham and they are now beginning to penetrate London.

The magpie prefers agricultural country with trees, hedges or scrub for nesting and is less frequently seen on moorland, heath and in treeless country. It occurs in bare countryside in the Isle of Man where the only cover is that of stone walls and gorse hedges. It dislikes dense woodland, but I have seen birds in and along the edge of broad-leaved woods of most tree species except beech; in Buchan it is frequent in the new plantations of the Forestry Commission. The magpie is very much a bird of ecotones – the forest edge and woodland clearings being two of its favourite haunts. It builds usually domed nests in tall trees, thorn bushes, hedgerows and scrub. Eight undomed nests have been recorded, but failure was high due to predation and the dome would seem to be a protection against crows and squirrels. A magpie's nest was noted in a gorse bush at Dungeness only 18 in. from the ground. In Ireland I have watched a dozen magpies foraging with rooks and jackdaws in the middle of a large pasture field; in England they tend to feed closer to cover.

Jay *Garrulus glandarius*

Resident; birds of Continental origin occur in autumn.

The jay's range in Europe reaches north to Scotland, central Norway, Sweden and Finland.

At the beginning of this century the jay was very local in much of England and Wales, scarce in northern England and Scotland and confined in Ireland to the south-east. An increase has been going on during the last fifty years and the jay is now generally distributed north as far as Argyll, Perth and Kincardine, but it is missing from the Isle of Man and parts of southern Scotland; in Ireland it does not breed in Kerry, Sligo, Leitrim, Donegal and Derry. Jays have penetrated the suburban areas of many towns – Birmingham, London. In 1932 a pair bred in Ladbroke Square and now jays nest in most of the central parks. In 1966 four pairs bred in London's Regent's Park alone. The first jays arrived at Dollis Hill in 1961.

The jay is very much a bird of woods, broad-leaved, coniferous and mixed, often but not invariably with a thick shrub layer and undergrowth, of plantations, scrub, orchards, large gardens and occasionally hedgerows. It is regular in oakwoods of both kinds and even frequents some sessile woods without much shrub growth. I have found that jays like English beech but not Scottish or Irish to the same degree, and they occur regularly in the fen alder carrs. In Ireland I found the Irish race in habitats which ranged from the mixed woodland of the Tollymore Forest Park to the sessile oakwoods of Co. Wicklow and the pines of Co. Waterford; it was

very common in the mixed oak, sycamore and beech of Co. Down. The
nests are usually built in trees or undergrowth, at not too great a height
from the ground, although an exception at 60 ft. has been recorded, often
in woods, plantations, scrub, orchards and large country and suburban
gardens. In London nests have been built in hawthorns, planes and even
in ventilators and on pipes of buildings. Jays may sometimes nest in the
holes of trees.

PARIDAE

Great Tit *Parus major*

British race is resident; Continental race is irregular autumn and winter
visitor.

The great tit breeds in Europe north to the British Isles, central Norway,
Sweden and Finland.

This common tit breeds throughout Britain and Ireland except for
some of the Scottish islands including the Northern Isles. The Outer
Hebrides were colonised in 1966, the same year that I heard its song in the
grounds of Lews Castle, Stornoway. The great tit is widespread in much
of Ireland, but is rare in Connemara. A big increase took place in north
Scotland during the present century, perhaps because of changes in the
winter climate. It also occurs in all but the most heavily built-up areas.

The great tit is very much a bird of woodlands and groves, generally
broad-leaved or mixed, of coppices, scrub, thickets, hedgerows, gardens
and orchards, but its hole-nesting habit is an important factor in deciding
whether it is present in a habitat or not. The great tit also tends to feed at
quite low levels and its presence is affected by the growth of the shrub
layer, coppice or undergrowth. I have recorded RAs of 7 for Scottish ash,
4 for English pedunculate oak, ash and beech, Scottish birch and Irish
beech, 3 for English sessile oak and Scottish alder, beech and mixed
broad-leaved woods, and Irish sessile oak, mixed broad-leaved woods and
plantations and 2 for Scottish sessile oak and Irish ash. It is rare in
coniferous plantations unless there are nestboxes, but I had 3 contacts in
the old pines at Loch Maree and it also occurred in some Scottish Norway
spruce plantations; I had only 1 contact in 9 Irish conifer thickets. I have
also recorded it in hazel and thorn scrub as well as fen alder carrs. Great
tits nest in the suburbs – and in all but the most highly developed parts
of towns. Fourteen pairs bred in 1966 in Regent's Park and at Primrose
Hill, and there were 12 territories in Kensington Gardens and Hyde
Park. Nests have been built in holes in trees, walls, the old nests of other

birds, nestboxes, letter-boxes, stack pipes, lamp-posts and many other sites.

Blue Tit *Parus caeruleus*

British race is resident; Continental race is an irregular autumn migrant.

The blue tit breeds from the Mediterranean north to the British Isles, southern Fenno-Scandia and the Urals.

This is an abundant species nesting in all the counties of Britain and Ireland except the Northern Isles, having colonised the Isles of Scilly in the late 1940s and the Outer Hebrides about 1962. It has spread with the increase in woodland and the provision of nestboxes since the 1920s.

The blue tit is a bird of broad-leaved woods and groves, of parks, orchards, hedgerows and gardens. I found it slightly commoner than the great tit in English pedunculate oak and Scottish and Irish sessile oak, about equally abundant in Scottish birch and beech, but less common in English and Welsh sessile oak and English and Irish beech. It is also regular in ash, alder woods and alder carrs. I have found it in the Scots pine of Speyside and Loch Maree and pine plantations in England. It is also present in English, Welsh and Scottish thicket stages, but was rare or absent in Irish ones. It is more common at Dollis Hill than the great tit and also in the central Parks. It nests in a great variety of situations. There was a considerable irruption of this species in 1957 and as a result there was an increase in the number of attacks on milk bottles, books, wallpaper, newspaper, lamp-shades, furnishings, washing on the line and putty.

Coal Tit *Parus ater*

Resident in Great Britain.

Breeds from the Mediterranean to the British Isles, central Fenno-Scandia and Archangel.

A numerous species breeding widely in the British Isles except in the Northern Isles; nesting took place in the Outer Hebrides in 1966. An increase occurred in the nineteenth century and again in the present one as the result of extensive coniferous afforestation. The Irish coal tit is resident except in the north-east of the country where its place is taken by the British coal tit.

In Europe the coal tit is found mainly in well-developed coniferous forests of spruce and pine, including the taiga and the subalpine forests. In Britain it has a marked but not exclusive preference for conifers and it can be found in mixed woods; in Italy it occurs in the montane beech-woods. It is the commonest tit in the birchwoods of northern and eastern Scotland and southern England and in the sessile oakwoods of England and Wales. In Irish sessile woods it was outnumbered by blue and great tits and in Scottish sessile oakwoods by the blue. I have records also in broad-leaved woods of coal tits in English ash (RA 1), pedunculate oak, Welsh birch and occasionally in Scottish and Irish ash, Scottish alder and Irish beech, but it did not appear in English beechwoods. In coniferous woodland it was the commonest tit in the native Scots pine forests of Scotland (the fourth most abundant species, in fact), in the Scots pine on the southern English heaths, in mature Scots pine plantations in Scotland (RA 17), in mature Norway and Sitka spruce and in mixed plantations north of the Border. At Kielder Forest it was co-dominant with the gold-crest in the spruce plantations, but showed a preference for Norway over Sitka spruce. The coal tit comes into the thickets at about 7 or 8 years and in many places is the third commonest bird; it was scarce in Ireland in the thickets, but was the most abundant tit in Irish mixed conifer planta-tions after brashing, and in mixed coniferous and broad-leaved plantations. Coal tits can be found in suburban areas where only single or scattered conifers occur and nesting has taken place within five miles of St Paul's Cathedral in London. At Dollis Hill it is a rare visitor since there are few conifers in the district.

Coal tits nest in holes in the ground and it has been suggested that because they are essentially hole-nesters they need not so much coniferous woodland as any woodland where the field layer is not too thick and holes are not hidden. Nestboxes are sometimes used. In winter the coal tit ranges widely and is frequent in plantations.

Crested Tit *Parus cristatus*

Resident in Scotland.

Crested tits breed in Europe from Spain, southern France, the Alps and the Balkans north to about the latitude of 64°–65°.

The crested tit is a scarce bird confined to eastern Inverness-shire and four counties on the Moray Firth. Its headquarters are in Speyside, but it has spread to coastal as well as upland plantations in Nairn, Moray and Banff. It has spread in Ross and has been seen in east Sutherland. Some 300–400 pairs are believed to breed in Scotland. Crested tits may be adversely affected by hard winters, but they seem to recover well.

These birds seem to prefer tracts of the old native pine-forest, often with plenty of dead stumps, but they will also accept a mixture of this with old and open birch and alder growth. The crested tit was the eighth commonest species in Speyside with about 6 contacts in each hour. These tits have moved into plantations and may use nestboxes. The nests are often in living or dead pines, pine stumps, alder and birches. In Europe the crested tit is very much a bird of coniferous forest. The ideal habitat possibly includes both oak and pine. The natural history of this bird has been described by Campbell.

Marsh Tit *Parus palustris*

Resident in Great Britain only.

Marsh tits can be found in Europe from northern Spain, France, Italy and the Balkans north to Britain, south Sweden and Norway and Leningrad.

Birds of this species breed commonly in every county in England and Wales (except perhaps Anglesey) and only thinly in northern England, north-west Wales and west Cornwall, but in Scotland they are confined to Berwick and a single breeding record in 1966 for East Lothian. The marsh tit is absent from Ireland and the Isle of Man.

These tits are very much birds of broad-leaved woods, especially open canopy oakwoods, groves, coppices, scrub and less frequently hedgerows, orchards and large gardens. In woodland it prefers a thick shrub layer. I have found marsh tits commonly in English pedunculate oakwoods (4–6 pairs bred in the 200 acres of Badby Wood), in beechwoods (RA 2), in the ashwoods of northern England and the birches of the south and in the fen alder carrs, but they are very scarce in sessile oak and, although I have seen them in mixed broad-leaved and coniferous woods, they are not birds of the latter culture. Two pairs nested in an open woodland strip about 100 yards long and some 20 yards wide on a farm in South Warwickshire. North of London they are quite common in the birches around Stanmore, but they avoid suburban districts without good tree and shrub cover. I have no records from Dollis Hill, but in 1937 I watched an adult feeding four young in the woodlands of Holland Park in London.

Nests are usually constructed in natural holes in trees such as willows, alders and birches and occasionally nestboxes and holes in walls will be used.

Willow Tit *Parus montanus*

Resident in Great Britain only.

The willow tit breeds from the Rhône Valley, north-eastern France, the Alps and the Danube north to Britain, northern Norway and Lapland.

This is a widely but thinly distributed species in England, Wales, the south-western and central Scottish Lowlands. It has not formally been proved to nest in every county in this area. There have been no recent instances of nesting in the Highlands, and it is absent from Ireland. It is difficult to be precise about its British range because of confusion with the marsh tit.

The willow tit's habitat is not clearly distinguishable from that of the marsh tit and I have found both species together in English pedunculate oakwoods, in fen alder carrs and damp willow and thorn scrub. It would seem that the willow tit may have some preference for damp, broad-leaved woods with some good secondary shrub growth and enough rotten timber to allow the birds to dig out their own nesting chamber, often in elder, alder, willow and birch. Willow tits were found in the Speyside pinewoods, but although I only recorded it in the Spey Valley in birch in 1953 and 1957 I have not seen it there since. Birds also occur in pine plantations in East Anglia (it outnumbered the marsh tit in Breckland) and in Lanarkshire. In Europe the willow tit is very much a bird of damp coniferous forest. Around London it favours damp, wooded commons. For general biology see Godfrey and Godfrey (1950).

Long-tailed Tit *Aegithalos caudatus*

Resident.

The long-tailed tit breeds from the Mediterranean north to northern Norway, central Sweden, southern Finland and the British Isles.

The species breeds thinly but widely in all the counties of Britain and Ireland except the Northern Isles, the Outer Hebrides and Caithness. Hard winters very much influence numbers. It may have decreased in the south as a result of hedge destruction.

The habitat of the long-tailed tit is chiefly that of broad-leaved wood-land edges, very open woods with good shrub growth, scrub, hedgerows, thickets, old orchards and more rarely gardens. I have found it in English, Welsh, Scottish and Irish oakwoods, as well as in alder, ash and beech. It had an RA of 2 in Irish beech and 1 in Scottish alder. In Ireland it was not uncommon in the mixed broad-leaved woods. It is very much a bird, too, of scrub and untidy hedges. I have recorded birds in the natural pines of Speyside, in the western pinewoods of Coille na Glas Leitir and in the plantations of East Anglia. It also favours the thicket stage of young coniferous plantations and in those of Ireland it had an RA of 3. In autumn birds may wander into towns and occurrences in Inner London outside the breeding season are frequent.

Nests are often built in thorns, gorse bushes, bramble clumps and shrubs, but in woodland they may be as much as 70 ft. above the ground against the trunk of a tree such as an oak or in a fork between the bole and a bough. For breeding see Lack and Lack (1958).

SITTIDAE

Nuthatch *Sitta europaea*

Resident.

Nuthatches breed from Spain and the Mediterranean Sea to England, south Sweden and south Norway.

This species breeds fairly commonly in England and Wales south of a line from the Mersey to the Wash and more thinly and locally north to Westmorland and Northumberland. Since about 1940 there have been signs of a spread in North Wales and Cheshire. It is scarce in Cornwall and absent from Scotland, Ireland and the Isle of Man.

The nuthatch is a bird of mixed broad-leaved woods of oak and beech as well as parkland, large gardens with old deciduous trees and avenues; it is a bird of the Siberian taiga, but is rare in conifers in Britain. Some authorities have claimed that the nuthatch is a species typical of oak-woods, and although it is regular in these woods (3 pairs nested in the 200 acres of Badby Wood) I have found it equally commonly in beech and mixed broad-leaved woods. Nuthatches occur from lowland situations up to heights of 1,000 ft. or more. It has been suggested that the distribution of this species is related to that of the beech, but it may well be that somewhat subtle climatic factors are at work. In Oxfordshire the nuthatch occurs widely where there are old elms and often nests in holes in them, and a liking for elms was observed in Worcestershire. Birds disappeared from many suburban areas of Middlesex in the nineteenth century, but they have persisted in some parks and woodlands. Their withdrawal may have been due to the accretion of soot on the trees. One or two have returned to Holland Park and Kensington Gardens in London. The nuthatch nests in holes or boxes, sealing them with mud.

CERTHIIDAE

Treecreeper *Certhia familiaris*

Resident.

In Europe the treecreeper occurs in the coniferous mountain woodlands

above 3,000 ft. in the Pyrenees, Corsica, Italy and the Alps, Germany,
Yugoslavia, eastern Europe, Denmark and in Fenno-Scandia almost to the
Arctic Circle. Below 5,000 ft. in parks and gardens it is generally replaced
by the Short-Toed Treecreeper (*Certhia brachydactyla*).

The treecreeper breeds in every county in the British Isles except
Orkney and Shetland; a few pairs breed at Stornoway in the Isle of Lewis
and others can be found on some of the wooded Inner Hebrides. The
population is generally stable, but there may have been some increase in
Scotland with afforestation.

It is very much a bird of well developed woodland, well-timbered
gardens, parks and avenues. It favours broad-leaved rather than coniferous
woods. Treecreepers are not on the whole very choosy about the tree
species they frequent provided the bark is rich in insects and there are
crevices in which to nest. The bird is regular in pedunculate and sessile
oakwoods. I found it common in the more remote sessile woods of Scotland
such as Glentanar and Ariundle and in Ireland south from Breen in Co.
Antrim to Killarney and east from Mossbrook in Co. Mayo to Glendalough in Co. Wicklow. It also appeared in the pedunculate woods at
Tullamore in Co. Offaly. I have seen it also in alder woods, old birches,
ashwoods, including the Rassal wood on the Durness limestone near Loch
Kishorn as well as in many mixed woods as far north as the Kyle of Tongue
and south-west to Bantry Bay. I have not found it very commonly in
beechwoods although these appear, with pines, in its European habitats.
In coniferous woodland I have records for the old Speyside pine-forest,
mature Scots pine plantations in England, Scotland and in Glen Poer in
Ireland, in English and Scottish larch and in the Sitka spruce at Castle
Caldwell in Northern Ireland. I have not found it in woods of yew. It is
occasionally found in town parks and the more wooded suburban areas.
Since 1923 birds have made use of the bark of Wellingtonias, introduced
in 1853, for roosting.

TROGLODYTIDAE

Wren *Troglodytes troglodytes*

Resident; partial migrant.

In Europe breeds from the Mediterranean to Iceland and central Fenno-
Scandia.

An abundant species breeding in all parts of Britain and Ireland with
racially distinct populations in the Outer Hebrides, St Kilda, Fair Isle
and Shetland. A stable population save for fluctuations due to bad

winters; from a grand total of birds counted in nearly 300 woods the second commonest bird.

The most favoured habitats are "damp, deciduous, mixed woods with much small growth and thick cover, overgrown valleys with streams, untended garden-woodland areas and sheltered, deep, tree-fringed lanes" (Armstrong 1955). It also occurs on rocky coasts, moorlands and reed-beds as well as in suburban and town areas. The wren can adapt itself to many different environments. I found that the wren was the commonest bird in Irish hazel scrub and conifer thickets (RA 15), the second commonest in Scottish mixed conifer plantations (RA 19), ashwoods (RA 14), alderwoods (RA 13), sessile oakwoods and old native Scots pine (RA 10). It was the third most abundant in English pedunculate oak (RA 10), Irish beech, mature spruce and mixed conifer thickets. The wren occupied fourth place in Irish and Scottish birch and Scottish pine and spruce plantations, and fifth place in English and Welsh sessile oak and birch as well as English and Scottish beech. It was sixth in Irish beech and sessile oak and seventh in Irish ash. These figures give a slight indication of certain preferences in habitat. In towns it stays away from the most heavily built-up areas; at Dollis Hill some 7 pairs nest each year in the parkland and allotment area amongst creeper and ivy on fences and sheds and in holes in old walls. For its natural history see Armstrong.

CINCLIDAE

Dipper *Cinclus cinclus*

This is not a woodland species and favours fast-flowing hill streams but where the burns or becks pass through woodland dippers may be seen flying through or above the trees. Nests are sometimes built on branches or among tree roots.

TURDIDAE

Mistle Thrush *Turdus viscivorus*

Resident, partial migrant and winter visitor.

This thrush breeds in Europe from the Mediterranean north to the British Isles, eastern Norway, Swedish and Finnish Lapland and Archangel. In the nineteenth century it spread from mountainous forests into the European plains.

A numerous and widespread species breeding in every county except Shetland and the Outer Hebrides, but only sporadically in Orkney and rather thinly in the extreme north and north-west of Scotland. It greatly increased during the early nineteenth century, colonising every Irish county by 1850 and spreading widely in Scotland perhaps because of replanting. This spread matches a similar one on the Continent into parkland and cultivated areas.

This is a bird of both broad-leaved and coniferous woods and plantations, of well-timbered parkland, orchards and gardens and occasionally of treeless areas (in Ireland it often builds its nest on stone walls, buildings or even on the ground). It occurs now in several ecotones but I have found birds regularly in English pedunculate woods (RA 1), less commonly in British sessile oakwoods, but more frequently in Irish sessile woods where its RA is 4. It also appears in Scottish alderwoods and English fen carrs. It is common in Irish beech (RA 6) but less so in English and Scottish. I have many records from English, Scottish and Irish birch but fewer from Wales. It is a bird I have often seen in mature plantations of Scots pine, Norway and Sitka spruce throughout the British Isles and in the conifer thickets and pole-stage plantations as well. It occurs in the Speyside native pinewoods. It has been described as "common" in the old forest, but I have found that in the forest proper it often keeps to the more secluded parts. It is very scarce (and absent sometimes) from ashwoods. Mistle thrushes are well distributed in many suburban and town areas. At Dollis Hill they are a marginal species, but birds nested in Ladbroke Square before the 1939–45 war and now breed frequently in the central London parks and squares.

In the late summer birds often flock on grassland and farms and I have seen parties of over a hundred, although from 20 to 40 are more usual.

Fieldfare *Turdus pilaris*

Winter visitor and passage migrant; has once bred.

The fieldfare breeds in Europe from Germany, Austria, Hungary north to the Arctic Ocean. Here it is a bird of light, mixed taiga and birch, spruce, pine and alder woods. In Scandinavia it also nests in parks and public gardens in towns and cities. Large numbers come to the British Isles from Scandinavia for the winter.

A common and widespread winter visitor. A pair reared 3 young in Orkney in 1967 – the first breeding record.

In winter the fieldfare prefers open country with rough pasture and arable land, but it also occurs regularly in woodland where there are berries such as those of rowan, holly, yew, dog-rose and hawthorn. It often roosts in young plantations, hedgerows, evergreen shrubs or trees and woodland. When forced to fly from the ground fieldfares often resort to trees and will sit, all facing the wind, on the tops of oaks, elms and ashes. Fieldfares are not so often reported in suburban areas as redwings, but they do pass over Dollis Hill; I counted some 2,500 over a period of a hundred minutes on 26th October, 1966. In cold weather they often shift their ground and in 1955 one remained in my garden, feeding on apples and chasing away all the local blackbirds from 20th February to 13th March. Another stayed nearly a month in January 1963. In December 1938 birds were feeding on haws in Ladbroke Square in London.

Song Thrush *Turdus philomelos*

Resident, passage migrant and winter visitor.

The song thrush nests from northern Spain, southern France, North Italy, northern Greece to North Norway and Lapland.

An abundant species breeding everywhere in the British Isles but only occasionally in Shetland. A decline in numbers appears to have taken place since about 1940, perhaps as a result of the increased incidence of cold winters.

This is a bird of woodlands, both broad-leaved and coniferous, of groves, clumps and small woods with a good shrub layer, of thickets, hedgerows, orchards, parks and gardens. In Scotland and Ireland it also occurs in desolate treeless districts and I have seen a song thrush on a rock singing a duet with a ring ouzel. I found the song thrush commonest in the sessile oakwoods of Scotland, then in the Irish sessile and English pedun-culate woods but much scarcer in the English and Welsh sessile oakwoods. I found it quite common in Irish and Scottish beech and birch, and young Irish conifer plantations, but less so in English and Irish ash and Speyside native pine and even less frequently in Scottish ash, and Scottish and Irish thickets. It is missing from the yew-woods although in autumn song thrushes feed extensively on the berries. Song thrushes are common in hedgerows and on farmland (forming about 7%–9% of the passerine population) as well as in scrub. There has been a decrease in the built-up areas of London since about 1900. It is very conservative in its choice of nesting site. Birds still breed in the parks of Inner London and in 1966 37 broods were raised in Regent's Park; they are now much rarer in the squares. The nesting success of the song thrush has been compared with that of the blackbird and mistle thrush (Snow 1955).

Redwing *Turdus iliacus*

A winter visitor and passage migrant; breeds almost annually in Scotland. The redwing nests regularly in Iceland, Norway, central and northern Sweden, Finland and north-east Poland and sporadically in Czechoslovakia, Austria, Germany, Belgium and France.

The redwing is a very common winter visitor from Iceland and Scandinavia. A pair nested in Sutherland in 1925 and since then a few pairs have bred sporadically in several areas of Scotland. In 1967 breeding was proved in Sutherland, Ross, Inverness and Shetland. A pair tried unsuccessfully to nest in Kerry in May 1951.

In Europe the redwing typically breeds in the light open taiga mixed with birch, willow and alder, along forest edges, in birch and willow scrub, even in parks and gardens in towns in Norway. The nests are built on tree stumps and in trees and bushes. In winter the birds come to open pasture and grassland and to open woods. They will go to trees or scrub when frightened, when seeking roosting places or when looking for berries. I have seen redwings in winter in both kinds of oakwood, in beech, ash and alder. In May I have found them in the Sutherland birchwoods and even more commonly at this time in mixed woods of sycamore, beech, wych elm, ash, birch and horse chestnut in woods as far apart as the Kyle of Tongue and Kylestrome. Migrants often pass over London and in the late winter flocks of several thousand may gather in hawthorn scrub on the outskirts. Cold weather may result in quite heavy passages over the built-up areas and birds may come to my garden in Dollis Hill to take apples and hips.

In December 1951 I heard a redwing giving full song at a roost in Staffordshire, and in March 1954 I succeeded in making a sound recording of the song and subsong of redwings in Kent.

Ring Ouzel *Turdus torquatus*

Summer resident and passage migrant.

This species breeds in the mountainous parts of Europe.

It is widely distributed on the moorlands of western and northern Britain from Caithness to Devon and on hill ranges in Ireland.

In the breeding season the ring ouzel is a bird of moorlands and hillsides especially those from 1,000–2,000 ft. On the Continent it enters the subalpine coniferous forests, fell woods and the birch zone. I have recorded it from the Scottish birchwoods and it has been seen in the Cumberland fell woods and in the Welsh scrub oakwoods. On autumn migration ring ouzels may occur in woods or along hedges and in scrub, and even in suburban areas as they look for berries. It is very scarce in London, but it has been recorded there feeding on the berries of elder, ivy and rowan.

Blackbird *Turdus merula*

Resident, partial migrant, passage migrant and winter visitor.

The blackbird can be found throughout Europe from the Mediterranean to central Norway, southern Sweden and Finland.

This is an abundant species breeding throughout Britain and Ireland. It has spread from its original woodland habitat to gardens and finally towns and cities. Blackbirds have also spread in the Scottish islands; of 204 nests in Shetland 50% were inside buildings and 19% in stone walls. There is also a tendency to breed at higher altitudes in England and Wales both in the new forests and on the more open hills. Estimates that there are about 10 million pairs in the British Isles have been made. From a grand total of birds counted in nearly 300 woods in the British Isles I found it to be the fourth most abundant bird.

The blackbird is a bird of a great variety of habitats from dense woodlands of various kinds with good shrub layers and soft ground to small woods, groves, thickets, hedgerows, shrubberies, gardens, town parks and open spaces, commons, moorlands, hillsides and rocky coasts. I have found it to be the most abundant species in Irish ashwoods (RA 27) and hazel scrub. It was the second commonest bird in English and Scottish beech (RA 12) and Irish sessile oak, beech, and mixed broad-leaved woods (all RAs 11). It came third in the mixed broad-leaved woods of Scotland, the mixed broad-leaved/coniferous woods of Ireland and in the suburban area of Dollis Hill. Blackbirds were not uncommon in English pedunculate oak, English and Scottish sessile oak, alder, ash and birch as well as English and Irish yew, Irish birch and Scottish sycamore. The blackbird is regular in the late thicket stages and in mature Norway spruce, Sitka spruce and mixed conifer plantations in Britain and Ireland. In Ireland it is to be found in the early thicket stages where the proportion to song thrushes is about 3 to 2. The blackbird was very scarce in *Tsuga* plantations and missing not only from the old Caledonian forest of Speyside, but also from 12 mature Scots pine plantations north of the Border. It is the commonest bird of lowland farmland. The densest populations of blackbirds occur in gardens, then in parkland, farmland and finally dense woodland where pairs are fewer and generally very retiring. In the

London parks the blackbird is the commonest land species after the house sparrow.

It is interesting to note that blackbirds start singing earlier and breeding earlier in towns than their relatives in woodland. A full account of the blackbird has been given by Snow.

Wheatear *Oenanthe oenanthe*

This is a heath bird of hillsides, downs, moors and rocky places, but I have found it on occasion in some of the light, open Scottish birchwoods and just inside the margins of the old Scots pine-forests in the Highlands where it sometimes perches on trees both of alder and pine. Wheatears will also survive for a time into the establishment stages of new forests, the planting of which has had an adverse effect on their habitats and numbers.

Stonechat *Saxicola torquata*

This is a bird of waste and neglected ground often with a few bushes or some small scrub. It has decreased in the British Isles as a result of a series of bad winters and destruction of its habitat. It is very much a bird of scrub and I have seen it amongst gorse in south-west England, in willow scrub under two and a half feet in south-west Ireland and in heather in Scotland. Recently stonechats have been breeding in young conifer plantations under 10 years of age, nesting in the undergrowth and using the young trees for look-out and song posts. They may continue to live along the edges and rides of plantations up to 10 to 20 ft. high. In 1967 I found many in south-west Ireland in this situation. In 1959 a stonechat was recorded from the highest oaks in the Birkrigg oakwood in Cumberland.

Whinchat *Saxicola rubetra*

This species favours a wide variety of open country including rough grasslands with bushes, marshes, heaths and upland pastures and moorlands. It often uses bushes and trees for perching and for song posts and I have seen birds singing in Scots pines in Rothiemurchus and in a small mixed wood on the Isle of Skye, in birches in the mixed birch and pinewoods of Glen Feshie and in an oak in a wood in Sunart. Whinchats have benefited from the new conifer plantations, too, and there is evidence that they have increased in parts of south-west and northern England, Wales and south-west Scotland for this reason.

PLATE 27. Woodland birds in town. A pair of blackbirds with their nest built on top of a clock in a workshop at the Post Office Research Station, Dollis Hill.

PLATE 28. Tawny Owl, a species whose breeding success depends on the density of its prey — wood mice and bank voles.

Redstart *Phoenicurus phoenicurus*

Summer resident and passage migrant.

Redstarts occur in Europe from the Mediterranean north to Britain, northern Scandinavia and the White Sea.

This is a fairly numerous species breeding regularly in the mainland counties of Britain except Cornwall, Cambridge and Caithness; it is most abundant in the north and west. It is absent from the Isle of Man and breeds only erratically in Ireland – Counties Kerry (1946), Antrim (1955), Tyrone (1955) and Wicklow (1959–60). Some decrease in numbers has occurred in Scotland, the Midlands and south-eastern England.

The redstart favours predominantly open-canopy broad-leaved forests and woods with a mixture of rich shrub layer and open space, of heaths and moors with scattered trees, of riversides with pollard willows, well-timbered parkland and old gardens and orchards. It also appears in mixed woods and even pure stands of pine. I have found the redstart most commonly in the sessile oakwoods of England, Wales and Scotland, in ashwoods in northern England and Scotland, in English beech and in Scottish birch. It is not so frequent in English pedunculate oakwoods and was seventh in the list for the old pinewoods of Speyside. Redstarts also occur in Scottish alder and occasionally in mature Scots pine plantations in Scotland. They nested in many old Warwickshire orchards and in Epping Forest, where 12 pairs were reported in 1966. I have seen nests in pollard willows along the river and on Otmoor near Oxford in 1939 and 1940. In 1967 I located a singing male in a sessile oakwood and a pair in a beechwood in Co. Wicklow in Ireland. Since the 1920s it has no longer been a suburban bird in the London area.

The nests are often built in holes in trees or stumps, but they may also be in the ground or in the hill country in old stone walls. It has been suggested that the redstart's original home was pine heath where it normally nested on the ground. Buxton has described its biology.

Nightingale *Luscinia megarhynchos*

Summer resident; vagrant elsewhere.

The nightingale breeds from the Mediterranean region to England, Holland, Denmark, central Germany and Poland.

It is not uncommon in England south of a line from Dorset to the Wash but it is more local west and north to Devon, Monmouth, Hereford, south-east Shropshire, Warwickshire, south Yorkshire and Lincolnshire.

There are isolated breeding records for Wales, Cheshire and Derby but the overall distribution has not altered greatly during the century although actual numbers seem to have declined. It is a vagrant to Scotland and Ireland where, however, birds have been reported in song. The nightingale may be limited to its present area by summer temperatures.

This species is largely confined to pedunculate oakwoods and beech-woods usually not more than 400 ft. above sea-level, to hazel coppices especially those with standard oaks, to thorn scrub often along the edges of woods and hedgerows and sometimes gardens. In woodland it likes broad-leaved trees with a thick shrub layer, shady places and a rich humus. It was seen to favour low coppices, and "the extensive grounds around London, which are cultivated by market-gardeners, are favourite haunts" (Jardine 1839). Nightingales were very common in 1949, and still are, in Preston Bushes near Stratford-upon-Avon; here very thick hawthorn scrub is mixed with oak and young ash but, as the trees grow, the birds retreat into the fringing scrub. Nightingales also bred in the over-grown thorn hedges along the old Shipston tramway outside Stratford but these were laid and the birds left. Birds are especially abundant in my experience in the mixed broad-leaved woods of Breckland, in Suffolk lane-sides with tangled thorn hedges, on Surrey commons, and in the scrub and spinneys of south Warwickshire. In 1944 I used to watch three pairs of nightingales in a small wood behind the Officers' Mess on the RAF station at Wickenby some 14 miles east of Lincoln. There were no nightin-gales in Badby Wood and I suspect that the shrub layer though rich was not quite luxuriant enough, and most of the wood is over 500 ft. above sea-level.

Robin *Erithacus rubecula*

Resident, partial migrant and winter visitor.

The range of the robin stretches north from the Mediterranean to Britain and central Fenno-Scandia.

This is an abundant species in the British Isles which also breeds on many islands, but not Shetland. Its status does not appear to have changed much over the last hundred years, apart from short-term fluctuations due to weather.

The robin is a bird of both broad-leaved and coniferous woods with undergrowth, of coppices, plantations, scrub, hedgerows, parkland and gardens and similar ecotones. When I totalled the contacts for nearly 300 woods in the British Isles it proved to be the third commonest species. The robin was co-dominant with the willow warbler (RA 17) in Irish birch, was the second commonest species in English pedunculate oakwoods and mixed broad-leaved and coniferous plantations over 20 ft. in Ireland and was third in Scottish ash and alderwoods, Irish sessile oak and mixed broad-leaved woods, mature plantations of Scots pine in Scotland and in the hazel scrub of the Burren. It was fourth in the birchwoods of Wales, northern England and Scotland and in the ash, beech and mixed broad-leaved/coniferous woods of Ireland. It was sixth in the sessile oakwoods of England, Wales and Scotland. Robins are fairly common in English beechwoods, in the fen alder carrs, scrub, hedges and farmland; in this last situation they occupy about 12% of the passerine population. I have seen them fairly commonly also in the Speyside pine-forest and in English yew. They come into the plantations early and increase as the thicket stage develops. Robins are common in all but the most developed parts of towns, but they do not nest as widely in the gardens at Dollis Hill as they might because of lack of suitable breeding places and disturbance and predation by cats. Lack (1943) has written extensively about this species.

SYLVIIDAE

Grasshopper Warbler *Locustella naevia*

Young conifer plantations form an important breeding habitat for this species. This extension of its breeding areas has been described as being particularly noticeable in the western half of Britain and in such southern counties as Berkshire and Buckingham. In Northern Ireland in the summer of 1967 I found it was regular in young pine, spruce and larch plantations up to about 6 feet in height (RA 7); it was very common at Cairnwood, Tully and Castle Archdale.

Sedge Warbler *Acrocephalus schoenobaenus*

The sedge warbler is primarily a bird of reed and osier beds, ditches and tangled growth on marshy ground. Birds sometimes sing in small trees and from scrub in these habitats, but recently the bird has shown a tendency to move into less damp situations to breed, including conifer plantations. I found, in fact, in 1967 that the sedge warbler was the dominant species in two dry plantations some 6–8 feet high at Cairnwood and Castle Archdale in Northern Ireland, although in both instances water was not too far away. In nine such Irish plantations it was commoner than the grass-hopper warbler and had an RA of 8. It has also been recorded in young plantations in Nairn in Scotland. In Suffolk in 1964 I found a sedge warbler singing in thorns some 600 yards from the nearest water.

Icterine Warbler *Hippolais icterina*

Eggs of this species, or the Melodious Warbler *H. polyglotta*, were taken in Sussex and Surrey in the nineteenth century and in May 1907 a nest was identified near Marlborough. From 28th–30th May, 1947, a singing male was present in Badby Wood and I had many opportunities of studying it. On the Continent the icterine warbler is a bird of woodland, broad-leaved and sunny, of parks, orchards and gardens.

Blackcap *Sylvia atricapilla*

Summer resident, occasional winter resident and passage migrant.

This warbler can be found in Europe in the summer from the Mediterranean north to Scotland, parts of Ireland and northern Fenno-Scandia.

The blackcap breeds commonly in nearly every county of England and Wales, locally north through the Scottish Lowlands and then sparsely to Inverness. Occasional breeding has taken place north to Ross as well as in Orkney (1949) and Shetland (1945–6, 1948). The blackcap is missing from the Isle of Man and has a small erratic fluctuating population in Ireland where an increase has been noted. Recently there has been an increase in north-east Ireland while breeding has taken place in Limerick and birds have been seen in Galway and Fermanagh. There seems to have been a decrease in Co. Wicklow.

The typical habitats consist of open mixed woodlands, with thick but not too dense shrub layers especially of brambles and dog-roses, of shrubberies and overgrown hedges with some tall timber; it has a similar habitat to that of the garden warbler, but is more partial to evergreens. The blackcap is perhaps commonest in English pedunculate oakwoods (RA 2) but it does also appear in sessile woods; in Ireland I have seen singing males in the sessile oakwoods at Crom Castle on Upper Lough Erne. In a mixed oak, ash, beechwood with a little spruce in Co. Fermanagh I counted 3 singing males in May 1967. Birds also appear in sessile oakwoods in Antrim and Wicklow. I have found blackcaps in many beechwoods, in some ashwoods in southern and northern England as well as mixed broad-leaved woods, but their density depends upon the nature of the shrub growth. Blackcaps appear in the pine plantations of Breckland at a density of 1–5 birds per 40 acres. They often nest in suburban areas without dense cover and have bred in many places much closer to the centre of London than the garden warbler; a pair bred at Dollis Hill in 1958. Some blackcaps winter in the British Isles, especially in the extreme south-west of England, around Dublin where they appear in the suburbs and to a lesser extent in southern England and Yorkshire.

Garden Warbler *Sylvia borin*

Summer resident; passage migrant.

The garden warbler breeds from central Portugal, Spain, France, Italy, Albania and Bulgaria north to the British Isles and northern Fenno-Scandia.

Its range in the British Isles is similar to that of the blackcap; it breeds in practically every county in England and Wales, but its northern distribution extends to south Argyll, Inverness and sometimes Easter Ross and Aberdeen. Males are sometimes heard singing in the northern birchwoods of Sutherland, but I have not found them myself. The garden warbler is absent from the Isle of Man but has nested in 11 counties in Ireland where it appears only to be well-established and stable in a few localities in the Shannon Valley.

This is also a species of broad-leaved and mixed woods with an abundant undergrowth of shrubs and brambles, but a shrub layer perhaps lower and denser than that needed by the blackcap. It also can be found in scrub, with or without trees, in large overgrown hedges and sometimes gardens and conifer plantations. Its habitat in Ireland has been described as "demesnes and islands where the natural wood has survived more or less, and where there are vast tangles of brambles, blackthorn and other scrub, intermixed with oak and other trees having sunny open spaces between them" (Ussher and Warren 1900). In Ireland, too, the presence of a lake is thought to be desirable. Certainly that is a very fair description of those sites near Upper Lough Erne where I have seen garden warblers; yet the species is missing from many apparently similar areas. The garden warbler is commonest in English pedunculate oak and less so in sessile oak, beech and ash. It is scarcer still in birch, although in northern Europe it breeds into the subarctic birch zone, and in some English pine plantations. The ecological distributions of the garden warbler and the blackcap appear very similar, but there are many discrepancies in relative numbers unaccounted for. In Badby Wood the garden warbler outnumbered the blackcap as it does in a number of Midland oakwoods, although near Stratford-upon-Avon and in some Staffordshire woods I have found the reverse to be true. A study of the West Midland Bird Reports from 1946–66 reveals that both species occur in equal numbers in the Severn and Stour

Valleys, that garden warblers at Hopwas and in the Wyre Forest may outnumber blackcaps 6 or 7 to 1, but in the Malverns blackcaps may outnumber garden warblers also by 7 to 1. The situation, too, can be complicated by quite serious annual fluctuations in numbers. The garden warbler does not normally enter towns except on migration; one was taking blackberries in my garden at Dollis Hill in August 1967. About five pairs bred in the Hampstead area of London until 1950 and a pair with two young was seen in July 1953 in St John's Wood Park.

Whitethroat *Sylvia communis*

Summer resident and passage migrant.

The whitethroat as a breeding species can be found in Europe from the Mediterranean north to the British Isles and southern Norway, Sweden and Finland.

This is a very common bird nesting in all the counties of the British Isles except the Northern Isles; it is local in north-west Scotland and the Hebrides. A stable population has shown only some general decrease in Ireland and a few local declines in southern England.

The whitethroat is very much a warbler of open tangled hedgerows often near cultivated ground, of scrub, rough bushy land, gorse-covered commons, osier beds and untidy gardens, but it also occurs along forest edges as well as in glades in open-canopy woodland. Pairs have sometimes bred in Badby Wood, but it is common in many wooded parts of the New Forest. I have records for both pedunculate and sessile oakwoods and for beech, ash and birch. Whitethroats occur thinly in the native pinewoods of Scotland and in mature conifer plantations if there is cover available. They come regularly into the young conifer thickets and reach their peak numbers about 8 years after planting. The whitethroat is common in thorny scrub and hedgerows and was the second commonest bird in the hazel scrub below four feet in the Burren. Birds will breed in suitable places in outer suburban areas and are very infrequent in the more built-up areas. A pair bred in London in 1953 in Regent's Park and birds carrying food where a nest was suspected were seen in 1960 in Holland Park.

Lesser Whitethroat *Sylvia curruca*

Summer resident and passage migrant.

The lesser whitethroat breeds regularly in Europe from central France, the Alps and the Balkans north to central Fenno-Scandia.

This is a not uncommon breeding bird in the southern half of England. It is then distributed locally west to east Devon and into Wales and north to the Lake District and Northumberland. It has bred, though not in recent years, in the Isle of Man and in 7 Scottish counties (most recently in 1948 in Argyll and in 1949 in Midlothian). The lesser whitethroat is absent from many districts in central and southern Wales and has bred only exceptionally in Cornwall. In Ireland it is a very scarce migrant with most records in the autumn.

The lesser whitethroat can be found in a number of habitats similar to those of the whitethroat including tall scrub, bushy overgrown hedgerows and thorny bushes but usually with taller, thicker growth and generally more and larger trees from which it may often sing. It is rarely found in the small hedges that the whitethroat will often choose. I have seen the present species in two pedunculate oakwoods with open glades and along woodland edges in the North Downs and in Worcestershire and southern Warwickshire, but it is not a typical woodland species. It rarely nests in towns.

Willow Warbler *Phylloscopus trochilus*

Summer resident and passage migrant.

The willow warbler breeds in Europe from central France, northern Italy, Yugoslavia and the Carpathians north to the British Isles and Lapland.

This is an abundant summer visitor breeding regularly in every county of Britain and Ireland except where local (the Outer Hebrides and Orkney) or sporadic (Shetland). There has been perhaps a recent decrease in southern England.

This species occurs in many different habitats including open broad-leaved woods, scrub and bushy regions, moorland with bushy patches and no trees, coniferous woods and plantations, hedges along roads, parkland, gardens and many other areas with grass tussocks and a few bushes or trees. In my lists it is the dominant bird of the Scottish birchwoods and is co-dominant with the robin in the Irish birch. The willow warbler also heads the lists for English ashwoods, was second after the blackbird in Irish ash and was pretty frequent in Scottish ash. With an RA of 15 it was also the dominant bird of the Irish conifer thickets. This species was second for the birches of the Lakes, Pennines and Wales, in the old Speyside pine (but was dominant by Loch Maree), and in Irish conifer plantations from 16 to 26 ft. in height. It came third in English and Welsh sessile oak and in the Irish mixed broad-leaved and coniferous as well as pure coniferous plantations over 26 ft. with some cover. Willow warblers came fourth in the Scottish alderwoods and fifth in English pedunculate and Scottish and Irish sessile oakwoods. Birds are also common on the southern heaths of England, in Scottish ash, in Irish mixed mature hardwoods, in conifer thickets and scrub including the Irish hazel scrub from 12 to 20 ft. in height. The willow warbler is quite common in English beech, but less so in Scottish and Irish. The species has tended to spread with the increase of afforestation coming into the new plantations in the fourth and fifth years, reaching a peak about the eleventh year in the late thicket stage when it is often the commonest species. It is also a very common scrub bird. I have seen willow warblers breeding up to 1,700 ft. in the birches of Glen Tromie and they clearly have a great preference for this species of tree. They are also common in suburban areas, but have only bred at Dollis Hill in 1957. They have bred in Inner London in Holland Park, Hyde Park, Kensington Gardens and Regent's Park, and are much more adaptable than the chiffchaff.

Chiffchaff *Phylloscopus collybita*

Summer resident, scarce winter resident and passage migrant.

The chiffchaff breeds from the Mediterranean north to the British Isles and central Fenno-Scandia.

This numerous species breeds in every county of England and Wales and the Scottish Lowlands but it is more local in the north, nesting as far up as Ross. Singing males have also been seen in Caithness, Sutherland and the Outer Hebrides following a spread in Scotland since the 1950s. In 1959 a pair bred for the first time in the Inner Hebrides. In Ireland the chiffchaff is common and widespread.

The chiffchaff breeds in woodlands, coppices, groves, shrubberies with luxuriant undergrowth, old hedgerows with good timber and is sometimes, but not always, more dependent on trees than the willow warbler. The reasons for this species having its present distribution and numbers in certain habitats are rather obscure. It occurs in the majority of English pedunculate woods and in Badby Wood was outnumbered 4 to 1 by the willow warbler. I have found chiffchaffs in sessile oakwoods, beech, ash, birch, mixed broad-leaved woods and conifer plantations from thicket stage to mature woods. The numbers of both species are about the same in Irish beech and spruce but the willow warbler outnumbered the present species 4 to 1 in old mixed conifer plantations in Ireland, 3 to 1 in Irish ash, birch and young conifer plantations, 5 to 2 in English beechwoods, 2 to 1 in Irish sessile oak and 9 to 7 in mixed young broad-leaved/coniferous plantations in Ireland. Around London the willow warbler is also the commoner of the two species, as it is in the Wyre Forest. The chiffchaff was slightly more common than its relative in the mixed broad-leaved and mature mixed broad-leaved/coniferous woods in Ireland. At Baronscourt in May 1967 in a twenty-five minute count I noted 14 singing chiffchaffs to 9 willow warblers and among the sessile oaks by Upper Lough Erne in half an hour I recorded 11 of the former to 6 willow warblers. At Woodford in Co. Galway the proportion was 2 to 1. Chiffchaffs are not uncommon in Scottish beech, mixed broad-leaved woods in Scotland, in English and Scottish conifer thickets and plantations and in mature Scots pine in Ireland. In northern Scotland I have found chiffchaffs in tall beeches at Kishorn and in beech, oak and ash near Ullapool and the shrub layer was largely composed of rhododendron which, it is believed, may offer some protection in adverse weather. In Ireland the chiffchaff was the dominant bird of the hazel scrub over 20 ft. in Co. Clare, was abundant in many small and varied roadside hedges in most of the country and in Co. Cork was regular in willow scrub under 2½ ft. in height. Birds may often breed in suburban areas with good timber and cover and I was fortunate enough to find the first nest in Inner London in 1937; this was in the grounds of Holland House.

Wood Warbler *Phylloscopus sibilatrix*

Summer resident and passage migrant.

This warbler has a breeding range from northern Spain, central France, Italy and the Balkans north to Britain and southern Fenno-Scandia with isolated highland groups in the southern part of Europe.

This is a not too uncommon species that breeds in mainland Britain, but is absent from Ireland and perhaps the Isle of Man. It is more frequent on the western side and is local or missing in the east from Yorkshire south to Kent. The wood warbler is also scarce in northern Scotland which it only reached in the 1940s. Decreases appear to have taken place in Worcester, Stafford, Cheshire, the Lakes and Ayr; it is very rare in or missing from East Anglia, Nottingham and perhaps Oxford.

Wood warblers like fairly open, mature broad-leaved woods, especially of oak and beech with very little secondary growth which could, if allowed to develop, exclude the species as a breeding bird. They also resort to stunted oak and birch growth in hilly country but rarely to conifers. The wood warbler is characteristic of the sessile oakwoods of Britain and comes fourth in my list for woods in England and Wales (RA 7); I have often seen birds in the open hillwoods of Wales and Cumberland and the oakwoods of Scottish Deeside. They also appear in many of the high-level birchwoods; Brown (1960–1) observed a wood warbler in a birchwood in Glen Tromie between 1,450 and 1,700 ft. above sea-level. Birds also appear in small numbers in the heath birchwoods in Kent and Surrey. The wood warbler also occurs in English and Scottish beechwoods. In the former I have found an RA of 2 which does not match with one assessment that it is "rare in beechwoods"; it was found in only one of the eight woods in which timed counts had been made, but I have listed it for nearly half of the English and a quarter of the Scottish woods. In north-east Scotland I have seen wood warblers in pure beech and mixed oak and beechwoods. In Hampshire they are frequent in several pure beechwoods and used to be in some of the Cotswold areas. Breeding took place in Cork in 1938. On the whole the wood warbler dislikes coniferous woodland, but although I have no personal records it has been recorded in larch.

Bonelli's Warbler *Phylloscopus bonelli*

This European species of low oak and beechwoods and dry areas of pine is a vagrant to the British Isles. It was not recorded before 1948 and now occurs almost annually; two were trapped in 1965. The species is spreading northward in Europe and might appear in Britain as a breeding bird; certainly some of the terrain might suit it.

REGULIDAE

Goldcrest *Regulus regulus*

Resident and partial migrant; also passage migrant.

The goldcrest occurs in Europe as a breeding species from central Spain, France, Italy and the Balkans north to the British Isles and central Norway, Sweden and Finland.

This is a fairly numerous species well distributed throughout the British Isles except in Shetland where it is absent, Orkney where it is irregular and the Outer Hebrides, north-west Scotland and parts of eastern England where it is local. The recent planting of coniferous woodland has helped its numbers which are likely to drop after severe winters. Its original home must have been in the old native Scots pine-forests, the indigenous yew-woods and broad-leaved woods containing yews.

The goldcrest is a very common bird in parts of the old pine-forest, in mature pine, spruce and mixed coniferous woodlands. At Kielder Forest in the Borders it was co-dominant with coal tits in the Sitka spruce and it was the second most abundant species in Irish spruce. At Dunkeld in fifty-year-old Norway spruce there were almost twice as many goldcrests as coal tits. These little birds are frequent in the pines of southern England and the mixed conifers of Ireland. They also occur in small numbers in pedunculate and sessile oak (RA of 2 in Irish sessile oak), alder, Irish and more rarely Scottish birch and in mixed woods primarily broad-leaved and with a small admixture of coniferous trees. I have single records in Scottish and Irish beech. Goldcrests appear more often in broad-leaved woods outside the breeding season. Birds enter the new conifer plantations when they are about 8 or 9 years old and then gradually overtake chaffinch and willow warbler in numbers until they become dominant or share dominance with the coal tit. In the Breckland pines in winter these two were the commonest species. I have no records from ashwoods. Birds will often breed in gardens provided there are a few yews about and I am sure many breeding pairs go unrecorded. However, it has not appeared at Dollis Hill and is very scarce as a breeding bird in the London area. Churchyards may well be worth a closer inspection.

Firecrest *Regulus ignicapillus*

This European species of broad-leaved and mixed broad-leaved/coniferous woodland has only recently arrived as a breeding species in Britain. Nests were found in the New Forest, Hampshire, in 1962 and 1965 while as many as 9 singing males have been heard in the same area since 1961. Since this species has some similarity to the goldcrest it may have been overlooked in the past. The English habitat is usually mature mixed woodland where spruce is dominant; however, conifers are almost absent from some of the localities and firecrests may have bred where oak and beech were dominant.

MUSCICAPIDAE

Spotted Flycatcher *Muscicapa striata*

Summer resident and passage migrant.

This flycatcher breeds from the Mediterranean north to the British Isles and Lapland.

It breeds in every county of Britain and Ireland except Shetland and is local in the Hebrides, Caithness and Orkney.

The favoured habitats of this species are open woodland, forest edges, parkland, churchyards, and roadsides with trees and gardens. It occurs in sessile oak (RA 2 in Ireland) and in pedunculate oak – 2 or 3 pairs nested every year in the 200 acres of Badby Wood as well as in several other nearby oakwoods. Birds also breed not uncommonly in English ash and beech as well as mixed woods and I have found them occasionally in birch in all four countries; in northern Europe it appears in the subarctic birch-forest. In Ireland the spotted flycatcher had an RA of 2 in the old broad-leaved/coniferous woodlands. I have watched several pairs in the old pine forest at Rothiemurchus and it also appears in Speyside larch groves and in several mature pine plantations that I know. Although never present anywhere in big numbers, the spotted flycatcher manages to hold on in many sheltered spots where flying insects are plentiful. One or two pairs breed each year at Dollis Hill and its status does not seem to have changed at all in the last 60 years although the area has become largely built-up. Birds breed in Ladbroke Square and Holland Park as well as in the central London parks; in 1966 twelve broods were reared in one park. The breeding biology of this bird has been discussed by Summers-Smith.

Pied Flycatcher *Muscicapa hypoleuca*

Summer resident and passage migrant.

This bird breeds locally in north Portugal, Spain, northern and eastern France, north Italy, northern Yugoslavia and Hungary north to Belgium, Holland, Denmark, northern Lapland and Finland.

The pied flycatcher is widely but not commonly spread through Wales and into Gloucester, Worcester, Shropshire and Cheshire; it occurs also from north Derby and mid-Yorkshire across northern England and southern Scotland. Its numbers are fairly high in the hillwoods of the Lake District, the Pennines, the north Yorkshire moors, Dumfries and Kirkcudbright. Elsewhere it breeds locally or sporadically, as in Perth and Inverness in the north, Exmoor and Devon in the south-west. From 1940–52 there was a spread, but this has slowed, or in some areas been reversed. The pied flycatcher has not bred in the Isle of Man or in Ireland. The history and range of this bird in Britain have been extensively studied by Campbell.

In the breeding season the pied flycatcher prefers old woodland of oak or birch often in wooded hillside combes or on hill slopes, sometimes but not always near water. It occurs most frequently in sessile oakwoods (RA 7), often on hillsides as in Merioneth, Montgomery and Denbighshire in Wales, and in the Lake District, Devon and the West Riding in England; these are the classical habitats. Nevertheless it also appears in more lowland woods of sessile and pedunculate oak. Other situations include mixed woods of oak, alder and birch, rowan and chestnut, riparian alders, sycamore and even beech. Campbell also noted nests in woods primarily of wych elm, ash and mixed conifers, in larch (with the aid of nestboxes), in parkland hawthorns and along roads and lanes in Herefordshire also provided with nestboxes. Around farms and large gardens in the Lake District the bird occupies a habitat it has preferred for many years. It has been pointed out that the greatest density in Cumberland and Wales occurs above the bracken limit where bilberry, grass and moss make up the field layers. This attractive bird with its delightful song is found in many wild parts of Britain and also in the area of London since the bird is a regular migrant through the region. I have seen birds in late summer in my garden at Dollis Hill and among the oaks in Gladstone Park. Migrants also appear in Inner London; I saw 11 in September 1951 in Regent's Park and in 1966 birds were recorded there on 13 dates in August and September.

PRUNELLIDAE

Hedgesparrow (or Dunnock) *Prunella modularis*

Resident, partial migrant and passage migrant.

This species breeds from Portugal, northern Spain, central Italy and Yugoslavia north to the British Isles and Lapland.

The hedgesparrow is abundant in the British Isles breeding everywhere except in Shetland. There may have been some general increase as well as a local one in the central London parks.

This species can be found in open woodlands with undergrowth and in waste places including low cover on islands and rocky coasts but it is more frequent in small woods, groves, plantations, scrub, hedgerows, shrubberies and gardens – marginal or fringe habitats. On the Continent it is a bird of young subalpine coniferous forests, mixed woods and forest edges and particularly in western Europe of parks, gardens, hedges and town eco-tones. The highest RA I have for the hedgesparrow is 8 and that was in the unbrashed conifer thickets of Ireland. It rated 4 in Irish conifer plantations over 16 ft., and in mixed conifer plantations in Scotland, but only 1 in mature spruce in Scotland, where it also rather disliked Sitka spruce. It was very scarce in the mature Scots pine plantations but commoner in the native pinewoods of Speyside and Loch Maree where its habitat often included juniper. In the broad-leaved woods its highest RA – 5 – occurred in Irish birchwoods although it was much less common in Scottish birch; it is fairly common in the Scandinavian birch-forests. It had an RA of 3 in English and Scottish beech, in Scottish sessile oak where it was commoner than in English or Welsh, and in Irish mature broad-leaved and young mixed woods. The hedgesparrow appeared in small numbers in Scottish ash and Irish beech (RAs of 2), Irish sessile oak and Scottish sycamore but was very scarce in English and Irish ash and missing from the alderwoods. The species occurred in a number of pedunculate oakwoods (RA 2) and there were from 8 to 11 pairs in the 200 acre Badby Wood. Numbers are high in many forms of scrub including thorn and Irish hazel. It is clear that as a species it depends very much on the presence of cover whether that be in association with broad-leaved or coniferous trees. In hedges and on farmland it comprises 8% – 16% of the passerine total. At Dollis Hill some 45 to 50 pairs breed every year although numbers were badly affected by the winter of 1962–3; it is very much a bird of the privet hedges. In 1966 Regent's Park had up to 50 breeding pairs.

The song posts in suburban areas are often very much higher than those used in more rural surroundings.

Meadow Pipit *Anthus pratensis*

The meadow pipit is a bird of open heath and moorland but it will also penetrate woods within its normal habitat. It occurs widely in the establishment stage of many moorland forests in Britain and Ireland but I have also found it regularly in Scottish birch, ash and sessile oakwoods, in 2 out of 6 Scottish alderwoods, in one English pedunculate oakwood, in the old pine forests of Speyside and one or two open mature plantations. It perches on trees and feeds beneath them, but I have only once found it nesting within a wood and that was an open sessile oakwood in Scotland.

Tree Pipit *Anthus trivialis*

Summer resident and passage migrant.

The tree pipit can be found breeding in Europe from northern Spain, southern France, Italy and the Balkans north to the British Isles and Lapland.

This is a fairly common species breeding throughout the British Isles with the exception of the Northern Isles, the Outer Hebrides, Caithness and Anglesey but it is less frequent in the woods of south-east Britain than in the hillwoods of the north and west. It breeds in the Isle of Man but not in Ireland. There has been a spread into Sutherland since the end of the nineteenth century and this corresponds to a move north in Norway at the same time. There appears to have been some decrease in south-eastern England and the west country although this would seem to be offset locally by a rise in numbers in new conifer forests.

The tree pipit is a bird of dry closed hillwoods in the west and north with little shrub layer, of some more open lowland woods, of wood borders, of heaths and parkland with scattered trees and hedges, and of young conifer plantations up to the thicket stage. It is the third commonest bird in the northern Scottish birchwoods as well as those of the Lakes, Pennines and Wales. I found more tree pipits in the northern rather than the eastern Scottish birchwoods. This species had an RA of 5 in the English, Welsh and Scottish sessile oakwoods where it is about as common as the redstart. It was the sixth commonest bird in the Speyside pinewoods where I have heard as many as four singing together in a small area of wood, and I have found it fairly regularly in English and Scottish ash. In the English and Welsh pedunculate oakwoods it has a low RA of 1 and from 1946–50 only one pair bred in Badby Wood, but the number rose in two years to 8 pairs when part of the wood was felled and opened up. It occurs occasionally in mature Scots pine plantations and more frequently in young early stage plantations. It does not occur in beech. In Warwickshire tree pipits used to breed in roadside situations; a typical habitat consisted of tussocky grass, brambles and a hawthorn hedge along a ditch with a single hedgerow ash for a song post. Around London the tree pipit often favours railway cuttings and commons and heaths.

Pied Wagtail *Motacilla alba*

I have occasionally found pied wagtails nesting in clearings or near buildings in quite dense woodland where they sometimes feed as well. Such woods may be of pine, ash and birch.

Grey Wagtail *Motacilla cinerea*

This wagtail often lives near fast-running becks and burns which may pass through woodland so that a great deal of time can be spent within a wood itself, especially of birch and Scots pine.

Waxwing *Bombycilla garrulus*

This spasmodic visitor from the European taiga when it comes to Britain and Ireland is usually to be found where berries or apples are plentiful and this can include open woodland, gardens and hedgerows. Waxwings often come to the fen alder carrs for the berries of the guelder rose.

Great Grey Shrike *Lanius excubitor*

This is a regular winter visitor in small numbers to the east and north of Britain and can be found on heaths with scattered trees and similar ground. I have seen birds frequenting bracken-covered land with scattered trees in Norfolk and Suffolk and for some days a bird stayed in an area of dense hawthorn in Middlesex. Birds are often annual visitors to the London area.

Red-backed Shrike *Lanius collurio*

Scarce summer resident.

The red-backed shrike's European range stretches from northern Portugal and Spain, France, Italy and the Balkans north to England, south-east Norway, south Sweden and Finland.

In the past this shrike has probably nested in every English and Welsh county, but after a great contraction in range and numbers (see Fig. 21) the breeding population by 1960 was down to under 200 pairs. It has not bred in Ireland or the Isle of Man. Its present range in England is bounded by Devon, Somerset, Wiltshire, Hampshire, Surrey, Middlesex, Buckinghamshire, Hertfordshire, Cambridgeshire and Norfolk with strongholds in Hampshire and Sussex and over 10 pairs in Surrey, Essex and Norfolk. This withdrawal has been attributed to the warmer, wetter summers that have resulted in fewer large flying insects and to the destruction of its habitats. The future of this bird is giving rise to concern.

This is very much a bird of scattered trees and bushes, old hedgerows, railway cuttings with thorns present for its larder on which it impales the insects and small birds that make up its prey. A pair I studied and filmed in Suffolk frequented the borders of an oakwood and its grassy fringes, studded with brambles and small willows and hawthorns. The male sang systematically from different bramble sprays and thorn tops. In other Suffolk sites I have seen territories among elder and privet along the roadside, but most in this country have been in thorny, bushy places sometimes in quite built-up areas.

STURNIDAE

Starling *Sturnus vulgaris*

Resident, partial migrant, passage migrant and winter visitor.

The starling nests in Europe from northern Spain and France, central Italy and the Balkans north to Iceland and Lapland.

This well-known and abundant bird breeds in every county of the British Isles; there is a separate race in Shetland and the Outer Hebrides. There was a remarkable decrease in its numbers and range just before 1800, but the species increased about 1850 again and extended its range once more. It has been estimated that the British population may be doubled by the migrants coming from the Baltic. The Irish hordes are swelled by starlings from the Baltic, Holland, north Britain and less so by birds from north Germany and Poland.

This bird can be found breeding in woodlands, on cultivated and untouched land, on heaths, coasts, bare islands, along roads, in parkland, orchards, gardens, suburban districts and quite well-developed built-up areas. Although starlings may nest in woods they generally feed outside them except during caterpillar plagues. They often breed semi-socially as well as feeding and roosting communally. Many now breed in association with man's buildings and may thrive in towns. At Dollis Hill some 250–275 pairs breed every year with a density of 50 nests per 100 acres compared with 6 for Badby Wood and 1–3 for more rural habitats. Although few records for sessile oakwoods were obtained by Yapp I found an RA of 8 in the sessile oak and beechwoods of Scotland and 7 in the beechwoods of Ireland; it was much less frequent in English, Welsh and Irish sessile oak (RA 1) and English beech (RA 2). It was interesting to find that the jackdaw and the starling were commoner in Scottish and Irish beech than in English. The starling was the fifth commonest bird in the Scottish alderwoods (RA 7) and was also regular in Scottish broad-leaved woods, but less so in Irish. I found it occasional in ash and pedunculate oakwoods and rare in birch. The starling's chief association with conifers is for roosting when spruce and other plantations may be almost submerged night after night by thousands of birds landing in the trees. Many kinds of tree and shrub may be used. At home my resident pair of starlings roost during the winter in their nesting place in the loft.

It may be of interest to repeat here some statistics on the feeding habits of this bird. A pair of starlings in Holland were found to feed their young from 118 to 525 times a day and to bring from 16,000 to 27,000 insects of which leather jackets formed from 14% to 26% in different years. Yet all the leather jackets collected by all the starlings in one area were only 1% of the total available.

FRINGILLIDAE

Hawfinch *Coccothraustes coccothraustes*

Resident.

The hawfinch breeds from the Mediterranean north to Britain, Denmark, southern Sweden and Leningrad.

It breeds in practically every county of England, except in Cornwall, and of Wales except for four. At the turn of the century the hawfinch increased in the Borders and the Lowlands, but there has been a decrease in these areas since. It has bred in three Highland counties including Perth. There are no breeding recordings for the Isle of Man but an adult was seen feeding young in Co. Kildare in Ireland in 1902.

This is an arboreal bird of well-developed broad-leaved or mixed woodlands, old wooded gardens, parklands with scattered thorns and orchards as well as occasional roadsides. The hawfinch has been observed on the Secondary and Tertiary deposits, living in partly hilly country, interspersed with mixed woodlands, coppices, thickets, orchards and hedges. It has sometimes been found only in ecotones, but I know the hawfinch best as a fast, shy, elusive and silent bird of mixed woodlands of small oak, birch, sycamore and even sweet chestnut with plenty of bracken, bramble and hawthorn along their borders. Here the nests are often 35 ft. above the ground in sycamores or high bushy hawthorns. The greatest density of hawfinches is on the chalklands from East Anglia to Berkshire, on the Severn lias and to a lesser extent on the Keuper marl and sandstones of the west Midlands. Mountfort, in his monograph on the hawfinch, listed 33 different species of tree (including 5 conifers) selected for 285 nests; of 244 nests 102 were in woodland, 76 in orchards and the rest in gardens, parks, along road edges and in thickets. Birds can also breed in the well-wooded parts of suburbs, but they are missing from the centre of towns and some inner suburbs where trees are few.

Hawfinches feed on the kernels and seeds of many trees and plants including cherry, damson, sloe, hawthorn and seeds of wych elm and hornbeam. To crack a cherry stone requires a crushing load of from 60 to 95 pounds.

Greenfinch *Chloris chloris*

Resident, partial migrant, passage migrant and winter visitor.

The greenfinch appears in the whole of western Europe from the Mediterranean to the British Isles and central Fenno-Scandia.

It breeds in every county except Shetland, having spread to the Northern Isles since the 1880s and into the Highlands and some of the other islands since the 1920s. The species is thought to have decreased generally in Ireland, but has made some advance locally in western Donegal.

The greenfinch likes a number of habitats with fairly tall trees and shrubs including demesnes and farms, avenues, roads, cultivated areas, gardens, orchards, bushy scrub and suburban districts, but it tends to avoid close woodland and keeps to the outer fringes and borders where it can perform without hindrance its erratic, butterfly-like display and song flights from tall trees. It is nowhere a very common bird and avoided the wood at Badby. I have found its highest numbers in parkland, scrub with tall trees and farmland. In woodland the highest RA of 4 occurred in the mixed, mature broad-leaved forests of Scotland and then in the unbrashed conifer thickets in the same country, as well as mature Sitka spruce plantations. Greenfinches were not so common in the Norway spruce. About equal numbers could be found in Scottish sessile oak and Irish beech (RA 2) and smaller numbers still in Scottish alder and mixed broad-leaved woods in Ireland. I had no records at all in the following Irish woods: ash, beech, birch, sessile oak, hazel scrub, conifer thickets and mixed conifer plantations. However, the bullfinch was regular in small numbers in all these woods except the ash and it seemed that the habitat could not support both species. Greenfinches flourished in small numbers in the Scottish conifer thickets and appeared in the Breckland plantations, but not in the Irish thickets. The bullfinch is, of course, more of a woodland bird whereas the greenfinch probably evolved in sparsely wooded areas and forest edges. The greenfinch with its short broad bill feeds on seeds relatively well exposed such as those of grasses or contained in pods and capsules; the bullfinch goes for buds and seeds from fleshy fruits such as appear in woodland. Three or four pairs manage to nest at Dollis Hill each year in overgrown hedges or shrubberies and birds certainly breed in other suburbs and in the centre of London; there were 12 territories in Hyde Park and Kensington Gardens and 10 broods in Regent's Park in 1966. Monk has described the breeding biology of the greenfinch.

Goldfinch *Carduelis carduelis*

Resident, and partial migrant.

The goldfinch breeds from the Mediterranean north to the British Isles and southern Fenno-Scandia.

It probably once bred throughout the whole of mainland Britain but, after years of persecution by bird-catchers together with reclamation of the marginal habitat it prefers, it was practically extinct in Scotland by 1900 and much reduced elsewhere. The goldfinch was described in 1909 as "decidedly scarce and local". It has not fully recovered in Scotland; it has bred in Ross but not yet in Caithness and Sutherland but it has returned to some of the islands. In Ireland it has extended its range in the west but suffered a reverse in some eastern counties.

In the breeding season the goldfinch is very much a bird of open cultivated land with scattered trees, orchards and gardens but small numbers may frequent open woodland for breeding or to take elm seeds, aphids and caterpillars. In autumn they resort to allotments, waste places and gardens for seeds of the Compositae which among Oxford birds formed 76% of their diet. I have seen birds in pedunculate oak and gold-finches have an RA of 1 in Irish mature mixed hardwoods. They also occurred in young mixed broad-leaved/coniferous woods in Ireland and I have 4 contacts in Irish sessile oak. A bird of its habits has done quite well in suburban areas and a pair – sometimes two pairs – may breed at Dollis Hill. Breeding also takes place in Inner London and a roost in Warwick Square in 1966 was used by 50 to 60 birds. Goldfinches have been recorded in the Breckland pine plantations.

Siskin *Carduelis spinus*

Resident, winter visitor and passage migrant.

The siskin breeds discontinuously in southern Europe in highland areas in the Pyrenees, and perhaps central France, but it spreads more continuously from the Alps east to Asia and north to central Norway, Sweden and Finland, Ireland and northern Britain.

This bird is commonest in Britain from Perth north to Caithness and Sutherland with populations also in the western Highlands and less stable ones in northern England and North Wales, although birds in the

Snowdonia Forest Park are probably spreading into mid-Wales. Siskins are now breeding in many new areas of forest in England.

The siskin's habitat is primarily coniferous woodland of pine, spruce and larch or of mixed woods with birch and alder. The highest RA I have is 5 for mature Scots pine plantations in the Highlands, but it is also regular in the more open parts of the old Caledonian forest. I have seen it in gardens in Braemar and Aviemore. The nest is built high up in these Highland conifers and spruce is often used; the nest is generally at the end of a branch. In Strathspey siskins breed up to 1,500 ft. In Ireland the birds are about equally common in mixed broad-leaved/coniferous, in brashed coniferous and in thicket woodlands about 10 years old (RAs all 1); they sometimes occur in Irish sessile oak too. After the breeding season siskins will visit many other areas; throughout its range birds are seen most often in conifers in summer, birches in autumn and alders in winter. They extract the seeds from cones previously opened by crossbills and they come to riparian alders in many parts of Britain as well as the fen alder carrs. They often travel and feed with redpolls but I have records of siskins alone in birches in Ladbroke Square and Holland Park in London. I have seen siskins in alders in many places from the Isle of Wight north to Sutherland; in the London area I have recorded them in alders in Brent Park, Richmond Park and along the River Colne. A party of 250 to 300 birds was seen in alders in Essex in 1966. I had a siskin in my garden every day from Christmas Day, 1961, to 29th March, 1962, and it fed for as much as six hours each day on "Swoop". Before it left it had started to sing. The numbers in the British Isles may be related to the size of the seed crops on its European breeding grounds.

Linnet *Acanthis cannabina*

This is a bird of heath, scrub, short hedgerows and bushy places, but it appears in numbers of the thicket conifer plantations of the north; it had an RA of 5 in Scottish thickets and was regular in many Irish ones. I have also seen birds in mature Sitka spruce plantations and an open wood of sycamore, elm, beech and horse chestnut on the Kyle of Tongue. Linnets also roost in winter in various woodlands, and a four acre patch of beech-trees has been known to hold as many as a thousand birds in September.

Twite *Acanthis flavirostris*

This species favours moorlands and rather barren rocky places in the north and west. I have occasionally observed it in the early establishment stages of Scottish conifer plantations.

Redpoll *Acanthis flammea*

Resident, partial migrant and winter visitor.

The lesser redpoll is smaller and browner than the other races of this highly variable passerine and breeds in the British Isles, the Alps and on the borders of Czechoslovakia; the larger, paler mealy redpoll breeds in the birch-forests from Norway to Siberia while the very large Greenland redpoll breeds in Greenland and on Baffin Island, and both these races may appear as irregular autumn and winter visitors in the British Isles. The taxonomy of the redpolls has been discussed by Williamson.

The British race may have nested in practically every county of the British Isles except Cornwall, the Isle of Wight and the Northern Isles. It has been recovering from a long period of persecution by bird-catchers and has been helped by reafforestation. Nevertheless, it is rather local except in many parts of Ireland, the Scottish Highlands and north Wales; there are signs of some further increase in the Highlands, in southern England, and especially in East Anglia and northern England.

The typical habitat of the redpoll is that of birchwoods and willow scrub, but new plantations must now be included since it breeds there and relies on weed seeds and not on those of birch. In the Irish conifer thickets the redpoll is the second commonest bird after the willow warbler with an RA of 14. It is also common (RA 11) in the young mixed conifer plantations from 16 to 26 ft. high that are so typical of much of Ireland; there it was the third commonest bird after wren and willow warbler. I found it most frequently after that in Scottish conifer thickets (RA 8) and in the Irish broad-leaved/conifer plantations (RA 5). Rather smaller numbers appeared in the Scottish birchwoods, mature Scots pine plantations and mixed coniferous woods, in the Irish mature conifers, in English and Welsh birch and thicket and in the English fen alder carrs. A few birds also appeared in one or two old pine-forests and even in mature broad-leaved woods in north Scotland. Redpolls also nest in small numbers in large mixed gardens and orchards close to London. They were garden birds in a number of Irish towns including Armagh, Omagh, and Carrick-on-Shannon. In autumn and winter redpolls are generally to be found (sometimes in the company of siskins) in birches and alders with a preference for the former, but I have seen them, too, in hedges, rough tussocky places, on sewage farms and rubbish dumps. They also frequent larch groves in Ireland and on Speyside. A flock of redpolls once visited my garden in cold weather in January 1958 while a flock of 800 to 1,000 was reported from Wimbledon Common in January 1966.

Serin *Serinus canarius*

This tiny finch which I once saw in Gladstone Park, Dollis Hill, in a holm oak, has ranged northwards across Europe arriving in Sweden in 1942 and on the Channel coast in 1956. It is an annual vagrant to England, but its numbers have been increasing recently. In 1966 there were 4 records of 9 birds in Cornwall as well as 2 birds reported from Devon and Hampshire and singletons from Dorset, Kent, Sussex and Yorkshire. This was two-thirds as many individuals as were observed in the whole period from 1958–65. Since all but one of the records was in the late part of the year this suggests a post-breeding season dispersal to another area. However, most observations are in April and May and a pair reared at least two young in southern England in May 1967. It is a bird of sunny forest margins and groves, avenues, orchards and gardens; in Spain I have found it ranging from riverside to subalpine coniferous woodland.

Bullfinch *Pyrrhula pyrrhula*

Resident.

The European range of the bullfinch stretches from northern Spain, southern France, central Italy and parts of the Balkans north to the British Isles and north central Fenno-Scandia.

This is a generally well-distributed species in suitable areas, but is rather scarce in parts of Scotland. In Ireland it has recently been extending its range and increasing its numbers and can now be found in all wooded areas.

The bullfinch is a bird of woodland, groves, parks, scrub, old hedgerows often with a good amount of tall and thick cover as well as of gardens and orchards. The highest RA I have recorded is 8 for Irish mixed conifer plantations over 26 ft.; these are entered when their age has reached some 7 to 9 years. The bullfinch is common in English thorn scrub and has an RA of 6 in the Irish hazel scrub of the west coast. It is regular in Scottish alder, slightly less so in Irish sessile oak, birch, mixed broad-leaved and young conifer plantations after brashing. It is to be found occasionally in pedunculate and other sessile oakwoods, in beech, fen alder carrs, the old Caledonian Forest, in pine plantations over 20 years old in Scotland, Wales and England, in spruce, in English yew and in the mixed broad-leaved/coniferous plantations of Ireland. It is very scarce in Scottish ash, much more frequent in English, and I have no records from Scottish birch, Irish ash or conifer thickets in the summer. In its ecotones of orchards and gardens it is a common nesting species in the Vale of

Evesham, Kent and elsewhere, and here its attacks on fruit buds are well known. It is very catholic in its choice of food and tends to go for buds in spring, insects in the first part of the summer, berries in the autumn and seeds in the late summer and winter. There is a tendency for the bird to feed far from cover in southern England and this may have helped the increase that has taken place there. The bullfinch will nest in suburban parks and orchards as well as large gardens but it is a very scarce winter visitor to Dollis Hill where cover is sparse. It does not readily come into towns but in 1966 2 pairs raised young in Regent's Park in London.

Crossbill *Loxia curvirostra*

The Scottish race (*L. c. scotica*) is resident in Scotland; the Continental race (*L. c. c.*) is resident in England and has bred in Wales and Ireland after periodic invasions from Europe. The Scottish crossbill has been held by some authorities to be referable to the Parrot Crossbill (*L. pityopsittacus*) which is a rare vagrant; a pair of the latter may have bred in 1963.

The Continental crossbill breeds in conifer woods, particularly spruce, in parts of Spain, south-eastern France, northern Italy and east to Russia and the Black Sea, in Denmark, Norway, the Baltic States and parts of Sweden and Finland. After irruptions it may breed outside its normal range.

Crossbills favour mature coniferous forests – of spruce, pine and larch – where these are fairly open and rich in seed production rather than smaller stands where the harvest may be limited and uncertain. The Scottish crossbill breeds in Perthshire, Nairn, Banff, Moray, Inverness, Ross and south-east Sutherland and possibly in Aberdeenshire. The main headquarters are in the old pine-forests and plantations of Strathspey and, although I have not seen birds in the woods near Beinn Eighe, I have picked up many cones worked by crossbills in the area. The common crossbill has bred in numbers of roadside Scots pines in Breckland and it was here that I studied it. After the irruption of 1962, breeding occurred in 17 counties in such trees as pine, larch and Douglas fir. Following an earlier invasion in 1956 breeding was proved in 9 English counties in 1957 and it was thought to have taken place in another 13. These periodic invasions are a feature of the crossbill's biology and it has been suggested that they are a way of avoiding a food shortage after a good breeding season; irruptions of crossbills have been recorded as far back as 1251. It was after the invasion of 1909 that the East Anglian colony was established and this received injections of new blood from subsequent irruptions. Most of the English breeding records come from East Anglia, Hampshire and perhaps Surrey. On the Continent, spruce is the favourite feeding tree, but after the 1962 invasion few birds were found in this species of tree in Britain. At Wytham in 1962 and 1963 98% of the records of birds feeding were in European larch. The parrot crossbill feeds chiefly in Europe on pine cones, the common crossbill on the softer spruce cones and the two-barred crossbill on larch. The common crossbill is less efficient than the parrot crossbill at extracting seed from pine cones. Immigrant crossbills also take the seeds of many fruit and berries, of grasses, thistles and other plants, while 16 birds in Essex in 1962 were seen feeding on beech-mast and hazel nuts. The Scottish crossbills feed largely on Scots pine seeds, but they will also take those of larch, spruce and rowan as well as buds and occasional insects. Feeding birds may attack the larger cones by hanging from them while smaller ones are nipped off below the joint and carried usually upwards to a branch where they are gripped by the foot while the crossed mandibles are employed to extract the seed. In a study of the Breckland crossbill Robertson has shown how the upper mandible bears down laterally on the space between the cone and a scale which are then forced apart. The points of the bill do not meet so that they act as guides to give the two halves of the beak the requisite shearing action; the seed is then withdrawn by the tongue. The populations of crossbills in the Highlands varies with the pine seed crop which runs in 3–4 year cycles. In good years Scottish crossbills may breed at a density of 16 pairs to 1,000 acres of pine-forest. I have watched Scottish crossbills in many parts of the Caledonian Forest as well as in mature pine plantations in Scotland where their RA is as high as 5. They are very much in evidence when parties come in summer to drink at gutters and water-butts for all crossbills are very thirsty birds. Common crossbills I have seen nesting in Suffolk, Norfolk, the New Forest and in Kew Gardens near London in 1936. I have also seen them in many areas where breeding could not be proved, including pine plantations in Glen Poer in south-east Ireland in 1967, on Surrey heaths and in Northamptonshire wind-breaks. Many eggs are laid in February and March since the crossbill is an early nester. For further information on the crossbill I would suggest consulting Robertson (1954) and Campbell (1962).

Chaffinch *Fringilla coelebs*

Resident, passage migrant and winter visitor.

The chaffinch breeds throughout Western Europe from the Mediterranean north to northern Norway, Sweden and Finland where its range is slowly moving north.

This abundant bird – the commonest finch in the British Isles – produced nearly twice as many contacts in the woods I visited than any other bird. The chaffinch breeds in every county; it has increased in Scotland with reafforestation but has declined in some parts of England.

This is a bird of broad-leaved, coniferous and mixed woods, of groves and plantations, parkland, farmlands, hedgerows, bushy commons, scrub, avenues, orchards and gardens; it is perhaps the most widely distributed of our woodland species of bird. The highest densities I have recorded have been in natural Scots pine, pine plantations, and in the young mixed broad-leaved/coniferous plantations of Ireland. The chaffinch is the dominant bird of the Scottish alderwoods (RA 17), the sessile oakwoods of England and Wales (RA 17), of Scotland (RA 16) and Ireland (RA 15) and of the English pedunculate woods (RA 13). I found that it was the commonest bird in the birchwoods of eastern Scotland, the Lake District, the Pennines and Wales, but it came second, after the willow warbler, in the birches of northern Scotland. The chaffinch was also the dominant species of the British and Irish beechwoods, of Scottish sycamore and ash, but it was ranked second in the ashwoods of northern England, and third in those of Ireland together with Irish birch. It came top of the list for the older mixed broad-leaved woods of Scotland. In coniferous woodland it was dominant again in the Speyside pine-forests, in the pure and mixed plantations of pine in England and Scotland, in spruce and mixed conifers in Ireland, but it came second in the Loch Maree pine, and Scottish Norway and Sitka spruce. The chaffinch was the most abundant species in the thicket stage of some conifer plantations coming in at about 7 or 8 years. Chaffinches also occur in the fen alder carrs and English yew-woods and I found some also in Irish yew. On farmland up to 12% of the passerine population is formed by chaffinches – a proportion about equal to that of the robins. Chaffinches have also adapted themselves to orchards, to suburbs and some of the larger parks and town gardens. Three pairs breed at Dollis Hill in almonds, hawthorns or apple-trees, but they are just holding on like the greenfinch and goldfinch. At the time of writing, new building projects have destroyed one of its habitats near my home. In Inner London chaffinches do well in some of the central parks; 19 territories were known in 1966 for Kensington Gardens and Hyde Park. A decline in numbers has been reported from oakwood and scrub at Bookham. For the behaviour of the chaffinch see Marler (1956), and for the breeding biology Newton (1964).

Brambling *Fringilla montifringilla*

Winter visitor and irregular passage migrant; has bred.

The brambling breeds in the birch and taiga regions of Norway, central and northern Sweden and Finland. It has bred sporadically outside its normal range, e.g., Estonia and Denmark.

The brambling is a regular winter visitor to England and south-west Scotland, but it comes less frequently in big numbers to the West of England, Wales, Ireland and parts of Scotland except in some years, depending on climatic factors and supplies of beech-mast. In winter it is normally found in beechwoods, plantations or under hornbeams as well as around farms and on agricultural land. At Badby birds come every year to a clump of beeches and feed with chaffinches under the trees, but the numbers and length of stay depend on how the cycle of beech-mast is going. I have seen several hundreds in flocks on the ploughlands of North Norfolk and in 1956 a flock of over a thousand was reported at Dartford in Kent. Birds quite often migrate over Dollis Hill in daylight and I have seen them feeding in Ladbroke Square in Kensington during hard weather. In 1963 many bramblings came to suburban gardens in Birmingham. Roosts are often in woodlands with dense cover such as the one in rhododendrons in 2 acres of wood at Westerham. The brambling has bred in Sutherland in 1920 and possibly also in Perth, Inverness and Ross.

On the Continent it is a bird of the dry taiga, birch-forests and willow and subarctic birch scrub. It was found to be the commonest bird after the meadow pipit and the willow warbler at Abisko in the Swedish sub-alpine birches. The scrubby birchwoods of northern Scotland may yet prove a suitable nesting terrain. In April 1952 I watched a male in full breeding plumage with a hen in a secluded part of Breckland.

Yellowhammer *Emberiza citrinella*

Resident and winter visitor.

This bunting breeds from northern Spain, south-central France, north Italy and the central Balkans to the British Isles and northern Fenno-Scandia.

The yellowhammer breeds in every county except the Outer Hebrides and Shetland. There are signs of a decrease in England as a result of hedge destruction and perhaps toxic chemicals. There has been a decline in parts of Ireland.

The habitats of the yellowhammer include farm and agricultural lands with hedgerows, where it forms perhaps 10% of the passerine population, as well as roadsides, commons, open heathy places without trees and the edges or glades of open woodland. On the Continent it will select edges and clearings in both broad-leaved and coniferous forests preferably of open oak and pinewoods with discontinuous vegetative growth on dry soils. I have located yellowhammers in a number of different kinds of wood which they use primarily for feeding. They have an RA of 1 in Scottish birch and I have watched small numbers in English and Welsh birchwoods. They occur in the hillside sessile oakwoods of England, Wales and Scotland, but I did not find them in Ireland. I have observed birds in English pedunculate oakwoods, in English and Scottish beech, Scottish alder and ashwoods almost everywhere. They come into the Scottish conifer thickets and have an RA of about 2 after ten years and will persist even into mature spruce plantations with some cover. Birds can be found in hawthorn scrub mixed with gorse and were regular in the Irish hazel scrub and the South Down yews. The yellowhammer retreats from suburbs as they become developed.

Cirl Bunting *Emberiza cirlus*

Local and restricted resident.

This is a bird of south-west Europe breeding in southern Britain, Belgium, France, the Rhineland, Spain, Portugal, Italy, the Dalmatian coast and the southern Balkans.

In Britain the cirl bunting is restricted as a regular but local breeding species to the south of a line from Hereford through Worcester, Gloucester, Oxford, Berkshire, Hertfordshire, Middlesex, Surrey and Kent. It nests only sporadically outside this line, but it has bred in 7 Welsh counties north to Denbigh and 26 English counties north to the Lake District.

Perhaps the favourite habitat of the cirl bunting is a combination of open areas of scattered trees and timber, often elms, with hedgerows, scrub or grassland and pasture with some herbage, not infrequently on chalk and limestone hills and downs. It is very much an ecotone bird: I have seen singing males on the lower slopes of scrubby hillsides on the Chilterns, in roadside elms in Hampshire, in a marginal area of tussocky fields, hedges and trees as well as in a cupressus-lined garden both in Somerset and in a fringe of fields and gardens in Hertfordshire. It sometimes favours sunny but sheltered southward-facing slopes and its distribution may be in part due to a mixture of such climatic factors as sunshine, low rainfall and warm winters together with certain topographical demands that an ecotone bird such as the cirl bunting needs to satisfy.

These factors could well set a limit on its distribution and numbers but the species is shy and unobtrusive and can escape notice. Its ecological relationship with the yellowhammer is unclear. It has been said that the cirl bunting arose from the group of yellowhammers by geographical isolation. In the Mediterranean countries it occurs at lower altitudes than the yellowhammer. Cirl buntings are rural birds and are extremely local around London.

Reed Bunting *Emberiza schoeniclus*

This is a species of reed and osier beds, bushy fens, wet sallow scrub, alder carrs and rich riverside vegetation but it can also be found in areas away from water. I have seen reed buntings in the breeding season in a conifer thicket in Northamptonshire some distance from water, in some of the dry Irish conifer thickets, in a Scottish birchwood and in dry willow scrub in Co. Cork. Birds have been recorded in a Yorkshire ashwood and a report listing a "tall mixed hedge (nowhere near water)" as a breeding site, showed that a substantial proportion of reed buntings in Nottinghamshire breed in typical yellowhammer habitats. Outside the breeding season birds may occur on grassy moorland and farmland and I have seen a bird in winter on an allotment at Dollis Hill. Very occasionally reed buntings appear in Inner London and an interesting 1966 record was of one in Hanover Gardens in a crab-apple tree.

House Sparrow *Passer domesticus*

It may seem rather surprising to include this species in a book about woodland birds, but it just qualifies because a very small proportion of sparrows in this country nest in trees or hedges, sometimes in or along the borders of small woods or scrub, but not too far from man's buildings. Although most nests are in dwellings and buildings some are built in the branches of trees or in holes, but the tree hole is not common. Open tree sites seem to be used when other sites are not available. Holes may be captured from the shyer, more retiring tree sparrow but I have seen a mixed colony in tall willows in Romney Marsh. In winter, birds often use hawthorn scrub for roosts and I have sometimes disturbed sparrows in woodland. Thousands have been observed among the hollies and beeches in Burnham Beeches on a January day. They also visit birches in winter.

Tree Sparrow *Passer montanus*

Resident, passage migrant and winter visitor.

The European range runs north from Spain, France, Italy, Yugoslavia, northern Greece to the Norwegian coast, central Sweden and Leningrad.

The tree sparrow's greatest breeding density lies in the Midlands, eastern and northern England, but it has bred either irregularly or sporadically in most of the counties of Britain. From 1959–60 it was apparently extinct in Ireland, but the species succeeded in breeding in 15, largely coastal, counties in 1966.

The tree sparrow is a bird of a countryside with scattered trees and cultivated parkland in moist situations such as river valleys. It likes old pollard willows and oaks, hedgerow trees, groves, clumps, orchards, gardens, old ruins and even rocky coasts and islands; it has even reached St Kilda and North Rona. In the London area, its preferred habitats were found to be river valleys with pollarded willows, gravel pits and open parkland with oaks and hornbeams; it was not a bird of dense woodland and any sites in woods were "on the periphery or in old trees left in cleared or open spaces". Nesting sites in suburban areas were generally in old isolated oaks and at Dollis Hill 2 pairs have bred in such a situation since 1953 and possibly earlier. In the London area 506 nest sites were listed of which 179 were in oaks, 123 in willows, 77 in elms, 21 in poplars and the rest in a variety of trees, including 5 conifers, buildings, machinery, old nests or hawthorn hedges where they built open untidy nests. In the Badby region in Northamptonshire tree sparrows nested from 1946–50 in old willows, parkland oaks and on the insulators of electricity pylons. Since that time birds have penetrated Badby Wood where previously they were unknown; by 1967 there were 18 pairs nesting both on the north-west fringe of the oakwoods and up to 450 yards inside the close-canopy wood. Similar colonisation had been going on in other nearby oakwoods. The nearest that the tree sparrow comes to St Paul's Cathedral in London is Dollis Hill (*c.* 6 miles) and the other inner limits lie from 7 to 11 miles away. Birds sometimes appear in Inner London and I have once had a tree sparrow on my bird-table. In Scandinavia, Russia and the Far East it is a bird of the towns and buildings often associating with house sparrows. The breeding biology of tree sparrows has been studied by Seel (1964).

SCIENTIFIC NAMES OF PLANTS
MENTIONED IN THE TEXT

Alder (*Alnus glutinosa*)
Alexanders (*Smyrnium olusatrum*)
Ash (*Fraxinus excelsior*)
   for Mountain, see Rowan
Aspen (*Populus tremula*)

Baneberry (*Actaea spicata*)
Beech (*Fagus sylvatica*)
Bell Heather (*Erica cinerea*)
Bilberry (*Vaccinium myrtillus*)
Birch, Downy (*Betula pubescens*)
     Dwarf (*B. nana*)
     Silver (*B. pendula*=*B. Alba*
     =*B. verrucosa*)
Black Horehound (*Ballota nigra*)
Blackthorn (*Prunus spinosa*)
Bloody Cranesbill (*Geranium
   sanguineum*)
Bluebell (*Endymion non-scripta*)
Box (*Buxus sempervirens*)
Bracken (*Pteridium aquilinum*)
Bramble (*Rubus fruticosus*)
Breckland Catchfly (*Silene otites*)
Broom (*Sarothamnus scoparius*)
Bryony (*Bryonia dioica*)
Buckthorn, Common (*Rhamnus
     catharticus*)
     Alder (*Frangula alnus*)
Bugle (*Ajuga reptans*)

Canadian Fleabane (*Conyza
     canadensis*)
Charlock (*Sinapis arvensis*)
Cherry, Bird (*Prunus padus*)
     Wild (*P. avium*)
Chestnut, Horse (*Aesculus
     hippocastanum*)

     Sweet (*Castanea sativa*)
Chickweed (*Cerastium sp.*)
Chickweed Wintergreen (*Trientalis
     europaea*)
Coltsfoot (*Tussilago farfara*)
Cowberry (*Vaccinium vitis-idaea*)
Cow-wheat (*Melampyrum pratense*)
Crab-apple (*Malus sylvestris*)
Creeping Buttercup (*Ranunculus repens*)
Creeping Lady's Tresses (*Goodyera
     repens*)
Crowberry (*Empetrum nigrum*)
Cuckoo Pint (*Arum maculatum*)
Currant, Black (*Ribes nigrum*)
     Red (*R. rubrum*)

Dewberry (*Rubus caesius*)
Dog's Mercury (*Mercurialis perennis*)
Dogwood (*Thelycrania sanguinea*)

Elder (*Sambucus nigra*)
Elm, Common or Field (*Ulmus
     procera*)
     Wych (*U. glabra*)
Enchanter's Nightshade (*Circaea
     lutetiana*)

False Acacia (*Robinia pseudoacacia*)
Fat-Hen (*Chenopodium album*)
Fennel (*Foeniculum vulgare*)
Fern, Broad Buckler (*Dryopteris sp.*)
     Hard (*Blechnum spicant*)
     Hartstongue (*Phyllitis
       scolopendrium*)
     Royal (*Osmunda regalis*)
Fine Bent (*Agrostis tenuis*)

Fir, Douglas (*Pseudotsuga menziesii*)
    European Silver (*Albies alba*)
    Grand Silver (*A. grandis*)
    Noble (*A. procera*)
Flowering Cherry (*Prunus serrulata*)
Foxglove (*Digitalis purpurea*)
Fuchsia (*Fuchsia magellanica*)
Fumitory (*Fumaria officinalis*)

Giant Bellflower (*Campanula latifolia*)
Globe Flower (*Trollius europaeus*)
Goosegrass (*Galium aparine*)
Gorse (*Ulex europaeus*)
Grass, Annual Meadow (*Poa annua*)
    Cocksfoot (*Dactylis glomerata*)
    Mat (*Nardus stricta*)
    Purple Moor (*Molinia caerulea*)
    Sweet Vernal (*Anthoxanthum odoratum*)
    Tufted Hair (*Deschampsia cespitosa*)
    Wavy Hair (*D. flexuosa*)
    Wood Soft (*Holcus mollis*)
Greater Bindweed (*Calystegia sepium*)
Ground Ivy (*Glechoma hederacea*)
Groundsel (*Senecio vulgaris*)
Guelder Rose (*Viburnum opulus*)

Hairy Brome (*Bromus ramosus*)
Hawthorn (*Crataegus monogyna*)
Hazel (*Corylus avellana*)
Hedge Mustard (*Sisymbrium officinale*)
Herb Bennet (*Geum urbanum*)
Herb Robert (*Geranium robertianum*)
Hogweed (*Heracleum sphondylium*)
Holly (*Ilex aquifolium*)
Honeysuckle (*Lonicera periclymenum*)
Hop (*Humulus lupulus*)
Hornbeam (*Carpinus betulus*)

Ironweed (*Polygonum aviculare*)
Ivy (*Hedera helix*)

Jack-by-the-Hedge (*Alliaria petiolata*)
Juniper (*Juniperus communis*)

Laburnum (*Laburnum anagyroides*)
Lady's Mantle (*Alchemilla vulgaris*)
Larch, European (*Larix decidua*)
    Hybrid (*L. eurolepis*)
    Japanese (*L. leptolepis*)
Lawson Cypress (*Chamaecyparis lawsoniana*)
Lesser Celandine (*Ranunculus ficaria*)
Lilac (*Syringa vulgaris*)
Lily-of-the-Valley (*Convallaria majalis*)
Lime, Common (*Tilia europaea*)
    Small-leaved (*T. cordata*)
Ling (*Calluna vulgaris*)
London Plane (*Platanus acerifolia*)

Maple, Field (*Acer campestre*)
    Norway (*A. platanoides*)
Marsh Marigold (*Caltha palustris*)
Meadowsweet (*Filipendula ulmaria*)
Milk Vetch (*Astragalus glycyphyllos*)
Milkwort (Chalk) (*Polygala calcarea*)
Moschatel (*Adoxa moschatellina*)
Mountain Avens (*Dryas octopetala*)

Nettle, Stinging (*Urtica dioica*)
    White Dead (*Lamium album*)

Oak, Holm (*Quercus ilex*)
    Pedunculate (*Q. robur*)
    Red (*Q. borealis* var. *maxima*)
    Sessile (*Q. petraea*)
    Turkey (*Q. cerris*)
Orchid, Birdsnest (*Neottia nidus-avis*)
    Coralroot (*Corallorhiza trifida*)
    Early Purple (*Orchis mascula*)
    Military (*O. militaris*)
    Spotted (*Dactylorchis fuchsii*)
    Twayblade (*Listera ovata*)
Oxford Ragwort (*Senecio squalidus*)

Parsley, Cow (*Anthriscus sylvestris*)
    Hedge (*Torilis japonica*)

Pennycress (*Thlaspi arvense*)
Pignut (*Conopodium majus*)
Pine, Corsican (*Pinus nigra*)
    Lodgepole (*P. contorta*)
    Maritime (*P. pinaster*)
    Monterey (*P. radiata*)
    Scots (*P. sylvestris*)
    Umbrella (*P. pinea*)
Plantain (*Plantago sp.*)
Poplar, Grey (*Populus canescens*)
    Lombardy (*P. nigra* var.
        italica)
    White (*P. alba*)
Poppy (*Papaver sp.*)
Primrose (*Primula vulgaris*)
Privet (*Ligustrum vulgare*)
Pulmonaria (*Pulmonaria officinalis*)
Purple Loosestrife (*Lythrum salicaria*)

Ramsons (*Allium ursinum*)
Red Campion (*Melandrium dioicum*)
Redwood (*Sequoia sempervirens*)
Rhododendron (*Rhododendron ponticum*)
Ribwort (*Plantago lanceolata*)
Rosebay (*Chamaenerion angustifolium*)
Rough Chervil (*Chaerophyllum
        temulentum*)
Rowan (*Sorbus aucuparia*)

Sallow (*Salix atrocinerea*)
Sanicle (*Sanicula europaea*)
Sedge, Pendulous (*Carex pendula*)
    Tussock (*C. paniculata*)
Sheep's Sorrel (*Rumex acetosella*)
Shepherd's Purse (*Capsella
        bursa-pastoris*)
Slender False Brome (*Brachypodium
        sylvaticum*)
Solomon's Seal (*Polygonatum
        multiflorum*)
Spiked Speedwell (*Veronica spicata*)
Spindle Tree (*Euonymus europaeus*)
Spring Gentian (*Gentiana verna*)
Spruce, Norway (*Picea abies*)
    Sitka (*P. sitchensis*)

Spurge Laurel (*Daphne laureola*)
Spurry (*Spergula arvensis*)
Stone Bramble (*Rubus saxatilis*)
Strawberry Tree (*Arbutus unedo*)
Sycamore (*Acer pseudoplatanus*)

Thistle, Melancholy (*Carduus
        heterophyllum*)
    Welted (*C. crispus*)
Tormentil (*Potentilla erecta*)
Traveller's Joy (*Clematis vitalba*)
Tree of Heaven (*Ailanthus altissima*)
Twinflower (*Linnaea borealis*)

Vetch, Horseshoe (*Hippocrepis comosa*)
Violet, Common Dog (*Viola riviniana*)
    Hairy (*V. hirta*)

Water Chestnut (*Trapa natans*)
Water Starwort (*Callitriche palustris*)
Wayfaring Tree (*Viburnum lantana*)
Western Hemlock (*Tsuga heterophylla*)
Western Red Cedar (*Thuja plicata*)
White Beam (*Sorbus aria*)
Wild Raspberry (*Rubus idaeus*)
Wild Rose (*Rosa canina*)
Wild Service Tree (*Sorbus torminalis*)
Wild Strawberry (*Fragaria vesca*)
Willow, Crack (*Salix fragilis*)
    Pussy (*S. caprea*)
Wintergreen (*Pyrola sp.*)
Wood Anemone (*Anemone nemorosa*)
Woodruff (*Galium odoratum*)
Woodrush, Great (*Luzula sylvatica*)
    Hairy (*L. pilosa*)
Wood Sage (*Teucrium scorodonia*)
Wood Sorrel (*Oxalis acetosella*)

Yellow Birdsnest (*Monotropa hypopitys*)
Yellow Dead Nettle (or Archangel)
        (*Galeobdolon luteum*)
Yellow Flag (*Iris pseudacorus*)
Yellow Pimpernel (*Lysimachia
        nemorum*)
Yew (*Taxus baccata*)

BIBLIOGRAPHY

ACLAND, Sir F. (1918). Final Report of the Forestry Sub-Committee, Ministry of Reconstruction. H.M.S.O. London.

ADAMS, M. C. (1966). Firecrests breeding in Hampshire. *Brit. Birds* 59: 240–6.

ALEXANDER, H. G., and HARTHAN, A. J. (1937). Redwings singing in November. *Brit. Birds* 30: 351–2.

ALEXANDER, W. B. (1946). The woodcock in the British Isles. *Ibis* 88: 1–24, 159–79, 271–86, 427–44.

ALTENKIRCH, W. (1965). Vogelschutz und Eichenwickler (*Tortrix viridana. L.*). *Z. angew. Zool.* 52: 197–244.

ANDREW, D. G. (1964). Birds in Ireland during 1960–62. *Brit. Birds* 57: 1–10.

ANDREW, R. J. (1957). A comparative study of the calls of *Emberiza* spp. (Buntings). *Ibis* 99: 27–42.

ANDREWARTHA, H. G., and BIRCH, L. C. (1954). *The distribution and abundance of animals*. Chicago.

APLIN, O. V. (1889). *The birds of Oxfordshire*. Oxford.

ARMSTRONG, E. A. (1954). The behaviour of birds in continuous daylight. *Ibis* 96: 1–30.

(1955). *The wren*. London.

(1963). *A study of bird song*. Oxford.

ASH, J. (1946). Barn owls roosting in conifers. *Brit. Birds* 39: 180.

AXELL, H. E. (1956). Predation and protection at Dungeness bird reserve. *Brit. Birds* 49: 193–212.

BALDWIN, S. P. (1960). Overwintering of woodpeckers in bark beetle-infested spruce-fir forests of Colorado. *Proc. 12 Orn. Congr.* 71–84.

BALDWIN, S. P., and KENDEIGH, S. C. (1938). Variations in the weights of birds. *Auk* 55: 416–67.

BARREAU, E. M. (1956). The crossbill invasion of Great Britain in 1953. *Brit. Birds* 49: 289–97.

BAXTER, E. V., and RINTOUL, L. J. (1953). *The birds of Scotland*. Edinburgh.

BETTS, M. M. (1955). The food of titmice in oak woodland. *Journ. Anim. Ecol.* 24: 282–323.

(1956). Further experiments with an artificial nestling gape. *Brit. Birds* 49: 213–15.

BEVAN, D. (1962). Starling roosts in woodland. *Quart. J. Forestry* 66: 59–62.

BEVEN, G. (1951). The bird population of an oakwood in Surrey (Eastern Wood, Bookham Common). *Lond. Nat.* 30: 57–72.

(1953). Further observations of the bird population of an oakwood in Surrey. *Lond. Nat.* 32: 51–77.

(1956). Further observations on the bird population of an oakwood in Surrey. *Lond. Nat.* 35: 21–32.

(1959). The feeding sites of birds in dense oakwood. *Lond. Nat.* 38: 64–73.

(1963). Population changes in a Surrey oakwood during fifteen years. *Brit. Birds* 56: 307–23.

(1963). Some additions and amendments to the check-list of birds of Bookham Common. *Lond. Nat.* 42: 98–100.

(1964). The feeding sites of birds in grassland with thick scrub. *Lond. Nat.* 43: 86–109.

(1965). The food of tawny owls in London. *London Bird Report* 29: 56–72.

(1966). "Birds" in Survey of Bookham Common. 25th Year. Progress Report for 1965. *Lond. Nat.* 45: 52–5.

(1967). "Birds" in Survey of Bookham Common. 26th Year. Progress Report for 1966. *Lond. Nat.* 46: 112–15.

BEWICK, T. (1804). *History of British Birds*. Newcastle.

BEZZEL, E. (1966). Blackcap imitating willow warbler's song. *Brit. Birds* 59: 502.

BLACKFORD, P. R. (1966). Song thrush imitating blackbird. *Brit. Birds* 59: 435.

BLAKE, A. R. M. (1959). The status and distribution of the nightjar in the West Midlands. *West Midland Bird Report* 25: 12–14.

BOASE, H. (1950). Calls of tawny owl. *Brit. Birds* 43: 86.

BOND, P. (1951). Timing the nightingale. *Field* 198: 695–6.

BORRER, W. (1891). *The birds of Sussex*. London.

BOSWALL, J. (1964). A discography of palaearctic bird sound recording. Special Supp. *Brit. Birds* 57.

(1966). New palaearctic bird sound recordings in 1964–65. *Brit. Birds* 59: 27–37.

BOURNE, W. R. P. (1952). Sub-song of magpie. *Brit Birds* 45: 405–6.

BOYD, A. W. (1949). Display of the tree sparrow. *Brit. Birds* 42: 213–14.

(1951). *A country parish*. London.

BREWER, R. (1963). Stability in bird populations. *Occ. Papers Adams Ctr. Ecol. Studies T. Kalamazoo, Michigan*. Pp. 1–12.

BROOKS, C. E. P. (1951). Geological and historical aspects of climate change. *Compendium of Meteorology* 1004–18. Boston (Mass.).

BROWN, E. P. (1963). The bird life of Holland Park. The effect of human interference. *London Bird Report* 26: 60–87.

BROWN, L. (1955). *Eagles*. London.

BROWN, P. E. (1957). The rarer birds of prey; their present status in the British Isles. Hobby. *Brit. Birds* 50: 149.

BROWN, P. E., DAVIES, M. G., and MYTUM, E. (1950). Duration of song of chiffchaff. *Brit. Birds* 43: 153–4.

BROWN, P., and WATERSTON, G. (1962). *The return of the osprey*. London.

BRUNS, H. (1960). The economic importance of birds in forests. *Bird Study* 7: 193–208.

BUCKNILL, J. A. (1900). *The birds of Surrey*. London.

Burns, P. S. (1957). Rook and jackdaw roosts around Bishop's Stortford. *Bird Study* 4: 62–71.

Buxton, J. (1950). *The redstart.* London.

Cadman, W. A. (1947). A Welsh raven roost. *Brit. Birds* 40: 209–10.

(1949). Distribution of black grouse in North Wales forests. *Brit. Birds* 42: 365–7.

Campbell, B. (1953). A comparison of bird populations upon "industrial" and "rural" farmland in South Wales. *Rep. Trans. Cardiff Nat. Soc.* 81: 4–65.

(1954–5). The breeding distribution and habitats of the pied flycatcher (*Muscicapa hypoleuca*) in Britain. *Bird Study* 1: 81–101; 2: 24–32, 179–91.

(1955). Crossbills. *Forestry Commission Leaflet,* 36. H.M.S.O. London.

(1957). The crested tit. *Forestry Commission Leaflet,* 41. H.M.S.O. London.

(1964). Birds and woodlands. *Forestry Commission Leaflet.* 47. H M.S.O. London.

(1964). Article "Nestboxes" in Thomson, A. L. (ed.). *New Dict. Birds.* London.

(1965). The British breeding distribution of the pied flycatcher. *Bird Study* 12: 305–18.

Campbell, J. W. (1957). The rarer birds of prey; their present status in the British Isles. Hen harrier. *Brit. Birds* 50: 143–6.

Carruthers, O. (1939). Cormorants roosting in trees in Dumfriesshire. *Brit. Birds* 33: 26–7.

Castell, C. P. (1958). The climate and vegetation of the London Area in prehistoric times. *Lond. Nat.* 38: 6–16.

(1959). The animal life of prehistoric London. *Lond. Nat.* 39: 5–16.

Chalke, S. H. (1954). Vertical zonation of some species of birds in oakwood (Eastern Wood, Bookham Common). *Lond. Nat.* 33: 47–51.

Chapman, W. M. M. (1939). Bird population of an Oxfordshire farm. *J. Anim. Ecol.* 8: 286–99.

Charlesworth, J. K. (1957). *The quaternary era, with special reference to its glaciation.* London.

Chessex, Ch., and Ribaut, J. P. (1966). Evolution d'une avifaune suburbaine et test d'une méthode de recensement. *Nos Oiseaux* 28: 193–211.

Chettleburgh, M. R. (1952). Observations on the collection and burial of acorns by jays in Hainault Forest. *Brit. Birds* 45: 359–64.

Clafton, F. R. (1959). Green sandpiper breeding in Inverness-shire. *Brit. Birds* 52: 430–2.

Clark, G. (1944). *Prehistoric England.* 3rd edition. London.

Cohen, E. (1961). *Nestboxes.* (British Trust for Ornithology Field Guide No. 3. Revised edition.) Oxford.

Collett, A. (1926). *The changing face of England.* London.

Colquhoun, M. K. (1940). The display and song of the turtle dove. *Brit. Birds* 33: 222–4.

(1940). Visual and auditory conspicuousness in a woodland bird community: a quantitative analysis. *Proc. Zool. Soc. Lond. A.* 110: 129–48.

(1940). The density of woodland birds determined by the sample count method. *J. Anim. Ecol.* 9: 53–67.

(1942). Notes on the social behaviour of blue tits. *Brit. Birds* 35: 234–6.

COLQUHOUN, M. K., and MORLEY, A. (1943). Vertical zonation in woodland bird communities. *J. Anim. Ecol.* 12: 75–81.

COMMITTEE OF THE LONDON NATURAL HISTORY SOCIETY. (1964). *The birds of the London area.* A new revised edition. London.

CONNOLD, E. T. (1908). *British oak galls.* London.

COOMBS, C. J. F. (1961). Rookeries and roosts of the rook and jackdaw in south-west Cornwall. Part 2. Roosting. *Bird Study* 8: 55–70.

COULSON, J. C. (1961). The post-fledging mortality of the blackbird in Great Britain. *Bird Study* 8: 89–97.

COUSENS, J. E. (1962). Notes on the status of the sessile and pedunculate oaks in Scotland and their identification. *Scot. For.* 16: 170–9.

COWARD, T. A. (1920). *The birds of the British Isles and their eggs.* London.

CRAMP, S. C. (1956). Summer in the Landes. *Bird Notes* 27: 113–17.

(1958). Territorial and other behaviour of the wood-pigeon. *Bird Study* 5: 55–66.

(1963). Toxic chemicals and birds of prey. *Brit. Birds* 56: 124–39.

CRAMP, S., CONDER, P. J., and ASH, J. S. (1962). *Death of birds and mammals from toxic chemicals, January–June 1961. The second report of the joint committee of the B.T.O. and R.S.P.B. on toxic chemicals, in collaboration with the game research association.*

CRAMP, S., PETTET, A., and SHARROCK, J. T. R. (1960). The irruption of tits in autumn 1957. *Brit. Birds* 53: 49–77.

CRAMP, S. C., and TEAGLE, W. G. (1952). The birds of Inner London, 1900–1950. *Brit. Birds* 45: 433–56.

CRAMP, S., and TEAGLE, W. G. (1952). A bird census of St James's Park and the Green Park, 1949–50. *London Bird Report* 15: 48–52.

CRAMP, S. C., and TOMLINS, A. D. (1966). The birds of Inner London, 1951–65. *Brit. Birds* 59: 209–32.

CRAWFORD, O. G. S., and KEILLER, A. (1928). *Wessex from the air.* Oxford.

CURIO, E. (1959). *Verhaltensstudien am Trauerschnäpper.* Berlin and Hamburg.

DANILIV, N. N. (1956). Measuring the accuracy of quantitative censuses of birds. (English summary). *Zool. Zh.* 35: 1697–1701.

DARBY, H. C. (1936). *An historical geography of England before A.D. 1800.* Cambridge.

DARE, P. J. (1962). Siskins breeding in Devon. *Brit. Birds* 55: 193–5.

DARLING, F. F., and BOYD, J. M. (1964). *The Highlands and Islands.* London.

DAVIES, P. W., and SNOW, D. W. (1965). Territory and food of the song thrush. *Brit. Birds* 58: 161–75.

DAVIES, S. J. J. F. (1958). The breeding of the meadow pipit in Swedish Lapland. *Bird Study* 5: 184–91.

DAVIS, P. (1964). Crossbills in Britain and Ireland in 1963. *Brit. Birds* 57: 477–501.

DES FORGES, G., and HARBER, D. D. (1963). A guide to the birds of Sussex.

DE WITT, J. B. (1955). Effect of chlorinated-hydrocarbon insecticides upon quail and pheasants. *J. Agric. Food Chem.* 3: 672–6.

(1956). Chronic toxicity to quail and pheasants of some chlorinated insecticides. *J. Agric. Food Chem.* 4: 863–6.

DIXON, C. (1909). *The bird life of London.* London.

DIXON, H. N. (1912). *Report on the mosses from the Arctic Bed, in Warren SH.*

DOBINSON, H. M., and RICHARDS, A. J. (1964). The effects of the severe winter of 1962/63 on birds in Britain. *Brit. Birds* 57: 373–434.

DUNNET, G. M. (1955). The breeding of the starling *Sturnus vulgaris* in relation to its food supply. *Ibis* 97: 619–62.

(1956). The autumn and winter mortality of starlings *Sturnus vulgaris* in relation to their food supply. *Ibis* 98: 220–30.

DURANGO, S. (1950). The influence of climate on the distribution of the red-backed shrike. *Fauna o. Flora* 46: 49–78.

(1956). Territory in the red-backed shrike. *Ibis* 98: 476–84.

D'URBAN, W. S. M., and MATTHEW, M. A. (1895). *The birds of Devon.* London.

EDLIN, H. L. (1956). *Trees, woods and man.* London.

(1958). *England's forests.* London.

(1960). *Wild life of wood and forest.* London.

(1965). *Know your conifers.* Forestry Commission Booklet 15. H.M.S.O. London.

EHRSTRÖM, C. (1954). Vinterfågelbeståndet i Sigtuna. *Vår Fågelvärld* 13: 76–83.

ELLIS, E. A. (1965). *The Broads.* London.

ELLIS, J. C. S. (1938). Effect of frost on distribution of the wood warbler. *Brit. Birds* 32: 116–17.

ELTON, C. S. (1935). A reconnaissance of woodland bird communities. *J. Anim. Ecol.* 4: 127–36.

(1958). *Ecology of invasions by animals and plants.* London.

(1966). *The pattern of animal communities.* London.

EMLEN, J. T. (1956). A method for describing and comparing avian habitats. *Ibis* 98: 565–76.

ENEMAR, A. (1959). On the determination of the size and composition of a passerine bird population during the breeding season. *Vår Fågelvärld* 18: suppl. 2.

(1962). A comparison between the bird census results of different ornithologists. *Vår Fågelvärld* 21: 109–20.

ENGLAND, M. D. (1951). Large roost of bramblings. *Brit. Birds* 44: 386.

FALCONER, D. S. (1941). Observations on the singing of the chaffinch. *Brit. Birds* 35: 98–104.

F.A.O. Forestry Mission to Ireland (1951). Proposed revision of Irish afforestation programme. February 15, 1951. *M.F.A.O./57/51.*

FERGUSON-LEES, I. J. (1946). Song of female greenfinch. *Brit. Birds* 39: 244.

(1957). The rarer birds of prey: their present status in the British Isles. *Peregrine. Brit. Birds* 50: 149–55.

(1968). Serins breeding in southern England. *Brit. Birds* 61: 87–8.

FINNIS, R. G. (1960). Road casualties among birds. *Bird Study* 7: 21–32.

FISHER, J. (1940). *Watching Birds.* London.

(1966). *The Shell bird book.* London.

FISHER, J. (ed.) (1967). *Thorburn's birds.* London.

FISHER, J., and PETERSON, R. T. (1964). *The world of birds.* London.

FISHER, J., *et al.* (1948). Rook investigation. *J. Min. Agric.* 55: 20–23.

FITTER, R. S. R. (1945). *London's natural history.* London.

(1949). *London's birds.* London.

FITZPATRICK, H. M. (ed.) (1966). *The forests of Ireland.*

FLÖSSNER, D. (1962). Die vogelgemeinschaft eines traubeneichen-buchen-waldes im norden der mark Brandenburg. *Beitr. Vogelkunde* 10: 148–75..

FORESTRY COMMISSION. (1943). *Report on post war forest policy.* H.M.S.O. London.

(1952–3). *Census Reports: No. 1 Census of woodlands 1947–1949: Woodlands of five acres and over. No. 2 Hedgerow and park timber and woods under five acres 1951. No. 3 Census of woodlands 1947–1949: Woods of five acres and over: Welsh county details. No. 4 Census of woodlands 1947–1949: Woods of five acres and over: Scottish county details. No. 5 Census of woodlands 1947–1949: Woods of five acres and over: English county details.* H.M.S.O. London.

(1961). *Guide to the New Forest.* H.M.S.O. London.

FORREST, H. E. (1899). *The fauna of Shropshire.*

FOSTER, J., and GODFREY, C. (1950). A study of the British willow tit. *Brit. Birds* 43: 351–61.

FREIBERGER. (1926–7). Zur vogelschutzfrage, inbesondere zur wissenschaftlichen begründung des wirtschaftlichen vogelschutzes. *Allg. Forst-u. Jagdzg.*

FRENZEL, B., and TROLL, C. (1952). Die vegetationszonen des nördlichen Eurasiens während der letzen eiszeit. *Eiszeitalter u. Gegenwart* 2: 154–67.

GAUSE, G. F. (1934). *The Struggle for existence.* Baltimore.

GIBB, J. (1950). The breeding biology of the great and blue titmice. *Ibis* 92: 507–39.

(1954). Population changes of titmice, 1947–1951. *Bird Study* 1: 40–8.

(1954). Feeding ecology of tits, with notes on treecreeper and goldcrest. *Ibis* 96: 513–43.

(1958). Predation by tits and squirrels on the eucosmid *Ernarmonia conicolana* (Heyl.). *J. Anim. Ecol.* 27: 375–96.

(1960). Population of tits and goldcrests and their food supply in pine plantations. *Ibis* 102: 163–208.

(1966). Tit predation and the abundance of *Ernarmonia conicolana* (Heyl.) on Weeting Heath, Norfolk, 1962–63. *J. Anim. Ecol.* 35: 43–53.

GIBB, J. A., and BETTS, M. M. (1963). Food and food supply of nestling tits (*Paridae*) in Breckland pine. *J. Anim. Ecol.* 32: 489–533.

GILMOUR, J., and WALTER, M. (1962). *Wild flowers.* London.

GLEGG, W. E. (1935). *A history of the birds of Middlesex.* London.

GODFREY, J. F., and GODFREY, C. (1950). A study of the British willow tit. *Brit. Birds* 43: 351–61.

GODWIN, H. (1934). Pollen analysis. *New Phytol.* 33: 278–305.

(1934). *Pollen analysis of peats from Scolt Head Island.* (ed.) Steers. Norwich.

(1935). In discussion on the origin and relationships of the British flora. *Proc. Roy. Soc. B.* 118: 210–15.

(1938). British forests in prehistoric times in *The New Naturalist*: a summary of British natural history.

GOMPERTZ, T. (1961). The vocabulary of the great tit. *Brit. Birds* 54: 369–94, 409–18.

GOODACRE, M. J., and LACK, D. (1959). Early breeding in 1957. *Brit. Birds* 52: 74–83.

GOODBODY, I. M. (1952). The post-fledging dispersal of juvenile titmice. *Brit. Birds* 45: 279–85.

GOODWIN, D. (1948). Notes on wood pigeon. *Brit. Birds* 41: 123–4.

(1949). Notes on voice and display of the jay. *Brit. Birds* 42: 278–87.

(1951). Some aspects of behaviour of the jay (*Garrulus glandarius*). Part 2. *Ibis* 93: 602–25.

(1952). Notes and display of the magpie. *Brit. Birds* 45: 113–22.

(1953). Jays nesting in hollow trees. *Brit. Birds* 46: 113.

(1956). Further observations on the behaviour of the jay (*Garrulus glandarius*). *Ibis* 98: 211–13.

(1964). Linnets and housesparrows feeding on birch seed. *Brit. Birds* 57: 82–3.

GORDON, S. (1927). *Days with the golden eagle.* London.

(1951). *The charm of the hills.* London.

(1955). *The golden eagle.* London.

GRACZYK, R. (1959). Forschungen über des auftreten und den quantitativen stand der amsel (*Turdus merula L.*) in Polen. Ekolesin Polska (A) 7: 55–82.

HAARTMAN, L. v. (1951). Der trauerfliegenschnäpper. Acta Zool. Fenn 67. Pp. 60.

(1956). Territory in the pied flycatcher *Muscicapa hypoleuca*. *Ibis* 98: 460–75.

(1957). Adaptation in hole-nesting birds. *Evolution* 11: 339–47.

HÄHNLE, H. (1946). *Das schutzgebiet Behr-Steckby (Anhalt) des reichsbundes für vogelschutz.* Giengen (Brenz).

HALL-CRAGGS, J. (1962). The development of song in the blackbird *Turdus merula*. *Ibis* 104: 277–300.

HANSEN, L. (1952). The diurnal and annual rhythm of the tawny owl (*Strix aluco L.*) Dansk. orn. Foren. Tidsskr. 46: 158–72.

HARRIS, M. P. (1962). Weights from five hundred birds found dead on Skomer Island in January 1962. *Brit. Birds* 55: 97–103.

HARRISON, C. J. O., and FORSTER, J. (1959). Woodlark territories. *Bird Study* 6: 60–8.

HARTHAN, A. J. (n.d.) *The birds of Worcestershire.* Worcester.

HARTING, J. E. (1866). *The birds of Middlesex*. London.

(1899). *A handbook of British birds*. London.

HARTLEY, P. H. T. (1946). Unusual forms of chaffinch song. *Brit. Birds* 39: 23–4.

(1953). An ecological study of the feeding habits of the English titmice. *J. Anim. Ecol.* 22: 261–88.

(1954). Wild fruits in the diet of British thrushes. A study in the ecology of closely allied species. *Brit. Birds* 47: 97–107.

HARTSHORNE, C. (1958). The relation of bird-song to music. *Ibis* 100: 421–45.

HAVLIN, J. (1963). Breeding density in the blackbird, *Turdus merula* Linn. *Zool. Listy* 12: 1–18.

(1963). Reproduction in the blackbird (*Turdus merula* L.) *Zool. Listy* 12: 195–216.

HAWKINS, H. E. L. (1953). A pinnacle of chalk penetrating the Eocene on the floor of a buried river-channel at Ashford Hill near Newbury, Berkshire. *Quart. J. Geol. Soc.* 108: 233.

HENDY, E. W. (1946). *Wild Exmoor through the year*. London.

HENSLEY, M. M., and COPE, J. B. (1951). Further data on removal and repopulation of the breeding birds in a spruce-fir forest community. *Auk* 68: 483–93.

HEREFORDSHIRE ORNITHOLOGICAL CLUB. (1966). *Annual Report for 1965*.

HINDE, R. A. (1952). The behaviour of the great tit (*Parus major*) and some other related species. *Behaviour, Suppl. 2, Leiden*.

(1959). Behaviour and speciation in birds and lower vertebrates. *Biol. Rev.* 34: 85–128.

HOFFMAN, H. J. (1951). Green and great spotted woodpeckers occupying the same hole. *Brit. Birds* 44: 282–3.

HOLT, E. G. (1966). Redwings breeding in Sutherland. *Brit. Birds* 59: 500–1.

HOLYOAK, D. (1967). Breeding biology of the Corvidae. *Bird Study* 14: 153–68.

HOWARD, H. E. (1907–14). *The British warblers*. London.

HUDSON, W. H. (1900). *Nature in Downland*. London.

(1909). *Afoot in England*. London.

HUNT, K. B. (1960). Song bird breeding populations in DDT-sprayed Dutch elm disease communities. *J. Wildlife Manag.* 24: 139–46.

HURRELL, H. G. (1956). A raven roost in Devon. *Brit. Birds* 49: 28–31.

HUXLEY, J. S. (1934). A natural experiment on the territorial instinct. *Brit. Birds* 27: 270–7.

(1947). Song variants in the yellowhammer. *Brit. Birds* 40: 162–4.

(1956). Abnormal song of willow warbler. *Brit. Birds* 49: 154.

HUXLEY, J. S., and BROWN, P. E. (1953). The song of the wood pigeon. *Brit. Birds* 46: 399–404.

JACKSON, R. D. (1954). Territory and pair-formation in the blackbird. *Brit. Birds* 47: 123–31.

JARDINE, W. (1839). *The natural history of the birds of Great Britain and Ireland*. Edinburgh, London.

JENNINGS, A. R. (1960). The major causes of death of wild birds in Great Britain. *Proc. 12 Int. Orn. Congr.* 353–7.

JESSEN, K. (1935). The composition of the forests in northern Europe in epi-palaeolithic time. *K. Dansk vidensk. Selsk. Biol. Med. 12.*

JOHNSTON, D. W., and ODUM, E. P. (1956). Breeding bird populations in relation to plant succession on the Piedmont of Georgia. *Ecology* 37: 50–62.

JONES, E. W. (1959). Biological flora of the British Isles: *Quercus* L. *J. Ecol.* 47: 169–222.

JONES, P. H. (1966). Effects of consecutive, contrasting winters on the bird population of an Anglesey pine plantation. *Bird Study* 13: 77–83.

(1966). The bird population succession at Newborough Warren. *Brit. Birds* 59: 180–90.

KENDALL, W. B. (1907). *The birds of Willesden.* Unpublished MS in Willesden Public Library, Brent.

KENNEDY, P. G., RUTTLEDGE, R. F., SCROOPE, C. F., and HUMPHREYS, G. R. (1954). *The birds of Ireland.*

KENT, A. K. (1964). The breeding habitats of the reed bunting and yellow-hammer in Nottinghamshire. *Bird Study* 11: 123–7.

KEVEN, D. K. McE. (1962). *Soil Animals.* London.

KIRKMAN, F. B., and HUTCHINSON, H. G. (1936). *British sporting birds.* London.

KLUYVER, H. N. (1938). The importance of the starling in agriculture. *Proc. 8 Int. Orn. Congr.* 720–5.

(1951). The population ecology of the great tit: *Parus m. major* L. *Ardea* 39: 1–135.

KLUYVER, H. N., and TINBERGEN, L. (1953). Territory and the regulation of density in titmice. *Arch. Nederland. Zool.* 10: 265–89.

KOROLJKOWA, C. E. (1956). Die bedeutung der vögel bei der vernichtung von in Massen auftretenden schadinsekten. *Soob. Inst. Lesa,* 2: 65–106.

KUHNELT, W. (1961). *Soil biology.*

LACK, D. (1933). Habitat selection in birds with special reference to the effects of afforestation on the Breckland avifauna. *J. Anim. Ecol.* 2: 239–62.

(1937). The psychological factor in bird distribution. *Brit. Birds* 31: 130–6.

(1939). The display of the blackcock. *Brit. Birds* 32: 290–303.

(1939). Further changes in the Breckland avifauna caused by afforestation. *J. Anim. Ecol.* 8: 277–85.

(1943). *The life of the robin.* London.

(1944). Ecological aspects of species formation in passeriform birds. *Ibis* 86: 260–86.

(1946). Clutch and brood size in the robin. *Brit. Birds* 39: 98–109, 130–5.

(1950). The breeding seasons of European birds. *Ibis* 92: 288–316.

(1954). *The natural regulation of animal numbers.* Oxford.

(1955). British tits (*Parus* spp.) in nesting boxes. *Ardea* 43: 50–84.

(1958). A qualitative study of British tits. *Ardea* 46: 91–124.

(1963). Cuckoo hosts in England. *Bird Study* 10: 185–201.

(1964). A long-term study of the great tit (*Parus major*). *J. Anim. Ecol.* 33 (Jubilee Suppl.). 159–73.

358   BIBLIOGRAPHY

(1964). Article "Population dynamics" in Thomson, A. L. (ed.) *New Dict. Birds*. London.

(1966). *Population studies of birds*. Oxford.

(1968). *Ecological adaptations for breeding in birds*. London.

LACK, D., and LACK, E. (1951). Further changes in bird life caused by afforestation. *J. Anim. Ecol.* 20: 173–9.

(1958). The nesting of the long-tailed tit. *Bird Study* 5: 1–19.

LACK, D., GIBB, J., and OWEN, D. F. (1957). Survival in relation to brood-size in tits. *Proc. Zool. Soc. Lond.* 128: 313–26.

LACK, D., and SOUTHERN, H. N. (1949). *Birds on Tenerife*.

LACK, D., and VENABLES, L. S. V. (1939). The habitat distribution of British woodland birds. *J. Anim. Ecol.* 8: 39–71.

LANCUM, F. H. (1946). Greenfinch singing at night. *Brit. Birds* 39: 78.

LIND, H. (1955). Bidtrag til solsortens (Turdus m. merula (L.)- biologi. *Dansk Orn. Foren. Tidsskr.* 49: 76–113 (Danish with English summary).

LLOYD, J. D. (1947). Redwing nesting in Sutherland. *Brit. Birds* 40: 277–8.

LLOYD, M. (1964). Article "Statistical significance" in Thomson, A. L. (ed.). *New Dict. Birds*. London.

LOCKE, G. M. (1962). A sample survey of field and other boundaries in Great Britain. *Quar. J. Forest.* 56: 137–44.

LOCKIE, J. D. (1955). The breeding habits and food of short-eared owls after a vole plague. *Bird Study* 2: 53–69.

(1955). The breeding and feeding of jackdaws and rooks with notes on carrion crows and other *Corvidae*. *Ibis* 97: 341–69.

LOCKIE, J. D., and RATCLIFFE, D. A. (1964). Insecticides and Scottish golden eagles. *Brit. Birds* 57: 89–101.

LOFTS, B., MURTON, R. K., and WESTWOOD, N. J. (1967). Photoresponses of the woodpigeon *Columba palumbus* in relation to the breeding season. *Ibis* 109: 338–51.

LÖHRL, H. (1958). Das verhalten des kleibers. *Z. Tierpsychol.* 15: 191–252.

LONG, D. A. C. (1950). Concealment of food by coal tit. *Brit. Birds* 43: 335–6.

LØPPERTHIN, B. (1955). Some isolated bird-populations and their possible origin. *Acta 11 Congr. Int. Orn.*

LOWE, F. A. (1954). *The heron*. London.

LUMSDEN, H. G. (1961). The display of the capercaillie. *Brit. Birds* 54: 257–72.

LUNDEVALL, C-L. (1952). The bird fauna in the Abisko national park and its surroundings. *Kungl. Svenska Vetenskapsakademiens Avhandlingar i Naturskyddsärenden* No. 7.

MACARTHUR, R. H. (1964). Article "Ecology" in Thomson, A. L. (ed.). *New Dict. Birds*. London.

MACKENZIE, J. M. D. (1945). The preference shown by birds for different species of trees in plantations. *Forestry* 19: 99–112.

(1950). Competition for nest sites among hole breeding species. *Brit. Birds* 43: 184–5.

(1957). Treecreepers roosting in Wellingtonias. *Bird Study* 4: 94–7.

(1959). Roosting of treecreepers. *Bird Study* 6: 8–14.

MACLELLAN, C. R. (1958). Role of woodpeckers in control of the codling moth in Nova Scotia. *Can. Entom.* 90: 18–22.

MADGE, D. (1966). How leaf litter disappears. Article in *New Scientist*, 20th October, 1966.

MAGEE, J. D. (1965). The breeding distribution of the stonechat in Britain and the causes of its decline. *Bird Study* 12: 83–9.

MANLEY, G. (1952). *Climate and the British scene*. London.

(1953). The mean temperature of central England 1698–1952. *Quart. J. Roy. Meteorol. Soc.* 79: 242–61.

MANNS, L. (1967). Leaf litter fauna in the ecology of ground-feeding birds. *Lond. Nat.* 46: 116–25.

MANSFELD, K. (1956). Zur vertilgung behaarter raupen durch singvögel. *Waldhygiene* 1: 160–4.

MARLER, P. (1952). Variation in the song of the chaffinch *Fringilla coelebs*. *Ibis* 94: 458–72.

(1956). The behaviour of the chaffinch *Fringilla coelebs*. *Behaviour* (Suppl.) 5: 1–184.

(1956). The voice of the chaffinch and its function as language. *Ibis* 98: 231–61.

(1956). The voice of the chaffinch. *New Biol.* 20: 70–87.

(1959). Developments in the study of animal communication. In *Darwin's Biological work; some aspects reconsidered*. Ed. P. R. Bell. 150–206. Cambridge.

MARSHALL, A. J. (1959). Internal and environmental control of breeding. *Ibis* 101: 456–78.

MARSHALL, R. V. A. (1961). Blackbird population imitating human whistle. *Brit. Birds* 54: 248–9.

MARTIN, N. D. (1960). An analysis of bird populations in relation to forest succession in Algonquin Provincial Park, Ontario. *Ecology* 41: 126–40.

MATHESON, C. (1963). The pheasant in Wales. *Brit. Birds* 56: 452–6.

MATTHEWS, J. R. (1955). *The origin and distribution of the British flora*. London.

MAY, D. J. (1947). Observations on the territory and breeding behaviour of the willow warbler. *Brit. Birds* 40: 2–11.

(1949). Studies on a community of willow warblers. *Ibis* 91: 25–54.

McVEAN, D. N., and RATCLIFFE, D. A. (1962). Plant communities of the Scottish Highlands: a study of Scottish mountain, moorland and forest vegetation. *Monographs of the Nature Conservancy*, 1. H.M.S.O. London.

MEIKLEJOHN, M. F. M. (1952). Habitat of chiffchaff in Scotland. *Scot. Nat.* 64: 114–16.

MEINERTZHAGEN, R. (1964). Article "Palaearctic Region" in Thomson, A. L. (ed.) *New Dict. Birds*. London.

MELCHER, R. (1951). Zaunammerbeobachtungen in Glarnerland, Churer Rheintal und Unterengadin. *Orn. Beob.* 48: 122–35.

MELLANBY, K. (1967). *Pesticides and pollution*. London.

MELLUISH, W. D. (1960). Recent changes in the bird population of grassland with encroaching scrub at Bookham Common. *Lond. Nat.* 39: 89–98.

MERIKALLIO, E. (1958). *Finnish Birds. Their distribution and numbers.* Fauna Fennica 5.

MESSMER, E., and MESSMER, I. (1956). Die entwicklung der lautäusserungen und einiger verhaltensweisen der amsel (*Turdus merula merula* L.) unter naturlichen bedingungen und nach einzelaufzucht in schalldichten raumen. *Z. Tierpsychol.* 13: 341–441.

MEUNIER, K. (1960). Grundsätzliches zur populationsdynamik der vögel. *Z. wiss. Zool.* 163: 397–445.

MILLS, D. H. (1962). The goosander and red-breasted merganser in Scotland. *Wildfowl Trust, 13th Ann. Rep.* 79–92.

MINISTER FOR LANDS IN THE REPUBLIC OF IRELAND. (1967). *Report on forestry for the period from 1st April, 1964 to 31st March, 1966.* S.O. Dublin.

MINISTRY OF AGRICULTURE, NORTHERN IRELAND (n.d.). *Forestry in Northern Ireland.* H.M.S.O. Belfast.

MONK, J. F. (1954). The breeding biology of the greenfinch. *Bird Study* 1: 2–14.

—— (1963). The past and present status of the wryneck in the British Isles. *Bird Study* 10: 112–32.

MOORE, N. W. (1957). The past and present status of the buzzard in the British Isles. *Brit. Birds* 50: 173–97.

—— (1962). Toxic chemicals and birds; the ecological background to conservation problems. *Brit. Birds* 55: 428–35.

—— (1962). The heaths of Dorset and their conservation. *J. Ecol.* 50: 369–91.

—— (1965). Pesticides and birds – a review of the situation in Great Britain in 1965. *Bird Study* 12: 222–52.

MOORE, N. W., HOOPER, M. D., and DAVIS, B. N. K. (1967). Hedges: 1. Introduction and reconnaissance studies. *J. Appl. Ecol.* 4: 201–20.

MOREAU, R. E. (1954). The main vicissitudes of the European avifauna since the Pliocene. *Ibis* 96: 411–31.

—— (1955). The bird-geography of Europe in the last glaciation. *Acta 11 Congr. Int. Orn.* 401–5.

MORLEY, A. (1940). Recolonisation by bird species on burnt woodland. *J. Anim. Ecol.* 9: 84–8.

—— (1953). Field observations on the biology of the marsh tit. *Brit. Birds* 46: 233–8, 273–87, 332–46.

MOUNTFORT, G. (1957). *The hawfinch.* London.

—— (1959). Great spotted woodpeckers killing nestling tits. *Brit. Birds* 52: 270–1.

—— (1962). Further notes on great spotted woodpeckers attacking nestboxes. *Brit. Birds* 55: 43–4.

MÜHLETHALER, F. (1952). Beobachtungen am bergfinken – Schlafplatz bei Thun 1950–51. *Orn. Beob.* 49: 173–82.

MUNSON, P. T. (1950). Note on the soaring flight of the reed bunting, with call and song. *Brit. Birds* 43: 222.

MURRAY, J. M. (1935). An outline of the history of forestry in Scotland up to the end of the nineteenth century. *Scot. For. Journ.* 49.

MURTON, R. K. (1965). *The wood pigeon*. London.

MURTON, R. K., WESTWOOD, N. J., and ISAACSON, A. J. (1964). A preliminary investigation of the factors regulating population size in the wood pigeon, *Columba palumbus*. *Ibis* 106: 482–507.

(1965). The feeding habits of the wood pigeon *Columba palumbus*, stock dove *C. oenas* and turtle dove *Streptopelia turtur*. *Ibis* 106: 174–88.

MYRES, M. T. (1955). The breeding of blackbird, song thrush and mistle thrush in Great Britain. Part 1. Breeding seasons. *Bird Study* 2: 2–24.

NEAL, E. G. (1953). *Woodland ecology*. London.

NETHERSOLE-THOMPSON, D. (1951). *The greenshank*. London.

(1966). *The snow bunting*. London.

NEWTON, I. (1960). The diet and feeding habits of the bullfinch. *Bird Study* 7: 1–9.

(1964). The breeding biology of the chaffinch. *Bird Study* 11: 47–68.

(1967). The adaptive radiation and feeding ecology of some British finches. *Ibis* 109: 33–96.

NICHOLLS, H. G. (1858). *The forest of Dean, a description and historical account.*

NICHOLSON, A. J. (1933). The balance of animal populations. *J. Anim. Ecol.* 2: 132–78.

NICHOLSON, E. M. (1951). *Birds and men*. London.

NICHOLSON, E. M., and KOCH, L. (1937). *Songs of wild birds*. London.

NICOLAI, J. (1956). Zur biologie und ethologie des gimpfels (*Pyrrhula pyrrhula* L.) *Z. Tierpsychol.* 13: 93–132.

NIETHAMMER, G. (1937). *Handbuch der deutschen vogelkunde.*

NOBLE, G. K. (1939). The role of dominance in the social life of birds. *Auk* 56: 263–73.

NORRIS, C. A. (1960). The breeding distribution of thirty bird species in 1952. *Bird Study* 7: 129–84.

NORTH, M. E. W. (1950). Transcribing bird-song. *Ibis* 92: 99–114.

NORTH, M., and SIMMS, E. (1958). *Witherby's Sound Guide to British Birds*. London.

NOVIKOV, G. A. (1960). Geographical variation in the density of forest birds in the European part of the U.S.S.R. and adjacent countries. *Zool. Zh.* 39: 433–7. (Russian with English summary.)

OLNEY, P. (1966). Berries and birds. *Birds* 1: 98–9.

ORIANS, G. H. (1962). Natural selection and ecological theory. *Amer. Nat.* 96: 257–63.

OWEN, D. F. (1954). The winter weights of titmice. *Ibis* 96: 299–309.

(1956). The food of nestling jays and magpies. *Bird Study* 4: 257–65.

(1959). The breeding season and clutch size of the rook *Corvus frugilegus*. *Ibis* 101: 235–9.

OWEN, J. H. (1945). Unusual feeding behaviour of tits. *Brit. Birds* 38: 173.

362   BIBLIOGRAPHY

PALMAR, C. E. (1965). The capercailzie. *Forestry Commission Leaflet*, 37. H.M.S.O. London.

—— (1966). Titmice in woodlands. *Forestry Commission Leaflet* 46. H.M.S.O. London.

—— (1968). Blackgame. *Forestry Commission: Forest Record No. 66*. H.M.S.O. London.

PARSLOW, J. L. F. (1967–8). Changes in status among breeding birds in Britain and Ireland. *Brit. Birds* 60: 2–47, 97–123, 177–202, 261–85, 396–404, 493–508: 61: 49–64, 241–55.

PAYN, W. H. (1962). *The birds of Suffolk*.

PEAKALL, D. B. (1962). The past and present status of the red-backed shrike in Great Britain. *Bird Study* 9: 198–216.

PEARSALL, W. H. (1950). *Mountains and moorland*. London.

PENNIE, I. D. (1946). Common gulls nesting on birch trees. *Brit. Birds* 39: 61.

—— (1950–1). The history and distribution of the capercailzie in Scotland. *Scot. Nat.* 62: 67–87, 157–78; 63: 4–17, 135.

PERRINS, C. M. (1963). Survival in the great tit, *Parus major. Proc. Int. Orn. Congr.* 13: 717–28.

—— (1965). Population fluctuations and clutch size in the great tit, *Parus major. J. Anim. Ecol.* 34: 601–47.

—— (1966). The effect of beech crops on great tit populations and movements. *Brit. Birds* 59: 419–32.

PERRY, R. (1948). *In the high Grampians*. London.

PETERSON, R., and FISHER, J. (1956). *Wild America*. London.

PEUS, F. (1951). Nüchterne analyse der massenvermehrung der misteldrossel (*Turdus viscivorus* L.) in nordwesteuropa. *Bonn Zool. Beitr.* 2: 55–82.

PFEIFER, S., and KEIL, W. (1958). Versuche zur steigerung der siedlungsdichte höhlen-und freibrütender vogelarten und ernährungsbiologische untersuchungen an nestlingen einiger singvogelarten in einem schadgebiet der eichenwicklers (*Tortrix viridana* L.) im osten von Frankfurt am Main. *Biol. Abhandl.* Pp. 52.

PHEMISTER, J. (1960). Scotland: the northern Highlands. *British Regional Geography*. H.M.S.O. London.

POTTS, G. R. (1967). Urban starling roosts in the British Isles. *Bird Study* 14: 25–42.

POULSEN, H. (1951). Inheritance and learning in the song of the chaffinch, *Fringilla coelebs* L. *Behaviour* 3: 216–28.

PRESST, I. (1965). An enquiry into the recent breeding status of the smaller birds-of-prey and crows in Britain. *Bird Study* 12: 196–221.

PRICE, M. P. (1934). A census of nightingales in Gloucestershire. *Brit. Birds* 28: 82–3.

—— (1938). Disappearance of wood warbler in Gloucester and Buckingham. *Brit. Birds* 32: 117.

—— (1961). Warbler fluctuations in oak woodland in the Severn valley. *Brit. Birds* 54: 100–6.

RATCLIFFE, D. A. (1962). Breeding density in the peregrine *Falco peregrinus* and raven *Corvus corax*. *Ibis* 104: 13–39.

(1965). Organo-chlorine residues in some raptor and corvid eggs from northern Britain. *Brit. Birds* 58: 65–81.

(1965). The peregrine situation in Great Britain 1963–64. *Bird Study* 12: 66–82.

(1967). The peregrine situation in Great Britain 1965–66. *Bird Study* 14: 238–46.

READ, H. H. (1949). *Geology*. Home University Library. London.

READ, H. H., and WATSON, J. (1963). *Introduction to geology. Vol. 1. Principles*. London.

RIBAUT, J-P, (1964). Dynamique d'une population de merles noirs, *Turdus merula* L.

RICHARDS, E. G. (1952). Song of female blackcap. *Brit. Birds* 45: 31.

RICHARDS, T. J. (1949). Concealment of food by nuthatch, coal tit and marsh tit. *Brit. Birds* 42: 360–1.

(1958). Concealment and recovery of food by birds with some relevant observations on squirrels. *Brit. Birds* 51: 497–508.

RICHARDSON, R. A. (1947). Courtship feeding of greenfinch and song of female. *Brit. Birds* 40: 307.

ROBERTSON, A. W. P. (1949). Subsong of female blackbird. *Brit. Birds* 42: 388–9.

(1954). *Bird pageant*. London.

ROLLIN, N. (1958). Late season singing of yellowhammer. *Brit. Birds* 51: 290–303.

ROYAMA, T. (1960). The theory and practice of line transects in animal ecology by means of visual and auditory recognition. *Misc. Rep. Yamashina Inst. Orn. Zool.* 35: 1–17.

(1966). A re-interpretation of courtship feeding. *Bird Study* 13: 116–29.

RUDD, R. L. (1964). *Pesticides and the living landscape*.

RUDEBECK, G. (1950–1). The choice of prey and modes of hunting of predatory birds with special reference to their selective effect. *Oikos* 2: 65–88; 3: 200–31.

RUTTLEDGE, R. F. (1961). *Ireland's birds*. London.

SAGE, B. (1963). The breeding distribution of the tree sparrow. *London Bird Report* 27: 56–65.

SALISBURY, E. J. (1918). The ecology of scrub in Hertfordshire. *Trans. Herts. Nat. Hist. Soc.*

(1961). *Weeds and aliens*. London.

SALMON, H. M. (1957). The rarer birds of prey; their present status in the British Isles. Kite. *Brit. Birds* 50: 137–41.

SALOMONSEN, F. (1948). The distribution of birds and the recent climatic change in the North Atlantic area. *Dansk. Orn. For. Tidsk.* 42: 85–99.

SAMMALISTO, L. (1957). The effect of the woodland-open peatland edge on some peatland birds in South Finland. *Orn. Fenn.* 34: 81–9.

SANDEMAN, P. W. (1955). The old Caledonian forest. *Bird Notes* 26: 174–5.

SANGAR, O. J. (1954). *The Chiltern project*. A paper presented to the Forestry Sub-Section, British Association Meeting, Oxford, 1954.

SAUER, F. (1954). Die entwicklung der lautäusserungen von ei ab schalldict gehalten grasmücken (*Sylvia communis* Latham). *Z. Tierpsychol.* 11: 10–93.

(1955). Uber variationen der artgesänge bei grasmücken. *J. Orn.* 96: 129–46.

SAUNDERS, H. (1899). *An illustrated manual of British birds.* 2nd Ed. London.

SCHUSTER, L. (1950). Uber den sammeltrieb des eichelhähers (*Garrulus glandarius*) *Vogelwelt* 71 (1); 9–17.

SCHÜTTE, F. (1956). Eichenwickler, waldameisen und vögel. *Waldhygiene* 1: 215–19.

SEEL, D. C. (1964). An analysis of the nest record cards of the tree sparrow. *Bird Study* 11: 265–71.

SELLAR, P. J. (1947). Crested tits in North Banffshire. *Brit. Birds* 40: 116.

SILVA, E. T. (1949). Nest records of the song thrush. *Brit. Birds* 42: 97–111.

SIMMS, E. (1952). *Bird migrants.* London.

(1957). *Voices of the wild.* London.

(1962). A study of suburban bird-life at Dollis Hill. *Brit. Birds* 55: 1–36.

(1965). Effects of the cold weather of 1962/63 on the blackbird population at Dollis Hill. *Brit. Birds* 58: 33–43.

SIMPSON, A. W. (1964). Some aspects of forestry in Northern Ireland since 1922 compared with those in Great Britain and Eire. *Quar. J. Forestry.* 58: 4: 287–301.

SMITH, B. D. (1966). Effects of parasites and predators on a natural population of the aphid (*Acyrthosiphon spartii*) (Koch) on broom (*Sarothamnus scoparius.* L.). *J. Anim. Ecol.* 35: 255–67.

SMITH, F. R., *et al.* (1967). Report on rare birds in Great Britain in 1966 (with 1964 and 1965 additions). *Brit. Birds* 60: 309–38.

SNOW, D. W. (1952). The winter avifauna of arctic Lapland. *Ibis* 94: 133–43.

(1954). The habitats of Eurasian tits (*Parus* spp.). *Ibis* 96: 565–85.

(1955). The breeding of blackbird, song thrush and mistle thrush in Great Britain. Part 3. Nesting success. *Bird Study* 4: 169–78.

(1956). Territory in the blackbird *Turdus merula. Ibis* 98: 438–47.

(1958). The breeding of the blackbird *Turdus merula* at Oxford. *Ibis* 100: 1–30.

(1958). *A study of blackbirds.* London.

(1966). The migration and dispersal of British blackbirds. *Bird Study* 13: 237–55.

(1966). The population dynamics of the blackbird. *Nature* No. 5055 (17th September). London.

(1967). Population changes of some common birds in gardens. *Brit. Birds* 60: 339–41.

SNOW, D. W., and MAYER-GROSS, H. (1967). Farmland as a nesting habitat. *Bird Study* 14: 43–52.

SOUTHERN, H. N. (1954). Tawny owls and their prey. *Ibis* 96: 384–410.

(1959). Mortality and population control. *Ibis* 101: 429–36.

SOUTHERN, H. N., and MORLEY, A. (1950). Marsh tit territories over six years. *Brit. Birds* 43: 33–45.

SOUTHERN, H. N., and VENABLES, L. S. V. (1939). Habitat selection among birds in a Lapland birchwood. *J. Anim. Ecol.* 8: 114–19.

SPENCER, K. G. (1967). Song thrush imitating other species. *Brit. Birds* 60: 91.

SPREADBURY, W. H. (1957). Bookham Common before 1914 and after. *Lond. Nat.* 36: 54–7.

STADLER, H. (1930). Vogeldialekt. *Alauda* 2 (Suppl.): 1–66.

STAFFORD, J. (1956). The wintering of blackcaps in the British Isles. *Bird Study* 4: 251–7.

— (1962). Nightjar enquiry, 1957–58. *Bird Study* 9: 104–15.

— (1963). The census of heronries, 1960–61. *Bird Study* 10: 29–33.

STAMP, L. D. (1946). *Britain's structure and scenery.* London.

— (1955). *Man and the land.* London.

— (1962). *The land of Britain.* London.

STEERS, J. A. (1954). *The sea coast.* London.

STEVEN, H. M., and CARLISLE, A. C. (1959). *The native pinewoods of Scotland.* Edinburgh.

STEWART, R. E., and ALDRICH, J. W. (1951). Removal and repopulation of breeding birds in a spruce-fir forest community. *Auk* 68: 471–82.

STOKES, A. W. (1960). Nest site selection and courtship behaviour of the blue tit *Parus caeruleus. Ibis* 102: 507–19.

SUMMERHAYES, V. S., COLE, L. W., and WILLIAMS, P. H. (1924). Studies on the ecology of English heaths. 1. *J. Ecol.* 12: 287–306.

SUMMERS-SMITH, D. (1952). Breeding biology of the spotted flycatcher. *Brit. Birds* 45: 153–67.

— (1963). *The house sparrow.* London.

SVÄRDSON, G. (1957). The "invasion type" of bird migration. *Brit. Birds* 50: 314–43.

SYMONDS, A. E. J. (1961). The counting of starlings at country roosts. *Bird Study* 8: 185–93.

TANSLEY, A. G. (1949). *The British islands and their vegetation.* London.

TAYLOR, S. M. (1965). The common birds census – some statistical aspects. *Bird Study* 12: 268–86.

THOMSON, A. L. (1950). Factors determining the breeding seasons of birds: an introductory review. *Ibis* 92: 173–84.

THORPE, W. H. (1955). Comments on *The Bird Fancyer's Delight*, together with notes on imitation in the sub-song of the chaffinch. *Ibis* 97: 247–51.

— (1956). *Learning and instinct in animals.* London.

— (1961). *Bird song: the biology of vocal communication and expression in birds.* Cambridge.

— (1963). Article "Singing" in Thomson, A. L. (ed.) *New Dict. Birds.* London.

THORPE, W. H., and LADE, B. I. (1961). The songs of some families of the passeriformes 1. Introduction. The analysis of bird songs and their expression in graphic notation. *Ibis* 103a: 231–45.

— (1961). The songs of some families of the passeriformes 2. The songs of the buntings (*Emberizidae*). *Ibis* 103a: 246–59.

THORPE, W. H., and PILCHER, P. M. (1958). The nature and characteristics of sub-song. *Brit. Birds* 51: 509–14.

TINBERGEN, L. (1949). Bosvogels en insekten. *Ned. Bosch Tijdschr.* 21: 91–105.

(1960). The dynamics of insect and bird populations in pinewoods. *Archs. neerl. Zool.* 13: 259–472.

TINBERGEN, N. (1957). The functions of territory. *Bird Study* 4: 14–27.

TURČEK, F. J. (1949). The bird population in some deciduous forests during a gipsy-moth outbreak. *Bulletin of the Institute for Forest Research of the Czecho-Slovak Republic.* (Slovak with English summary.)

(1950). O vztahu sojky (*Garrulus glandarius*) k obnove dubu (*Quercus sp.*). *Lesnická Práce* 29: 385–96.

(1954). The ringing of trees by some European woodpeckers. *Ornis Fenn.* 31: 33–41.

(1954). A contribution to the function of forest bird populations from the point of view of biocoenology and forest managements. *Aquila* 55–8, 51–73.

(1955). Bird populations of some lowland forests near the Danube in Southern Slovakia. *Acta 11 Congr. Int. Orn.* 532–6.

(1956). On the bird population of the spruce forest community in Slovakia. *Ibis* 98: 24–33.

(1957). The bird succession in the conifer plantations on mat-grass land in Slovakia. *Ibis* 99: 587–93.

(1957). Der nahrungsbedarf der kohlmeise und klappergrasmücke an raupen vom tannentriebwickler (*Cacoecia murinana*) in gefangenschaft. *Orn. Mitt.* Gottingen 9: 229.

(1960). Uber das fehlen der amsel in den menslichen siedlungen der Nord-slowakei (ŠSR). *Orn. Mitt. Gottingen* 12: 172–3.

(1960). Some aspects of the trophic and topic relations of birds, forest pest insects and woody plants. *Vedecke Práce* 1960: 259–80.

(1961). *Ökologische beziehungen der vögel und gehölze.* Bratislava.

(1961). Uber einige wechselbeziehungen zwischen gehölzen, vögeln und forstschädlingen. *Z. angew. Zool.* 48: 423–40.

TURRILL, W. B. (1948). *British plant life.* London.

TUTT, H. R. (1953). Notes on the nesting of a pair of jays inside a hollow tree. *Brit. Birds* 46: 98–9.

ULFSTRAND, S. (1962). On the non-breeding ecology and migratory movements of the great tit (*Parus major*) and the blue tit (*Parus caeruleus*) in southern Sweden. *Vår Fågelv. (Suppl.).* 3: 1–145.

UPTON, R. (1962). Crossbills feeding on beechmast and hazel nuts. *Brit. Birds* 55: 592.

USSHER, R. J., and WARREN, R. (1900). *The birds of Ireland.* London.

VENABLES, L. S. V. (1937). Bird distribution on Surrey greensand heaths. *J. Anim. Ecol.* 6: 80–5.

VENABLES, L. S. V., and VENABLES, U. M. (1952). The blackbird in Shetland. *Ibis* 94: 636–53.

(1955). *Birds and mammals of Shetland.* Edinburgh.

VOOUS, K. H. (1960). *Atlas of European birds.* London.

VOÛTE, A. D. (1946). Regulation of the density of the insect-populations in virgin forests and cultivated woods. *Arch. Neerl. Zool.* 7: 435–70.

WALLACE, D. I. M. (1961). The birds of Regent's Park and Primrose Hill, 1959. *London Bird Report* 24: 81–107.

(1967). Birds in Ireland during 1963–65. *Brit. Birds* 60: 205–13.

WARDLE, P. (1961). Biological flora of the British Isles, *Fraxinus excelsior* L. *J. Ecol.* 49: 739–51.

WARREN, S. H. (1912). On a late glacial stage in the valley of the River Lea, subsequent to the epoch of river-drift man. *Quart. J. Geol. Soc.* 68: 213.

WATSON, A. (1967). The Hatton Castle rookery and roosts in Aberdeenshire. *Bird Study* 14: 116–19.

WATT, A. S. (1919). On the causes of failure of natural regeneration in British oakwoods. *J. Ecol.* 7: 173–203.

(1923). On the ecology of British beechwoods with special reference to their regeneration. *J. Ecol.* 11: 1–48.

(1926). Yew communities of the South Downs. *J. Ecol.* 14: 282–316.

(1936). Studies on the ecology of Breckland. Climate, soil and vegetation. *J. Ecol.* 24: 117–38.

WEST MIDLAND BIRD CLUB. (1962). *Bulletin No. 134.* Cannock Chase Nest-Box Scheme.

WHITE, G. (1788). *The natural history of Selborne.*

WILLIAMSON, K. (1961). The taxonomy of redpolls. *Brit. Birds* 54: 238–41.

(1964). Bird census work in woodland. *Bird Study* 11: 1–22.

(1967). The bird community of farmland. *Bird Study* 14: 210–26.

WILLIAMSON, K., and HOMES, R. C. (1964). Methods of preliminary results of the Common Birds Census, 1962–63. *Bird Study* 11: 24–56.

WITHERBY, H. F., JOURDAIN, F. C. R., TICEHURST, N. F., and TUCKER, B. W. (1947). *The handbook of British Birds.* 4th Impression.

WRIGHT, A. A. (1946). Blackcap imitating notes of nuthatch. *Brit. Birds* 39: 247.

WYNNE-EDWARDS, V. C. (1959). The control of population-density through social behaviour: a hypothesis. *Ibis* 101: 436–41.

(1962). *Animal dispersion in relation to social behaviour.*

YARRELL, W. (1856). *A history of British birds.* London.

YAPP, W. B. (1953). The high-level woodlands of the English Lake District. *Northwestern Naturalist* 24: 190–207, 370–83.

(1953). The bird community of the fellwoods of the English Lake District. *Northwestern Naturalist* 24: 503–12.

(1955). A classification of the habitats of British birds. *Bird Study* 2: 111–21.

(1956). The theory of line transects. *Bird Study* 3: 93–104.

(1956). The birds of high level woodlands. The breeding community. *Bird Study* 3: 191–204.

(1959). The birds of high level woodlands. The winter population. *Bird Study* 6: 136–40.

(1962). *Birds and woods*. London.

(1969). The bird population of an oakwood (Wyre Forest) over eighteen years. *Proc. Birm. Nat. Hist. Soc.* 21: 199–216.

YEATES, G. K. (1934). *The life of the rook.*

INDEX

INDEX OF BIRDS

The page numbers in bold type show where the summaries for each species can be found in the Systematic List.

SUBJECT INDEX